LIVING IN A CRYSTAL BOX

MAP OF DOCTOR ARROYO IN 1960

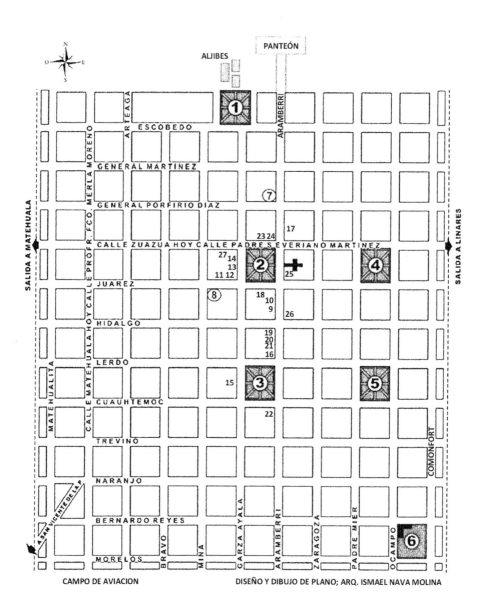

CAMPO DE AVIACION   DISEÑO Y DIBUJO DE PLANO; ARQ. ISMAEL NAVA MOLINA

CITY PLAN OF DOCTOR ARROYO
IN 1960

1. PLAZA HIDALGO
2. PLAZA DE ARMAS
3. PLAZA JUÁREZ
4. PLAZA REVOLUCIÓN
5. PLAZA 5 DE MAYO
6. LIC. BENITO JUÁREZ, MIDDLE SCHOOL
7. COSME ARAMBERRI, BOYS ELEMENTARY SCHOOL
8. LEONA VICARIO, GIRLS ELEMENTARY SCHOOL
9. *DOÑA* SUSANA'S HOTEL
10. POOL AND CANTINA
11. THEATER
12. COURT
13. TOWN HALL
14. JAIL
15. MILITARY POST
16. LA NACIONAL
17. *DOÑA* MARCELINA'S HOTEL / BUS STOP
18. LA SIMPATÍA, HARDWARE STORE
19. EL PRECIO FIJO/ EL SPUTNIK
20. CASA RODRÍGUEZ,
21. *DON* JUAN AND NENA LÓPEZ PORTILLO' S STORE
22. LA LIBERTAD/ CASA CONTRERAS
23. HOTEL DEL COMERCIO
24. LAS AMAZONAS
25. CHURCH LA PURÍSIMA CONCEPCIÓN
26. EL TRIUNFO
27. PHARMACY LA PAZ

LIVING IN
A CRYSTAL BOX

*Experiences of a Teacher
in Rural México in the 1950s*

MARÍA SOCORRO "COCO" MARTÍNEZ

Cover photo by Andrés Huerta† courtesy of Saskia Juárez
Cover by Aundrea Hernández
Interior by Cynthia Lee
Editing by Lillie Ammann and Jan McClintock

ISBN: 978-1-7378711-0-1

DEDICATION

This book is dedicated with much love to:
my husband Martín
my children Patricia, Carlos, and Omar
my parents Arcadio† and Petrita†
my siblings
the people of Doctor Arroyo
the memory of Professor Francisco Merla Moreno†

TABLE OF CONTENTS

FOREWORD

Courage, a strong set of values, and a deep desire to become a teacher flow through Coco Martínez's memoir *Living in a Crystal Box*. Reluctantly, she leaves her family behind in Monterrey as she begins her career in the isolated rural town of Doctor Arroyo. She must prove herself as a teacher and as a woman going off on her own in the late 1950s, a time when women stayed with family until they married. She tells her remarkable story with humor, transparency, and deep insight into herself and those around her who helped her fulfill her dream.

Hearing her story unfold as she brought each chapter to class was truly a gift. Coco took us with her to Doctor Arroyo. We walked the dusty streets and watched her students as she earned their respect and they, hers. Their voices and those of her peers and family resound with the flavor of place, as authentic as if we were hearing them ourselves. The language and images she uses to convey her story are delicious.

Her strength, humor, intimacy, openheartedness, values, and confidence shine through her words.

—*Jean Jackson, instructor, the Academy of Learning in Retirement*

PREFACE

The 1950s were for me a very romantic and innocent time, perhaps because I saw these years through the eyes of a young woman who grew up protected by her family and surrounded by their love.

At that time, we still attended dances accompanied by chaperones. Those were the years when, according to my mother and the rest of Mexican society, "no decent lady walks alone down the street after ten at night." However, at the end of that decade, my life took an unexpected turn. Circumstances forced me to separate from my family in the city of Monterrey, Nuevo León, México.

Having achieved my dream of becoming a teacher, I found myself in a dilemma: accept a job in a public school in a remote location, far from the safety of my home, or reject it and give up teaching.

In México at that time, a woman left her home only when she got married. So, my main problem was convincing my father to allow me to accept the teaching opportunity.

My destiny took me to Doctor Arroyo, an isolated little town, with no main paved road, no drinking water, and electricity for only two hours a day. There, I faced the taboo of being a single woman, working and living with only male teachers, plus the circumstance of having students almost my age.

Another challenge was to earn the respect and affection of the people. My weapon would be to apply my mother's wise advice: "Never forget that you will live in a *crystal box*. Everyone will see and judge what you do."

In this book, *Living in a Crystal Box: Experiences of a Teacher in Rural México in the 1950s*, I share my experiences of small-town taboos, superstitions, and new customs. My adventure began in 1958. I describe not only my loneliness and frustrations, but also the joy of seeing my students advance toward their goals. I show how circumstances influenced the course of my love relationship, the people and projects I had to give up, and the vicissitudes of my family during my absence.

This memoir is written for Spanish- and English-speaking readers. For this reason, I use descriptions of events that are familiar to those born in México, but that might be unknown or little known to readers in other countries.

In this story, I have changed the names of some people to protect their privacy.

This book is my love letter to the people with whom I shared my experiences as a teacher in Doctor Arroyo, Nuevo León, and to the wonderful neighbors of the endearing little town, to the love of my life, and to the members of my family who enriched my existence. It is also a tribute of gratitude to my former *director*, guide, and friend, the unforgettable professor Francisco Merla Moreno.

ACKNOWLEDGMENTS

This book was made possible because of the valuable help of several people who believed in me. Their knowledge, advice, encouragement, friendship, and love contributed to its completion. I offer my sincere thanks to all of them.

To my husband Martín, for believing in my potential as a writer and supporting me in the writing classes offered by the Academy of Learning in Retirement (ALIR) program in San Antonio, Texas, and for his understanding of my time invested in writing my book.

To my children Patricia, Carlos, and Omar, whose comments on this project were a great inspiration to complete it.

To Jean Jackson, my ALIR writing class teacher, who gave me the writing tools to embark on my literary adventure.

To all my fellow students in my ALIR Writing II class who helped me by critiquing the drafts of my book. I am especially grateful to Jane Dreyfus, Susan Chandler, Val Pierce, and Janet Alyn, who along with my teacher Jean Jackson, read my manuscript from its inception.

To Jan Kilby, another writing class teacher, and now a friend, who helped me edit my book and who has wisely guided me with her advice on various aspects of my writing career.

To my dear brother Arcadio "Cayito" Camero, who applied his experience in the literary field and his knowledge of the Spanish language to edit the Spanish translation of this book.

To the people who kindly contributed photographs and other information used in the book: Andrés Huerta†, through his wife, Saskia Juárez, Trini Rodríguez, Arturo Quiroz, and former students at the Doctor Arroyo middle school: Matilde Briones, Rodolfo Contreras, *arquitecto* Ismael Nava, *profesora* Lilia Nava, *profesor* Víctor Manuel Nava, and Lupita Torres†.

To Lillie Ammann, for editing and coordinating the publication of my book.

To each of you, I offer my eternal and sincere gratitude.

—*María Socorro "Coco" Martínez*

CHAPTER ONE

TAKE IT OR LEAVE IT!

One early morning in August 1958, the atrium of *la Dirección General*, today *Secretaría de Educación*, in Monterrey, México, vibrated with laughter and animated conversations. Everything related to education in the State of Nuevo León—school planning and programs, job assignments, salaries, and changes of workplace, among other things—were handled in this place.

One hundred eighty-eight recently graduated young teachers, including me, waited impatiently for our names to be called. It was the Big Day! One by one we would be notified of our new teaching assignments.

Divided into small groups, we sat wherever we could. For the men, it was easy to find a place, even on the stairs leading to the second floor, but we women had a harder time with our tight skirts or starched petticoats. When sitting down, we had to make sure our knees were modestly covered.

Mexican women did not wear dress pants in those years. It would still take a few years before pants became an everyday garment.

I wore a pretty yellow dress that my mother had made for me for such a special occasion. The color of the dress contrasted against my cinnamon skin. My jet-black hair sported a modern haircut that framed my face nicely. My makeup was discreet, and the only jewelry I wore were a pair of gold earrings and the gold bracelet my father gave me when I turned fifteen.

I closed my eyes for few seconds, reliving in my memory the blessing of my mother and her soft kiss on my cheek before I left home. *"¡Buena suerte, hijita!* I'll be praying for you!" she had told me as I boarded the bus that brought me here. With her words and her blessing, I felt protected.

The day was as bright as the faces of the young crowd around me. A light breeze helped to dissipate the static heat in the place. From time to time, some of the girls discreetly checked their hair or makeup in their pocket mirrors. A comb or a lipstick corrected any imperfection, and, once satisfied, they continued with their talk. Others tried to keep cool by using their hand fans or improvising fans with a sheet of paper. The water fountain gained popularity as the day got hotter. It was the first week of August, so Monterrey was extremely hot.

We knew it would be a long wait. Many of the graduates brought something to nibble on and to drink. By midmorning, several of them were already sharing their lunches or snacks with those around them. Others made plans to buy some *tortas* or *tacos* in the small stands close by. I had an apple and a banana with me, but the aroma and the looks of the *tacos* and *tortas* were becoming irresistible!

Amidst all the gaiety, there were lots of concerns, too. Not all of the 1955–58 generation of aspiring teachers had graduated. I was one of the lucky ones. More than good luck, it was the great effort I put into studying as much as I could in the spare time I had after working two jobs and helping my mom with chores at home. For three years, I had worked exhaustingly, studied hard, and slept little. My only time for enjoyment was a few free hours after work on Sunday afternoons. I usually went to the movies with Bertha, my friend and next-door neighbor, and occasionally to some parties with her and another group of friends.

At the beginning of our last year of study, the *Director General of Educación* came to our school, the Normal del Estado, the teachers' university. All of the students aspiring to graduate as teachers gathered in the building's auditorium.

"Do you have any idea of why the *Director General is* here?" whispered the girl sitting next to me.

"No, but we'll find out soon. I'm afraid it isn't good news. Look at the face of *profesora* Rebequita," I said.

We observed the assistant principal who accompanied the *Director General.* Instead of her usual pleasant smile, at this time she wore a stern expression.

After a short greeting, the *Director General* cleared his throat and said, "The reason for my visit is to let you know that next year there won't be many teacher positions available. For this reason, you are forewarned that we'll try to retain as many of you as possible."

His words were followed by many gasps and whispers from the students. Several people in the audience fidgeted in their seats; others frowned.

As if that information was not disturbing enough, he added, "And, to those who'll graduate, be aware that for the first time, many of you will have to work outside Monterrey."

A heavy silence followed this last statement. Afterward, the *Director General* thanked us for our attention and departed.

When he left, accompanied by *profesora* Rebequita, a general murmur of frustration was heard. It did not last long, because she returned immediately to dismiss us. "Okay, students, you heard the *Director General*. My best advice to you is to study hard if you don't want to be back next year. Now, please return to your classrooms. The teachers are waiting for you."

As we left the auditorium, I looked around me and noticed a lot of faces with furrowed brows or forced smiles. Others simply had an absent gaze. Undoubtedly, each of us was thinking about what our future would be.

I heard a student ask, "Do you really think this can happen, or they are just trying to scare us?"

"You better believe it," replied his classmate. "These people don't joke around!"

Now, almost a year later, we were sitting at *la Dirección General*, the Central Office. The predicted bad news had become a reality. Not everybody graduated, and some schoolmates were being sent to work outside Monterrey, not only to big towns, but to small communities, as well. This was causing a stir among all of us.

"If I don't get a position here in the city," one young male teacher said, "there are two municipalities in this state of Nuevo León where I don't want to work: China and Doctor Arroyo!"

"From what I hear on the news, those towns are quite dangerous," a young woman added.

"Well, I won't accept any one of those assignments for sure," another young man said. "They better give me a job in Monterrey or in a nice town, or I won't take it."

I wonder if this young man will really keep his word if the Director General sends him to work in a place he doesn't like. I think it's just bravado. If he needs to help his family or if he loves this career, he'll accept anything that is offered to him.

Several people added negative comments. Soon, it was the general consensus that an assignment to either of the small towns of Doctor Arroyo or China in Nuevo León would be a bad one. Afterward, the theme of the conversation changed, and my attention centered on the *director's* closed office door. My unpredictable future was behind it. When it opened, each of us hoped to hear our name called. For brief moments there was a tense silence. Once it closed, the noise started again.

As each schoolmate came out of the office, everybody wanted to know his or her assignment. So far, most of the teaching positions accepted had been in Monterrey, and a few in some towns close to the city. *If I'm going to be sent away to work, I hope it will be in one of the nearby towns so that I can come home every day or at least once a week.*

Early in the afternoon, the young man who was talking bravado was called inside the office. He left us with a sly smile. After a relatively short time, he came out with a dejected expression.

His friends surrounded him immediately. "What kind of assignment did you get?" they asked.

After a brief silence, he answered in a sour mood, "China, Nuevo León!"

"Aww! And did you accept it?" one of his friends asked him.

"Of course not!" he answered sharply, raising his eyebrow. "I told all of you that I wouldn't accept such a place. And don't even think I'm worried. I'm sure they'll call me back later with a better option."

Afterward he described his interview. Everybody around him listened intently.

At that moment, the *director's* secretary opened the door once again. The noise stopped almost completely. Here and there, a nervous cough broke the silence. The hours of tense waiting had brought good news to several people and sadness and frustration to others. Now, full of restlessness, all of us fixed our eyes on the secretary by the door. Everybody awaited her words. She opened her notebook, adjusted her eyeglasses over the bridge of her nose and read a name on her list.

"María del Socorro Camero Haro!" she called.

"That's me!" I said raising my hand. My heart started beating furiously. *Oh God, I hope it is just me who can hear my heart beating like a drum!*

"*¡Buena suerte, Socorro!*" some of my friends said.

"Thanks! I sure need lots of good luck." I stood up, blushing at being the focus of attention.

I smoothed my dress and followed the secretary into the office. A slight shudder ran through my body. In a few moments I would know my destiny. The friendly woman smiled and wished me good luck on my new assignment. Then she opened a second door and motioned for me to go in. I breathed deeply and walked into what I envisioned as *la cueva del león.* I smiled thinking about what the *Director General* would say if he knew I called his office "the lion's cave."

The *director* sat behind his desk with several folders in front of him. He was tall and robust. With his dark suit, balding head, and black-rimmed glasses, he reminded me of a judge. He greeted me with a firm handshake. *God, I hope he didn't notice the trembling of my hand!*

After we had exchanged pleasantries, he pointed to the chair in front of him. I sat with my hands in a tight grip on my lap. He opened a tan folder that had my name on the front.

"*Señorita Camero*, I have a special job for you," he said with a friendly smile.

I felt my skin crawl. I imagined what would come next—the position that the previous person had declined!

"Is it ... China, Nuevo León?" I asked in a strained voice. I was sitting on the edge of the chair with a knot in my stomach.

"Why do you say that?" The *director* tilted his head and smiled. "No, this position is in another place and a lot better."

I sat back on the chair and started to relax. I got ready to receive good news.

"It's a middle school in Doctor Arroyo, and your salary will be one thousand pesos."

I was dumbfounded. Doctor Arroyo! The other place where nobody wanted to go! My mind began to race. My parents depended on my help! Being the oldest of seven siblings, I didn't have too much of a choice. I thought about all of the information I'd heard before and remembered Doctor Arroyo was almost at the most southern end of the state. I would see my family only during long vacations. On the other hand, my salary would be double what I had earned as a student teacher. I clenched my hands. *What should I do?*

"So, what's your answer, *señorita Camero?*" The *director's* voice startled me. He was tapping on my open folder.

I looked at him and bit my lower lip without saying a word.

"I have to remind you that there won't be another chance to make a decision. You either take it or leave it." This time there was a warning in his voice. "The young man who left a moment ago will have to look for work elsewhere since he declined my offer."

"Excuse me, *señor Director*, but I hope you can understand that I have to consult with my parents first before I make this important decision," I said to him.

To my surprise, he showed understanding. He kindly agreed to wait until the next day for my final answer.

Before I left, he added, "If it makes you and your parents feel better, I want you to know I'm planning to send two more ladies to Doctor Arroyo. You should know also that there is a possibility we might bring you back next year if a position becomes available in the city."

"Gracias, señor Director. I'll explain that to my parents."

"I'll see you tomorrow then, and I hope you'll make a wise decision." He stood up and shook my hand.

I left his office in a hurry. Immediately the classmates started asking questions.

"I might go to Doctor Arroyo," I said. "I still have until tomorrow to think about it."

In reality, all I needed was my parents' consent. In my mind, I had already decided to go, not only because my family needed my economic help but because working as a teacher would be worth any sacrifice.

My first date with Martín in 1956

However, for a few moments fear assailed me. How would my boyfriend Martín react to my decision to work away from home? We had a long-distance relationship because he resided in the United States. For more than two years we had communicated only through letters. We had met in Monterrey when he came on vacation with his family. He later joined the US Air Force, and his assignments to other parts of the world had prevented him from visiting me.

Although Martín had grown up abroad, I knew that his family still preserved Mexican customs. According to them, single women stayed home until they were married. However, by the time he would receive my letter letting him know of my job offer, I would already be working in Doctor Arroyo. I sighed. Martín would have to trust me just as I trusted him. After all, getting away from my family was at that time a need, not a pleasure.

CHAPTER TWO

ALLOW ME TO FLY!

I went back home with a myriad of mixed emotions. I had been offered an assignment—even though it was not what I wanted. If I were to accept it, it would be a radical change for me and my family.

I thought about all of the positive aspects. The extra salary I would earn would be of great benefit in my home. Besides, becoming independent for the first time was exciting. I tried to dismiss the negatives, like going to an unknown, faraway town with such a bad reputation, plus the fact that I would rarely see my family and friends.

What kind of coworkers would I have? Would the people of Doctor Arroyo like me? I remembered the saying: *"Pueblo chico, infierno grande."* A chill ran through my entire body just thinking about this, "Small town, big hell." I was so deeply submerged in my thoughts that I almost missed my bus stop.

Before entering my home, I breathed deeply. I would need of all my courage and diplomacy to let my parents know about my assignment and get their permission to work out of town. For sure, my mother would agree, even if it broke her heart to see me go. It was my father who would be hard to convince.

I heard the music from the radio coming from the kitchen. My little sisters Norma and Julie came to greet me with tender hugs as I walked by where they were playing.

"Where are the boys?" I asked.

"Javier went to the library, Héctor and Cayito are running some errands, and Ernesto is playing with his friends in the river," Norma said.

I smiled, thinking that people who had never been in Monterrey probably didn't realize that the Santa Catarina river was completely dry. Many years before, it had flooded parts of the city, so the government decided to make it wider and channel it. Only when it rained hard could you see a narrow stream running in the middle of the huge riverbed.

I was hoping to give the news to all the family, but maybe it was better this way. I saw my father at the kitchen table reading his newspaper and drinking a cup of steaming coffee. My mother stood next to the stove, cooking something that smelled delicious. Not even the aromas of garlic and spices were able to arouse my appetite.

As soon as they saw me, my father closed his newspaper, and my mom turned off the stove. I kissed both of them while they looked at me expectantly. They knew right away that I had some serious news to share.

"How did it go, *hijita?*" they asked almost simultaneously with a tinge of anxiety in their voices.

"Well ..." I cleared my throat a little and took a breath.

Without delay, I explained the situation to both of them. When I finished, my mother was silent, with a dejected expression on her pale face. My father's jaw tightened.

He frowned and said, "It's out of the question. We are not even going to discuss it." He stood up, emptied the rest of his coffee in the sink, and turned around to walk away.

I stepped into his path. Holding him by the arm, I forced him to stop.

"*¡Escuche, papá!*", I said. I felt his muscles tensing under my hand.

Shaking his index finger at me, and frowning, he said, "You listen. You are a young lady with a home, and I won't allow you to go anywhere away from us."

Norma and Julie had heard I was asking permission to leave home and had tears in their eyes. My heart tightened, but I couldn't let my feelings get in the way. If my father didn't allow me to go, I might never get a job as a teacher for the state.

"This is 1958, Dad. These are modern times. Women have more freedom," I said. I swallowed hard, trying not to cry.

It was ironic for me to say such a thing, since I still behaved old style. My mom went with me to all the dances I was invited to, and if my bus was late coming back from school, she would be standing on the corner waiting for me.

"What are you doing here alone, *madrecita*?" I always asked her.

"A decent young lady can't be on the street after ten o'clock," she used to answer. "*¡Qué dirà la gente!*" My mom would always worry about "what people would say."

There I was now, waiting for an answer. My father had a stern expression. He looked at me sideways in silence. Then he tried to remove my hand from his arm, but I didn't let him. He knew I wasn't going to give up easily.

"The *Director General* is just trying to scare you. He will give you work in another place," he said stubbornly.

"No, he won't, Dad. Didn't you hear what I said before? He's already advising the people who didn't accept their assignment to start looking for another kind of job. I don't want to be one of them."

I was frustrated that my father didn't want to give in. I finally dissolved into bitter tears. "Have you forgotten how hard the last three years were for me?"

For the previous three years, I had worked as a secretary during the morning and as a student teacher in the afternoon. At the same time, I had attended school at night in order to earn my teacher's degree. Every day before going to bed I did my homework, wrote my teaching plans for the week, and tried to help my mother with some household chores. Many times, I stayed up until after midnight. That was my routine from Monday to Friday.

On weekends, I worked twelve hours on Saturdays and eight hours on Sundays in a curio store's office. My only free time was after I had collected the money from the store's cashiers on Sunday afternoon. I hardly had any time to rest during those years. I did it for my family and because of my longing to become a teacher. Now, I felt my father was cutting my wings, not allowing me to fly.

I wiped away my tears. "Dad, I've always been obedient to you two; both of you know perfectly well you can trust me! I know in such a place I will be expected to uphold the highest moral conduct at all times. I've never disappointed you, and I never will. You have to give me your permission to go. I'm not a little girl anymore. I'm already twenty years old."

My parents knew how much I longed to be a teacher. My father finally agreed to let me go. I don't know if it was because he couldn't stand to see me cry or because I informed him that two other girls would also go to Doctor Arroyo.

"Well, *hijita,* if two other *señoritas* are assigned there too, it's different. You just go to see if you adapt, but if you feel uncomfortable, promise you'll come back right away," he said in a conciliatory tone of voice. He hugged me and kissed my forehead.

I understood how hard was for him to let me be free. There had always existed a strong bond between us because I was not only his firstborn but also a girl.

With my heart full of joy, I promised to do that. I kissed my parents with a surge of elation. The rest of the day, I tried to focus only on the positive aspects of my assignment.

The following day I returned to the *Dirección General* to accept the position. As I entered the office that I no longer thought was *la cueva del león,* the *Director General* stood up to greet me with a handshake and a kind smile.

He stared at me, opened the tan folder with my name, and offered me a pen. "That beaming face tells me you are going to Doctor Arroyo, true?"

"*Sí, señor director*", I said. "*Muchas gracias* for giving me the opportunity to consult with my parents about it."

"That was because you came here with the right attitude, and I could see you really wanted the job. So, you are welcome. Now let's finish this business."

The *Director General* and I signed the contract, and he congratulated me on my decision. He assured me it was a good assignment.

After thanking him again, I was surprised when he stood and followed me to the exit. As he opened it, I could see everybody in the room staring at us in silence.

"I want you to learn from this young lady," he told the waiting teachers in a loud voice. "*La profesora Camero* is not afraid to work outside the city. She has accepted the position in Doctor Arroyo." He shook my hand again and repeated, "Congratulations and good luck, *profesora*. We'll bring you back as soon as possible." With that, he softly closed the door behind me.

Some of the young teachers said they were sorry about my assignment to Doctor Arroyo. The rest of them, I'm sure, were secretly relieved that the assignment had gone to somebody else.

When I returned home, I told my parents the *Director General's* reaction. They listened in silence. I found it hard to see the wounded look in my mother's eyes, the pensive expression on my father's face, and the anxiety of all of my siblings who couldn't understand why I had to go away.

"I have to go, not because I want to, but because if I hadn't accepted this opportunity, they wouldn't give me work in any other school," I said to them. They listened silently. "Dad needs my help to support the family, but I'll be back as soon as I can."

My closest friends, Alicia Rodríguez and Mari Paz Rodríguez—who were not related to each other—received with dismay the news that we could be separated for a long time. They didn't want me to go and tried to dissuade me. Yet, the idea that I would contribute to providing a better life for my family gave me the courage to continue getting ready to leave the nest. There were still three long weeks ahead of me before I would do so.

Despite all of my concerns, I could hardly wait!

CHAPTER THREE

PAINFUL FAREWELL

The day for me to depart for my new job finally arrived. It was the last week in August 1958. I woke up very early and waited impatiently for the sun to come out. When the sky turned pinkish, I ran to bathe. With nine people in our family, I didn't want to wait for my turn to use the only bathroom in the house.

I put on a new dress that my mom had so lovingly made for me. I was lucky that she was a good seamstress. Sometimes I would see a dress I liked in a magazine, and she would make it for me. I couldn't wait to wear my new wardrobe that was carefully packed in my two suitcases.

We all sat down to share my last breakfast at home. I wanted to enjoy those last minutes. There was always a sense of happiness when we gathered around the dining table. That was when we shared food, stories, and laughter. On that morning, however, there was a different atmosphere. There were long silences. My mother was unusually quiet, and my dad left half of his breakfast on his plate. Soon I was ready to go. But before leaving, I had to observe a special tradition.

I put a cushion on the floor and knelt down to receive my parents' blessing. We did this whenever we were going to be away for a long time.

"¡La bendición de Dios Padre, de Dios Hijo y del Espíritu Santo, te acompañen y después de la de Dios, la mía!". As my parents recited these words, "The blessing of God the Father, God the Son, and the Holy Spirit be with you, and my blessing after God's!" they made the sign of the cross over my forehead, my lips, and my chest. This was meant to shield me from all the dangers of the world.

"*¡Qué Dios te acompañe siempre, hijita!*", said my father. It felt good to hear the words "May God be with you always, my little daughter."

He kissed my forehead and helped me to stand up. I held his hand for a few seconds. That strong hand had held mine so many times throughout my life. I let it go and felt a knot in my throat. I was moving away from the nest toward the unknown.

"*¡Cuídate mucho, hijita!*", my mother whispered in my ear. "Take lots of care of yourself, my daughter." Then, she added something that would be my guide of conduct in the future: "And remember that you'll be living in a *crystal box* where everybody will see and judge what you do!"

That was perfect advice. She wiped away her tears and smiled. My mother was such a courageous and wise woman. She would always be my role model.

"*¡No se preocupe madrecita, recordaré todos sus consejos!*". I knew she would feel better after I assured her not to worry and that I would follow her advice. I hugged her long and hard, wanting to take all the warmth of her flesh with me. She was not only my mother, but also my best friend, and I had to leave her behind. I swallowed the lump in my throat, hoping she wouldn't notice my pain.

All my family went with me to the bus station. We settled into a taxi with the usual giggling from the younger ones. My father was noticeably somber, and my mom kept quiet. I tried to make light conversation to cheer them up, but they just nodded. Occasionally, my mom answered with a sad smile.

I looked at my siblings and wondered who would miss me the most. Javier and Héctor were sixteen and fourteen respectively. As young teenagers, they understood everything better, so I knew they would keep each other company. On the other hand, Ernesto and Julie were the youngest, so my mom would comfort them for sure if they started missing me.

I had been Ernesto's first grade teacher. His classmates didn't find out we were related until almost the end of school. Ernesto was a respectful little boy who called me *"señorita Socorro"* in the classroom and always used the formal word *"usted"* when he talked to me. He did it on his own, and my fellow teachers found it amusing. He understood that in the school I wasn't his sister, I was his teacher. When Ernesto was a baby, he was very sick, and I kept vigil over him with my mom. During his convalescence, I carried him in my arms all the time, but he never got spoiled. He was a good boy. I knew he would miss me.

Julie was the baby, smart and hyperactive, and for these reasons, she was always getting in trouble. One day she was walking on the roof of the house after my mom had advised her several times not to do it. Unfortunately, my mom delegated the discipline to me. It was a different time and culture. Helping supervise the younger children was always expected of the oldest in any Mexican family. I smiled, thinking Julie might be happy to see me go. It worried me that she would get out of control. I wished I could take her with me because I knew she would behave well around me.

Cayito and Norma, on the other hand, had a special attachment to me and vice versa. Norma was the long-awaited sister, and for years we shared the same bed. When I started earning money, I took her to the stores with me and always bought something for her. Cayito was more like a little son to me than a brother. When he was born, I was expecting a little sister, but when I bent over the bed and saw him lying next to my mom, so dark, *"tan morenito!"* as I said, and with his head full of black curls, I forgot my disappointment. He looked more like a toy doll to me than a baby. I thought that three boys would be too much for my mom.

"Mom, you already have two boys. Could this one be mine?" I asked her with expectation.

"Sure, he is yours." My mother smiled. I guess she thought it was a simple occurrence because I was only eight years old, but I took her seriously. After that day, I took responsibility for changing him and entertaining him, and, when it was time, I was the one who taught him to walk. Luckily for me, he was a very patient baby, so it wasn't hard taking care of him.

Now, all of them were standing together at the bus station to see me go far away. Norma stood by my mom as if trying to draw strength from her. I noticed both had teary eyes.

Javier, Héctor, and Cayito tried to be strong. *"¡Los hombres no lloran!"*, I thought. They were raised with the concept "Men don't cry," so although my departure surely hurt them, they weren't going to manifest it. Ernesto, perhaps because he was the youngest of the boys, turned around and furtively wiped his eyes. My father was more serious and silent than ever. Looking at them, I felt my heart sink.

While my two suitcases were being checked in, my youngest sister, Julie, started crying.

"I want to go with you," she said. She grabbed my hand and pulled me toward the bus.

"No, *hijita*, you don't even have your clothes," my mom intervened. She tried to get Julie's hand away from mine.

Julie didn't want to listen. She glanced at me with despair while continuing to pull me toward the bus. Her reaction took me by surprise and for the moment all I could think of was to say: "Mom, that's not a problem. I can buy some clothes for her."

When Julie heard this, she pulled my hand harder and was ready to get on the bus. Then everybody started telling her other reasons why she couldn't go, which made her cry more intensely.

"Is just that ... you don't want to ... know ... *Doctora-Rollo*," she said sobbing.

My siblings were amused by her mistake. "It's Doctor Arroyo, silly."

It broke my heart. I wanted to take her with me.

At that moment, I saw my sister Norma's face full of anguish. There was no way I could insist on taking Julie with me. It was enough for Norma that I was leaving. To be apart from her younger sister would be devastating for her. I couldn't do that to her. In addition, I recognized that taking her with me was impossible, as Julie, at four years old, was not of school age and I had no way of taking care of her during my working hours.

It was hard for me to get her to release my hand. When she did, Norma grabbed her firmly and pulled her. She wanted to be sure Julie would stay. I felt a tug in my heart to see my baby sister crying, but I knew it was the right thing to do.

I gave last hugs and kisses to my family and finally boarded the bus. I found my seat next to a window. When the bus started moving, I waved to them for the last time. They waved back sadly.

"I'll be back at Christmas with lots of presents," I promised them through the open window, trying to cheer them up.

"*¡Ve con Dios, hijita, y escribe pronto!*", my mother said with trembling lips.

"Yes, mom, I'll write to you as soon as I can. I love you!" I yelled, afraid she couldn't hear me over the sound of the loudspeakers in the area.

My mother followed the bus, almost running while it was leaving the terminal. She sent me blessings with her hand, and then she stood in the middle of the street, still wiping her tears. My siblings hugged her, while my father stayed alone next to the curb. This image oppressed my heart.

Oh, Dad. You must be feeling the same way I felt when I had to let go of Julie's hand! You had to set me free, despite your pain! Thanks, Mom and Dad! I love you.

The bus turned the corner slowly until I couldn't see them anymore. It was my turn to cry. I let my tears flow freely like an overflowing stream. What came to my mind were the words to a song my mother loved:

> *Dicen que no se sienten las despedidas*
>> They say that farewells don't hurt
>
> *Dile a quien te lo dijo, que esto es mentira*
>> Tell whoever told you this, that it's a lie.
>
> *El que se queda, se queda llorando*
>> The one who stays is left crying,
>
> *Y el que se va, se va suspirando.*
>> and the one who leaves, leaves sighing.

We'd always been a very tight-knit family, and now, with a broken heart, I was the first one to leave the nest.

"One year will go by fast," I told myself. But would I be able to survive for a full year away from my family?

I thought it was better not to anticipate and just live one day at a time.

CHAPTER FOUR

UNEXPECTED EXCHANGE

The bus drove through Monterrey's light traffic. I wiped my tears and watched in the distance the majestic *Cerro de la Silla*. It was named Saddle Mountain for its two peaks that resembled a horse's saddle. This huge mountain, southeast of the city, dominates Monterrey's landscape. It covers an area of twenty-three square miles, and its highest peak is almost 6000 feet high.

Cerro de la Silla in Monterrey. Photo provided by Mati Briones.

I enjoyed viewing this landmark every day on my way to work. I found it a treat to watch the sun rise behind the mountain, and it was a wonderful experience when a full moon rose over its peaks. *Cerro de la Silla* reminded me of a silent giant whose silhouette could be appreciated against the blue sky from far away. That time, I watched it with sadness in my heart, knowing I would miss it, just as I would miss all of the other rugged mountains that surround Monterrey.

Farther down the road, the bus went near *Cerro del Obispado*, a small hill with the Bishop's Palace on top. I remembered the stories about supposedly secret tunnels underground that connected this with the Cathedral, four or five kilometers away. This historic place is now a museum, and for me and my family, it was a place full of unforgettable memories. I sighed, evoking the many times we went there just to admire the city lights. In my mind, I saw again my brothers playing and clambering over the silent cannons that safeguarded this place against the American troops in 1846.

Little by little, we left Monterrey behind. Once on the open road, I enjoyed the view of the stunning *Sierra Madre Oriental*. This chain of mountains at times looked bluish and, at others, very green. The landscape changed as we approached Saltillo City. Here, there were more green valleys and fewer mountains.

Sierra Madre next to Monterrey

Lulled by the gentle rocking of the bus and the whispering of the passengers, I fell asleep, exhausted from the emotions of the day.

Four hours later, I arrived at the bus terminal in Matehuala, in the state of San Luis Potosí. I felt rested and a little calmer. This was halfway to my destination. From there, I would take the only bus to Doctor Arroyo, which ran only once a day. It was scheduled to leave at 3:00 p.m. I looked at my watch. It was only 1:00 p.m. I still had two hours ahead of me.

I asked for directions to the Doctor Arroyo bus station, but I couldn't find anyone at the terminal to help me carry my two heavy suitcases to it. It wasn't easy to walk in high heels on cobblestone streets. I tried to keep my balance so that I wouldn't twist an ankle. Fortunately, Matehuala was a small city, and the bus office wasn't far away. I would check in my luggage and then look for a place to eat.

I wondered if the other female teachers had already arrived, because they were not on my bus. Only an elderly couple, a family with several children, and I had stopped in Matehuala. I was eager to meet the teachers and hoped we would become good friends. With their company and friendship, I wouldn't feel so lonely away from my family. *What if I already know them? That would be fabulous!*

Soon, I arrived at a small office that served as the bus terminal. My shoulders dropped. Contrary to what I expected, there were no women there. There was only an employee behind the counter and a young man sitting on a bench. This young man was staring at the entrance door. When I went inside, he stood up and approached me, smiling. He was slightly taller than me, which meant he was short, too. He had a thick moustache, heavy eyebrows, and black curly hair. He carried a folded jacket on his arm.

"Are you Socorrito Camero, the new middle school teacher in Doctor Arroyo?" he asked gently.

"Yes, but how do you know my name?"

"I'm *profesor* Andrés Tejada Zúñiga, and we'll be working together. They gave me your name at the *Dirección General de Educación*." He extended his hand to me.

I stared at him, trying to make sense of what he was saying. I finally said, "*¡Mucho gusto!* But I don't understand... I was told two lady teachers would be coming to Doctor Arroyo with me."

"They changed their minds or didn't accept, and I'm the only one who got a position." He tilted his head to one side and chuckled.

I was dumbfounded. *A male teacher instead of the two females! If this meeting had happened at the Monterrey bus terminal, my father probably wouldn't have let me come!* I shivered at the thought.

"Don't worry. I'll be better company, you'll see." He grinned and winked at me.

I was embarrassed that he had noticed my disappointment.

We decided to go find some place to eat. We had time. I asked the office attendant to watch our luggage. We looked for a restaurant close by, and we started getting acquainted while we ate. It was the first time Andrés had left his family, too. He seemed to be very close to his mom. I could hear the emotion in his words.

"If one day my mom would come to live with me, I would rent a house and you could move in with us if you wanted," he said. "It would be like having another sister."

"That would be very nice, Andrés. Thanks, especially since nobody from my family can come to live with me."

I told him about my mom's having to attend my dad and my siblings and also about my baby sister Julie's wanting to come with me and how sad I felt to leave her crying. My voice broke, and he patted my hand.

After we finished eating, we returned to the bus stop. By that time there were other passengers waiting. They observed us openly.

"*¡Buenas tardes, maestros!*", several of them said.

The office attendant, who knew everybody, had found out who we were and had informed the others.

"*¡Buenas tardes!*", we answered and sat on one of the three benches to wait for the arrival of the bus.

It was funny to us to observe how curious the townspeople were. Once their interest about us was satisfied, they turned their attention to some items kept inside a small room in the back of the office. They walked over to look at them and took turns asking the attendant to whom they belonged. Then he mentioned the names of the owners.

"I know them and their families," one of the onlookers said. "They have been working in the United States for almost two years."

"I bet you they're coming back with their pockets full of dollars," a third man added with a sigh.

We were amused listening to the *rancheros'* comments. Moments later, a good-looking man came into the office. He wore a *guayabera* that matched the color of his blue eyes. He looked different from the rest of the people. Everybody greeted him respectfully. We were surprised when we saw the white stripe around his neck. He was a priest.

"*¡Hola, buenas tardes!*", he said, smiling. "I'm Father Jesús Rangel. I heard you are Doctor Arroyo's new middle school teachers."

Andrés and I introduced ourselves.

He told us that there were some other priests assigned to the town's church too, and they took turns visiting the surrounding communities. He was on his way back to Doctor Arroyo.

The bus finally arrived. It was old. I just hoped it would take us to our destination without problems. The owners of the items stored in the small room returned, as well. Several people approached them to ask about their experiences in the United States and listened to the men with attention and wide eyes. Afterward, some volunteers helped them to carry outside a Singer sewing machine and some other large boxes. The men placed those items carefully on top of the bus, next to a fighting rooster in a cage and everyone's suitcases. Most of us watched all of this activity. People laughed while they pulled a heavy cord from side to side to secure everything on top of the bus. When they finished, we were ready to leave.

We boarded the bus, and Andrés and I occupied the front seats with Father Rangel. The driver, known to all as Chepa, said hello to several passengers calling them by their names. He then took his place behind the wheel, and we were on our way. We had been told the bus normally arrived in Doctor Arroyo around 7:00 p.m.

"Today, the trip will take longer because it rained this morning," Chepa said, looking at us in the mirror in front of him. He was a middle-aged man with big shoulders. He covered his straight black hair with a straw hat.

I didn't understand why it would take longer, since the rain had stopped, not even remotely imagining how the day would end.

"There is only a dirt road to Doctor Arroyo, and when it rains, the ground becomes muddy," explained Father Rangel. "Frequently the bus gets stuck and, consequently, arrives late in town."

Chepa drove fast for a short time on a dry, uneven road, which made us bounce up and down repeatedly. The people screamed and laughed with every bump. The rooster in the cage on top of the bus made a lot of fuss, too. Suddenly, the bus sank in the mud and stopped. When everyone was convinced the bus would not move, several men got out to push it. After a while, we were on the road again. The volunteers cleaned their muddy shoes as best as they could. Even so, they left a trail in the bus aisle.

The bus advanced slowly, swaying side to side on a sea of mud. The next time it got stuck, another group of men took turns pushing, while the rest cheered them. This happened several times. Soon the floor of the bus was full of mud, and there was a strong odor of sweat.

"Excuse me, *señor*. How far are we from Doctor Arroyo?" I asked Chepa.

"*¡Ahí nomás tras las lomitas, seño!*", he said. "Over there, just behind the hills, Miss," he answered in a humorous tone of voice.

I was glad to hear this. It was already the time we were supposed to arrive in town, but we passed many hills, and the town was nowhere to be seen.

CHAPTER FIVE

PARANORMAL ACTIVITY

When Andrés or I asked if we were close, Chepa's answer had been always the same, *"¡Ahi nomás tras las lomitas!"* We finally stopped asking.

We noticed that whenever people saw lights coming in our direction they started asking, *"¡¿Es ese el camión fantasma?!"* "Is that the Ghost Bus?" Afterward they were quiet and expectant, craning to see the road ahead of us. Some of them even stood up to see well. When an actual truck went by, the passengers identified it right away. Andrés and I couldn't understand how they could identify who owned the vehicles. At the same time, we were extremely curious to hear about the mysterious bus they mentioned so often.

"What's the Ghost Bus?" Andrés asked Father Rangel.

"Well sometimes you see lights coming your way and you hope to find another vehicle on the road because there are no other roads than this. All of a sudden, the lights disappear," Father Rangel said. After a brief pause, he continued. "Where did they go? What happened with them? Nobody knows. These mysterious lights started appearing after an accident in which many men died. They were riding in the back of a truck that overturned in this area. People think that's the Ghost Bus."

"Do you believe that story?" I asked Father Rangel.

"Yes, I have seen the lights of the Ghost Bus several times, and many people testify to it. It's possible that one day you'll see them, too," he murmured.

It was 3:30 in the morning when we arrived in Doctor Arroyo. Instead of four hours, our trip took twelve! The town was almost dark, with a few lights here and there.

"Is there a blackout in town?" I asked.

"We have a small electric plant that provides energy from seven to nine o'clock at night," Father Rangel answered. "After that, everybody uses oil lamps."

"No paved road and no electricity?" Andrés was surprised. "I didn't know that. Did you, Socorrito?"

"Of course not. Probably they were afraid I wouldn't come." I laughed.

"Hmm ... There isn't running water either," the priest added calmly. "The *aguadores* deliver the water on their *burros*, house by house. There are three big *aljibes* where the water from the rain is collected. So, if there isn't any rain, we are in big trouble, but don't you worry about it."

Andrés and I looked at each other and grinned. What else did we not know?

Los aljibes or cisternas in Doctor Arroyo.
Photo provided by Saskia Juárez.

The bus started slowing down, and people who were asleep stirred in their seats.

"Do you have a place to stay?" Father Rangel asked. "If you don't, there is a hotel where the bus stops. I'm sure they'll have rooms available."

We thanked him, and, as he suggested, we rented two rooms in the hotel, which was a big old house with rooms around a large square patio.

An elderly woman showed me to my room. Besides the bed and a chair, it had a washstand in one corner. She handed me a small kerosene lamp and a big stick to secure my door.

After placing the lamp on the chair next to the bed, I put on my nightgown and lay down. I was exhausted and sleepy. I turned on my side and lowered the lamp's wick. I closed my eyes, said a small prayer, and thought about my family back home. Then I started to doze.

In the silence of the night, an unfamiliar sound startled me. It was somebody's rhythmical snoring. It was an unwelcome, recurrent sound. I tried to ignore it, but as the snoring continued my sleep was gone momentarily. I turned the lantern up again. I listened intently and realized the noise had stopped. *Great! Whoever is snoring in the next room is dreaming soundly now, and I'm completely awake.*

Soon, my eyelids started to close. I dimmed the light for a second time, plumped my pillow, and tried to find a comfortable position to rest. I was almost asleep when suddenly, the annoying noise disturbed me again, but this time it was louder. "Will I ever be able to sleep?" I said to myself. Frustrated, I raised the lamp's flame again. Astoundingly, the sound stopped immediately. This called my attention. *What's this? What's going on? How can I hear noises through such thick walls?*

I looked at the flame, a blue and yellow tongue licking at the glass. A small statue and a glass bottle next to the lamp formed gigantic dancing figures on the wall. *My imagination is playing tricks on me. I'm not surrounded by familiar sounds, so anything different is going to disturb me.*

After a while, the only sound was some crickets outside my door. I fixed my pillow and lowered the flame to a tiny tongue. Everything was quiet. I finally got ready to have a good rest, even if it were for a short time.

I was so wrong! The snoring started ... again. With my entire senses alert, I paid attention. This time the sound was closer and clearer. I held my breath and stayed still, listening: the snoring was coming from ... my own bed! The hairs on the back of my neck stood up, and my breathing quickened. For a few minutes, I was paralyzed with fear and tried to get up unsuccessfully. I finally was able to move and sat up quickly. With my heart pounding, I turned up the flame of the lamp as high as possible. When the room was full of light, the snoring stopped immediately as before. I waited for a long time, and it never recurred. I realized this wasn't a coincidence or a product of my imagination.

I had never been a fearful person, but that night I couldn't wait for the sun to come out! I finally fell asleep, sitting up in the bed, with the light of the kerosene lamp on and the rosary that my mother gave me tight in my hands.

Was there a ghost in my room? More importantly, would anybody believe me?

CHAPTER SIX

MY COWORKERS

A soft knock on my door and a voice calling me woke me from a deep sleep. I looked around, trying to figure out where I was and shuddered remembering the incident before I fell asleep. *Thank God for the daylight. I won't spend another night here. But what if there isn't any other place available? What will I do then?*

There was a second and harder knock on the door. "Time to get up, Socorrito," Andrés said in a loud voice.

"I'm up, Andrés. I'll see you in ten minutes," I yelled.

"Okay. I'll be waiting for you."

I got ready as fast as I could and went looking for him. He was smoking a cigarette in the middle of the patio. "Good morning, Andrés. Did you rest?"

"I hardly closed my eyes." He let out a heavy sigh. "They gave me the front room, and as soon as I went to bed, several people started talking just outside my window. They were waiting for the bus leaving for Matehuala and kept me awake for a long time with their noise."

"Oh, that's too bad. By the way, do you realize that Chepa only slept for two hours? There isn't another driver to help him."

"That's true. And then he'll turn around to come back this afternoon."

"Incredible; poor Chepa." I shook my head.

"What about you? Did you sleep well?" Andrés asked.

"Three hours at the most." I proceeded to tell him about my strange experience. He held his chin with one hand and listened attentively.

"I can't find a reasonable explanation for what happened in my room. Now I believe in ghosts."

"Are you sure you weren't asleep?" Andrés looked at me sideways.

"I was completely awake. The worst experience was the third time. Luckily, I didn't scream. Can you imagine how embarrassing it would've been? Finally sleep overcame me sitting up and with the light on." I couldn't help shuddering again.

"Hmm, I guess I'd have been scared, too," Andrés said. "Well, that's over; now let's have breakfast. We haven't eaten for eighteen hours, and I'm starving."

"That's a good idea. The banana and chips we ate during the trip weren't enough," I said. "As soon as we finish, we'll go introduce ourselves to the school principal and the other teachers."

In the small restaurant in the hotel there were only six tables covered with colorful tablecloths protected with plastic. Four chairs surrounded each table. The dining room walls were painted in a bright yellow. On the windows that faced the patio, we could see some pots with red begonias. Singing birds in a couple of cages delighted us with their songs. The aroma of fresh coffee and recently made *tortillas* spread throughout the dining room. For breakfast we had *chorizo* with scrambled eggs, refried beans, fluffy flour *tortillas*, a cup of coffee, and delicious *pan dulce.* This more than satisfied our hungry stomachs. We paid the bill and went back to pick up our suitcases.

A medium-built, dark-skinned woman met us near the door.

"*¡Buenos días, maestros!* I'm *doña* Marcelina, the owner of this place. I wanted to let you know I have nice rooms for rent for a very reasonable price. My hotel is very popular," she said, with a big smile on her thick red lips.

"Thanks a lot, *doña* Marcelina, but we have to meet our school's principal and see what kind of arrangements he has made for us," I said.

That was only an excuse because I knew for sure I would never stay there again. One night was enough, but I didn't want to hurt her feelings.

"That's fine. I'm sure you don't want to be walking around carrying your suitcases. You can leave them here while you find out if you already have a place to stay."

She was right. It would be an inconvenience to walk around with all of our belongings. I looked at Andrés, and he nodded in agreement.

"Very kind on your part, *doña* Marcelina. We accept your offer. We'll let you know about the rooms later," I said. "Now, could you please tell us where the middle school is?"

Doña Marcelina said the school was a block away, around the main square. She described the building to us. After thanking her again, we went on our way. It was a bright morning, and the temperature was very pleasant. The cobblestone streets looked clean, and the trees in the plaza looked healthy and green, thanks to the previous rain.

We were going to meet the other teachers, and we wanted to make a good impression. Thus, Andrés wore a suit and tie. I had chosen an aqua-green dress to wear on such an important occasion, high-heeled white shoes, and a white purse.

"*¡Te ves muy guapa,* Socorrito!", Andrés said. His compliment put a smile on my face.

"*Gracias.* You look very nice too, Andrés." He smiled with satisfaction at my reassurance.

By that time, it was as if Andrés and I'd been friends for a long time. And to think that twenty-four hours before I hadn't known about his existence. Andrés was funny and easy to get along with. I was overjoyed we would be working together in Doctor Arroyo.

"*¡Buenos días, maestros*!" Several persons greeted us on our way to the school. Every time they did, Andrés and I gave each other puzzled looks. They had never seen us before, and yet they called us *maestros*, teachers.

"News travels fast," Andrés said. "We arrived when people slept, yet already everyone knows who we are."

"My mother advised me, 'Don't forget that a small town is like a *crystal box.* Everyone can see what others do.' I'll try to remember her wise words all the time." I sighed.

"I wonder what kind of coworkers we will have," Andrés said.

"Don't worry. At least you know we can count on each other." I smiled.

We found the school just around the plaza. It was a big old house with a wide front door, as *doña* Marcelina described it. We were a little nervous, but we wished each other good luck before we entered.

Immediately to the left was the school's office. Inside, a man around fifty years old sat behind a big desk. Two younger male teachers stood up to greet us.

"*¡Pasen, bienvenidos!*", one of them told us. "We were waiting for you."

The other young teacher motioned us to take a seat. Then, the older man introduced himself. "*¡Bienvenidos, maestros!* I'm *profesor* Francisco Merla Moreno, the school principal." He was of medium height, heavy set, and dark skinned. His black straight hair was combed back. He wore a white shirt with the long sleeves rolled up and a loose striped tie.

"*¡Mucho gusto, profesor Merla!*", we answered at the same time.

Afterward, we introduced ourselves.

Profesor Merla had a stern look, and he seldom smiled. He wiped the sides of his mouth occasionally as he talked.

The young teacher who welcomed us first said his name was José Luis Pérez. He was of medium height, with a fair complexion, straight black hair, and a slightly aquiline nose. I noticed he frowned often, which made him look stern. When he smiled, however, he showed a warm personality. The other teacher was Lauro Villarreal. He was tall and slim and had curly black hair. Even without smiling, he had a spark in his eyes.

José Luis and Lauro were around our same age. Both were very cordial and made us feel welcome.

"We'll need a place to stay," Andrés said. "*Doña* Marcelina offered us lodging, but we wanted to check with all of you first."

"There are rooms available where I'm staying," José Luis suggested. "I would like some company since Lauro lives in another place."

Andrés and I agreed that this would be the best, especially after *profesor* Merla assured us that we would be fine there.

"Great! You can come with me to check the place after we finish with the orientation meeting," José Luis concluded with enthusiasm.

I thought that any place would be better than the hotel with ghosts, and I was happy to know that there was accommodation for Andrés and me. He was my only family at the moment.

CHAPTER SEVEN

A HOTEL WITHOUT GHOSTS AND A TOUR OF THE TOWN

The orientation went smoothly. Although we were a small school, we had to meet the curriculum of the *Secretaría de Educación Pública del Estado*. Because I was the only female, I was in charge of teaching Home Economics to the girls in each of the three levels. My other classes would be Civics in first-level class, Human Geography and Universal History in second level, and Chemistry, History of New León, and Modeling with Plasticine in the third.

After we finished, we all walked to what they called *doña Susana's* hotel. This was another old house with a restaurant at the front where we could eat our meals. A separate entrance allowed passage into a wide corridor with potted plants. Inside the house, eight rooms surrounded a square courtyard filled with mismatched flowerpots. A big fig tree in the center of the patio extended its branches toward several bird cages. Four of the small rooms in the house were available. Each one had a metal headboard bed covered with a faded bedspread, a chair with a woven straw seat, a small table, a medium-sized mirror, and a washstand in the corner.

José Luis introduced us to *doña* Susana, the owner of the hotel. She was a tall, heavy-set, older woman with a wrinkled face. She had black-tinted hair combed to the back in a bun. Some small curls fell over her forehead. *Doña* Susana wore a gray apron on top of a navy-blue cotton dress with a small floral pattern.

She looked at us coldly. I had second thoughts about staying there. I was disturbed by her intimidating personality. Apparently, Andrés felt the same way. *Maybe we should check the place where Lauro stays.*

"Where did you sleep last night?" asked the woman with a cold and raspy voice.

"At *doña* Marcelina's hotel," I told her.

"Hmm. Did you two get a scare?" A malicious smile accompanied her question.

"Wha ... what do you mean?" I asked.

"Well, everybody knows there are ghosts in that place. We hear about them all the time."

I felt the hairs on the back of my head stand up but didn't say anything.

She added that the same thing happened in the hotel across the main plaza. This was one reason travel agents hated it. She smiled in amusement.

"I heard that guests are pulled by their legs when they are asleep. Other times, their bed covers are pulled." She paused for a few seconds. "Only people who don't know these facts stay there. There aren't any ghosts in my hotel. You can ask *profesor* José Luis."

Andrés and I exchanged a look. What she said was enough to convince us. *Doña* Marcelina's hotel really had ghosts! I hadn't been dreaming!

"No ghosts here," José Luis affirmed, smiling.

"We'll take the rooms," Andrés and I said at the same time.

"Do we pay you for the room now?" I asked *doña* Susana.

"Go and get your things before *doña* Marcelina thinks you're staying with her," she suggested. "We'll get your rooms ready. Ahh! Don't let that woman convince you otherwise."

"We certainly wouldn't stay there, even for free," I said.

Doña Susana walked back to the kitchen, cleaning her hands on her apron. Then she stopped and turned around. "I wish I could see *doña* Marcelina's face when you tell her you'll stay with me. That woman won't be happy at all." She smiled wickedly, showing a gold tooth.

"*Doña* Susana!" said José Luis, shaking his index finger.

She shrugged and went inside the kitchen.

"I promise this lady isn't that bad," José Luis commented. "I wouldn't live in her place otherwise. Now, let's go to pick up your belongings. Welcome to Doctor Arroyo and to your new home!"

When we walked past a couple of businesses, people stepped outside to have a good look at us. José Luis didn't pay attention, but we did because were not used to such curiosity.

"Welcome to the *crystal box*, Andrés," I whispered.

He winked and smiled.

"What *crystal box*?" José Luis asked.

"We'll tell you later," I replied, as we reached *doña* Marcelina's hotel.

The kind woman accepted without question our thanks and the excuse that *profesor* Merla had already made arrangements for our stay in town. One night of paranormal phenomena in that bedroom had been enough for me.

When we returned with our suitcases to *doña* Susana's hotel, our rooms were ready. They were next to José Luis's.

"Socorrito, your bedroom is in the middle; just knock on either wall if you need anything, and Andrés or I will come right away," José Luis said.

"*Gracias*, José Luis." I was relieved knowing both of them would watch over me, especially because foreigners came to stay in this hotel quite often. For the first time I was going to live away from my family, so I still had to adjust to this new situation.

I went into my small room. It looked sad, cold, and impersonal. I sighed deeply. *As soon as I can afford it, I'll buy a nice bedspread, make a matching long skirt to cover the table and a ruffle to go around the mirror. I also need a curtain to cover the corner where I'll hang my clothes and some pictures to hang on the bare walls.*

That afternoon, *profesor* Merla and Lauro joined us for dinner. We talked and learned from each other. *Profesor* Merla had his own home a couple of blocks away from *doña* Susana's place. His two teenage daughters, Lydia and Delia, were studying in Monterrey. They had graduated that year with the first generation of high school graduates.

"Good students, both of them," said José Luis, and Lauro supported the comment.

Lydia, Profesor Merla, and Delia. Photo provided by Delia Merla.

Profesor Merla smiled proudly and then changed the subject. He said he loved reading and offered to lend us his books. I thought that was a kind gesture on his part.

"I love reading, too. In fact, I started doing it before I was five years old, but because of work and my studies, extra reading hasn't been present for quite some time," I said.

"Well, you'll have plenty of time to read here. Tomorrow I'll bring you a historical novel I just finished reading. I'm sure you'll enjoy it as much as I did." He smiled, and this time his smile was amiable.

The talk then moved on to other topics.

"Lauro and I are from Villaldama, Nuevo León," José Luis said. "We attended the same schools, and we graduated as teachers together. We were lucky to be assigned to work in the same place."

"We have been friends for a long time," Lauro added placing a hand on José Luis' shoulder, "and we will be for the rest of our lives."

The sincere friendship between the two of them was obvious. It made me think of my friends Mari Paz and Licha. I wished the three of us were working together as we had for the past year.

One thing that puzzled me was that José Luis and Lauro lived in separate places even though they were so close. Lauro mentioned that he only came to eat at *doña* Susana's place from time to time. I knew that I would find the reason without asking.

Before leaving, the *director* gave us the list of the subjects that we would teach and our weekly work schedule. He said he might come back later on to have coffee with us.

"Would you like to take a tour of the town?" José Luis asked Andrés and me after *profesor* Merla and Lauro went home.

We enthusiastically accepted, so the three of us went out and headed north. One block away from our new home was the Plaza de Armas. It was a classic town square with a medium-sized gazebo in the center. Trees abounded and several benches invited rest on both sides of the sidewalks. East of the plaza, there was a white church with an atrium at the front and a single bell tower. On the opposite side were the municipal offices and the jail, the walls painted in yellow. North of the plaza were the town's main hotel, *Hotel del Comercio*; some houses; and the large store *Las Amazonas*. On the south side was an ice cream parlor; a hardware store, *La Simpatía*; the commerce school; and other small businesses.

From there we went to the *aljibes*, large cisterns where the rain was collected. José Luis explained to us that the two largest supplied the town, and the third was intended for the animals. Several men were placing large cans with water on their donkeys' backs.

We greeted them and they responded, removing their straw hats and looking at us curiously. Then they put their hats back on and continued their work.

José Luis told us the *aguadores* would deliver the water house by house for a small fee. I noticed the men's faded clothing and worn-out *huaraches*. I wondered how they could feed their families with the small amount of money they earned. Looking at the dark color of their skin, I could only guess the many hours they spent under the harsh sun.

We left the *aljibes* and walked on straight cobblestone streets. It amused us to see people peering out of their doors or windows as we passed in front of their homes.

"Are they always this curious, José Luis, or is it only because we're newcomers?" I asked him.

"No, it's always like this. You can be sure that in a couple of hours, at the most, everybody in town will know that we strolled through the town's streets."

We continued with our walk. We visited plaza Juárez, which was of regular size; it had some games for the children and a few trees and benches. There were two large stores and a smaller one plus some private homes in front of the plaza. Later we saw two other small plazas, both unremarkable. Soon, we had seen most of the town.

Rodolfo Contreras across plaza Juárez. Photo provided by Rodolfo Contreras.

José Luis told us about the town's most influential people as we walked past their businesses. South of the main plaza was *don* Ramón Perales' hardware store. Across from our hotel, on Aramberri Street, was *don* Peregrino de la Garza's store *El Triunfo*. Everything was sold there, from groceries to clothes, fabrics, blankets, cots, and mattresses. He also owned *La Paz* pharmacy, located on General Zuazua street, half a block from the main square. *Don* Peregrino was recognized as a poet and a politician. He was married to *doña* Magdalena Macias, a lady well-liked by the townspeople. They had many children, but two of them, Paco and Socorrito, would be our students that year, followed by Cuquita and Malena later on.

Then José Luis mentioned *don* Candelario Contreras, a much-respected man who was owner of *La Libertad*, a large grocery store across Plaza Juárez. José Luis said that two of *don* Candelario's boys, Héctor and Rodolfo, had just graduated from our school.

In front of the same plaza was *La Nacional*, the largest store in town, with the most variety. The store

La Nacional store, across plaza Juárez

also had its own merchandise warehouses right there. It was owned by *don* Amancio Berrones, whom the people called *El Patrón*, The Boss. It was said that "he owned half the town." One of his daughters, Irma, would attend our school this year and the youngest, Alicia and Petrita, later on.

A few meters ahead from there, also on Aramberri street one block from our lodging, three other clothing stores were lined up in a row. The smallest belonged to *don* Juan López Portillo, *doña* Susana's ex-husband. Next in line came a large establishment, *Casa Rodríguez*, owned by *doña* María Eguía and *don* Max Rodríguez. It was a very well-stocked store, where in addition to clothing and footwear, they sold everything from mattresses and coffins to plows and other agricultural items. Four of the Rodriguez children would attend our school. This family was to play a very important role in my life later. Last but not least, there was *doña* Lupita's clothing store. This nice lady was the grandmother of the Rodríguez-Eguía children, and later she would transfer her business to her grandson Antonio, who would call his store *El Sputnik.*

I wondered what the townspeople did for fun. I had always lived in a large city where there were many things to see or to do, so this was a new experience for me.

"Don't worry. We'll find ways to kill time," José Luis answered when I asked him. "It won't take long for you to get used to it. Besides, we have movies twice a week, and sometimes, they even exhibit *estrenos*, you'll see."

The inflection of his voice made me think there was something funny about these *premiers* he mentioned. I was curious about it.

CHAPTER EIGHT

THE FIRST NIGHT IN MY NEW HOME

At seven o'clock in the evening, the small power plant's lights came on. I felt happy to listen, if only for a couple of hours, to the small radio I'd brought from home. This was a way of connecting with my family at a distance. I promised to mention it to my mom at the first opportunity. In that way, we would listen to the same program at the same time. I thought about my family in Monterrey, and that made me feel homesick.

The aroma that filled the air distracted my sad thoughts. It came from the bakery next door. We couldn't resist the temptation of freshly baked bread, and soon, José Luis, Andrés, and I enjoyed some *pan dulce* and a cup of Mexican frothy hot chocolate in the dining room. There were some other customers in the restaurant who kept looking at us then whispered among themselves. We pretended we didn't notice and kept our conversation in a low voice. *Doña* Susana ensured that everybody was well served.

"*Doña* Susana, do you want me to go and wait for the bus to arrive?" a vivacious young girl asked while pulling la *señora's* apron. The *niñita* tapped the floor with her foot waiting for a response. Her name was Claudia, and she was around ten years old. Her round face was framed by a pageboy haircut. She was short with a well-proportioned body and ran small errands for the owner.

"*¡Por supuesto! ¡Corre, muchacha, y pregunta quien llegó!*". The three of us smiled when we heard *doña* Susana saying, "But of course! Run, girl, and inquire who arrived."

Claudia left in a rush. We were still in the dining room when she ran back almost out of breath. She gave a detailed report to the landlady about who had arrived on the bus. Claudia named several persons who *doña* Susana apparently knew because she nodded at every mention. The young girl took a deep breath and then continued. "Besides the people I told you about and a bunch of *rancheros* that I don't know, there were three salesmen, and a family came to visit *don* Peregrino. Everybody looked funny, covered with dust from head to toe, as always."

When she finished, Claudia put her hand out. *Doña* Susana got a coin from her apron pocket, and frowning, she gave it to her. "Now go and buy a candy, *muchacha chismosa*," she said.

Claudia didn't care that *doña* Susana called her "gossip girl." She just smiled and ran to buy her candy.

"That's one of the entertainments," José Luis said. "Many people sit on the plaza benches just to wait for the arrival of the bus. They like to know who comes into town, and they spread the news immediately. You were lucky it rained when you came, or you would also have looked like white ghosts."

Andrés and I exchanged a look and smiled. We then understood why everybody knew who we were, although they had never seen us.

Lauro arrived and José Luis invited us to his room to play cards. He tuned into a station with good music on his small radio. While we played, he shared some other information with us.

"Before I forget, let me advise you. Don't drink any water unless it is filtered and boiled. I'll tell you why."

He went outside and came back with a glass of water recently delivered, which he placed close to the light.

I saw many tiny tadpoles swimming in the cloudy water. "Wow! You can be sure those disgusting creatures won't go into my throat! Just to see them gave me chills," I said.

Andrés took the glass of water from José Luis's hand and observed it with half-closed eyes. Then he shivered and poured the water in a flowerpot.

"Whenever you want to take a bath, ask the maids to warm a couple of buckets of water. They'll take it to the small room where we bathe. Just be sure to lock the door. You won't want to get a draft of air if somebody opens it," José Luis joked.

"There isn't too much water here, so the popular saying is, 'What would you rather have, a cup of coffee or a bath? You have to choose one or the other,'" Lauro said with a straight face. Then he laughed, and so did we.

It was hard to believe, but time would show us how true this was.

Ten minutes before nine o'clock, the lights started flickering, announcing they would go off. Teresa, one of the three maids, had already given us an oil lamp.

At that time, she came back to see if I needed anything. At more than thirty years old, Teresa was *doña* Susana's oldest maid. She was of medium height and slightly plump. Her face was framed by short, permed hair. Teresa was serious, but helpful and friendly.

I asked her to accompany me to the bathroom before she went to bed. She lit my lamp, and the scent of the kerosene filled up my bedroom. Afterward we headed toward the farthest part of the house.

With the light of the lamp, the branches of the fig tree in the middle of the patio seemed to writhe in a strange dance. The birds were already asleep in their cages covered with blankets. We walked quietly so as not to wake them up. Suddenly, as we approached the bathroom, someone raised the curtain that covered the door and a person stepped out. I jumped back.

"*¡Buenas noches, maestra!*", a huge man with a big straw hat and bell-bottomed overalls said. "I'll be back," he told Teresa in a husky voice.

Before we could answer him, he was already lost in the *patio's* darkness. Only the sound of his pants dragging on the floor let me know the direction that he went.

"He's Juan, my husband," Teresa said. "The other person you haven't met yet is Horacio, *doña* Susana's grandson. He's out of town but will be back tomorrow, just in time to attend school. He'll be one of your students, and he's a handful."

"I'm sure Horacio and I will get along. I'm looking forward to meeting him."

When I entered the adobe room where the septic tank was, Teresa advised, "Check the floor for snakes, *señorita!*"

I looked around the place with the lamp. I didn't know if Teresa was joking or if she was serious. I prayed never to have to use the bathroom in the middle of the night. Besides my concern about snakes, I now felt intimidated by Juan and was still shaken after meeting him.

I returned to playing cards with the other teachers. Around ten o'clock, we all retired to our rooms. The sound of the radio was replaced by an eerie silence, only interrupted by the chirping of some lonely cricket. I missed all of the familiar noises of my home: my siblings' jokes and their happy laughter, the baseball broadcasts my father listened to on the radio, my mother's engaging conversation, her singing, and the sound of her guitar. Here, in Doctor Arroyo, there weren't any traffic noises outside, nor the laughs and yelling of children playing in the middle of the street. It was a sleepy town.

Me at 20 years old   *Martín in uniform*

I said my prayers and lay in bed with mixed emotions. I was homesick, but at the same time, pleased at being on my own for the first time in my life. Before I fell asleep, I looked at my boyfriend's picture on top of the table. He wore his uniform of the US Air Force.

CHAPTER 8

I wonder if Martín has received my letter letting him know about my assignment here. Is he thinking of me, too? After all, he has a lot of things to do and to see wherever he is right now.

I knew Martín enjoyed learning about other cultures and he went looking around in his free time. Occasionally he sent me some pictures. How I longed to see those places with him! He had promised me one day we would travel the world together, and I looked forward to that day.

CHAPTER NINE

A VERY INTERESTING SUNDAY

Sunday morning, I was awakened by the ringing of the church bells. The deep rich sound reverberated in the air, inviting the faithful to attend the five o'clock Mass, *La Misa de Gallo,* whose literary translation means *Rooster's Mass*. It's called this because it starts when the roosters announce the new day. I heard *doña* Susana and her maids closing the front door and leaving the house to attend Mass.

I wasn't planning to get up early, so I fixed my pillow and went back to sleep. After breakfast, Andrés and I went to church. The place was full because many people came from the surroundings of Doctor Arroyo. We sat at the back of the church. When the service finished, we were among the first to leave.

We noticed several young men sitting on the benches across from the church's entrance. Some of them waved discreetly at us and we waved back. *Will they be our students?* We walked around the square for a while and then went home.

"Surely there was a large male audience outside the church, true?" José Luis, who was finishing breakfast, asked. "That's another kind of distraction here. The men might not attend Mass, but without doubt they'll be there outside to admire the *señoritas* when they come out."

"Well, you weren't there attending Mass or watching the *señoritas*," I joked.

He just smiled and took a sip of coffee without responding to my comment. Teresa, who was picking up José Luis's empty dishes, wore a funny expression on her face when she overheard the conversation. Later on, she came by my room, ready to clean it.

"I overheard what you told *profesor* José Luis," Teresa said while making up my bed. "The reason why he doesn't go to look at girls is because he already has a girlfriend."

"Oh, I see."

"By the way, a sister of hers will be your student because she will be in third grade." Teresa mentioned the young woman's name.

"*Profesor* Lauro has a girlfriend, too," Teresa continued. "She is *profesora* Esperanza, whom you came to replace. Nice person. She and *profesor* Lauro were renting two rooms at her grandmother's house, here in Doctor Arroyo. *Profesor* Merla told *doña* Susana that *profesora* Esperanza was transferred to a school in Monterrey. So, he and his wife offered *profesor* Lauro to move in with them and he accepted," Teresa said, as she finished cleaning my room.

"I am sorry that they had to separate, but at least Lauro has his best friend, José Luis, here, besides a good place to stay."

Teresa nodded in agreement, then she left.

I looked at Martín's picture. By this time, his absence of news didn't surprise me. Sometimes weeks passed between one letter and another. This happened every time he was sent to a new assignment outside of the United States. In a way, this delay was fine, as it gave me the opportunity to send him my new address. Otherwise, my mom would have to forward his most recent correspondence to me. *If only he could come see me next Christmas.*

I sighed deeply.

Sunday afternoon I was ready for the first day of school. I had planned my lessons, and the clothes I would wear during the week hung neatly in the corner of my room.

When Teresa told Andrés and me that she could do our laundry and ironing for a reasonable amount of money, we accepted without hesitation. I didn't want to worry about going home and having to take care of those extra chores. And I knew them perfectly.

I thought about the hardships of the last three years. How had I survived them? Living in Monterrey, we couldn't afford a maid as we had done previously in San Luis Potosí. Certainly, my brothers Héctor and Cayito helped my mother by going on errands, and my little sister Norma, under the age of ten, was beginning to learn the secrets of order and cleanliness in the house. But there were tasks that would have been very difficult for them, with which my mother needed help. Those were the washing and ironing of the clothes for our family of nine. Since we didn't have a washing machine yet, washing, rinsing, and squeezing had to be done by hand.

My day had been completely busy working in the mornings as a secretary and in the afternoons as a student teacher. At night, I attended classes at the Normal, the teacher's university. I could help my mother only late at night.

In those years, there were no wrinkle-free materials, so everything had to be ironed, including sheets and bedspreads.

Besides, my father's shirts had to be starched. Ironing was even more tiring during the hot Monterrey summers. I always ended my routine by going to bed late and started the next one by getting up early.

Sometimes I felt so tired that I wanted to give in for a day. But I reflected on how hard my family struggled—my mother at home, my father in his enslaving job, and my six siblings attaining the first places of achievement in their school. This energized me, and I made an effort to continue. The word surrender did not exist in my family's vocabulary.

Now, without my help, I knew it would be hard for my mom to do it alone. However, she promised me that she would hire a laundress as soon as she started receiving my contribution. This gave me a little peace of mind.

My adrenaline was high in anticipation of my new job. This would be the first time I would be teaching teenagers. *Profesor* Merla gave Andrés and me some helpful advice.

"This school was created recently and many of our students are almost your age because the town had never had a middle school before, only the six elementary grades. This year will be the second generation of students to graduate. There are several eighteen-year-olds, and one of them is nineteen."

Profesor Merla was right. They were almost our age, since I was only twenty years old and I figured Andrés was about the same.

"You should apply strong discipline and remind them when necessary of who's in charge. Basically, they are good kids, but they'll try to see how far they can go."

"You'll find very soon who are the troublemakers," Lauro said.

"Don't let them get away with anything," José Luis added. "Not even Horacio, *doña* Susana's grandson. If he disrupts the class, all you have to do is tell her, and the lady will take care of his discipline."

That was the second time I had heard comments about Horacio. I was curious about meeting him and finding out for myself what kind of kid he was.

I didn't have to wait long. Before dinner time, the sound of the strings of a guitar called my attention.

"Who is playing the guitar?" I asked Claudia, who was playing with her hula hoop outside my room. It was the toy that was causing a sensation around the world. Her skirt and her hair moved from side to side, following the turn of her waist.

"Oh, it's Horacio. He came home today when you were in church." At that moment, Claudia ran when she heard *doña* Susana calling her.

I sat and listened with pleasure, thinking of my mom and her guitar. Suddenly, the music stopped. A few minutes later, someone stopped in front of my room's open door.

"*¡Maestra, buenas tardes! Soy Horacio López Portillo, a sus órdenes*".

I turned around to face a tall, thin young man with kinky black hair. The twinkle in his dark eyes and the jovial smile made me overlook his teenage acne. He had the guitar in one hand and a Coke bottle in the other.

"¡Hola! ¡Mucho gusto, Horacio! Soy la maestra Socorro Camero".

"¡Bienvenida a Doctor Arroyo, maestra!", he said politely, shaking my extended hand. "I just came to introduce myself."

"Well, thanks, Horacio. I was looking forward to meeting you. I've already been told about you."

"If it's something bad, don't pay attention, but if it's something good, you better believe it!" he joked.

We both laughed.

"I'll be the judge of that. By the way, you play the guitar beautifully!"

"I'm glad you liked it. Anytime you want me to play something for you, just call me. Oh, and before I forget, I mostly came to tell you that if anybody bothers you in the school or outside the school, all you have to do is to let me know and I'll take care of business."

His vehemence and sincerity made me laugh.

"Gracias, Horacio, espero no sea necesario".

He smiled at my saying I hoped it wouldn't be necessary.

"I'll teach Duque to look after you, too." He pointed to the big black dog asleep in the middle of the hall.

He was so big because he ate the restaurant leftovers. Duque was very intimidating, especially when he picked up his big head to look at you with his yellow eyes. Somebody had shot one of his back legs, and as a result, he was crippled. When he ran, he didn't put weight on that leg. *Doña* Susana had told us not to be afraid of him because he was mean only to strangers. I thought that, at that point, Andrés and I were still strangers, so we tried to avoid him.

Horacio and I chatted for a little bit. His personality and sense of humor radiated sympathy. Surely, we would get along well.

"Well, now you'll excuse me. I'll have to hurry up to meet up with my friends," he said.

He waved at me and left, whistling. Duque stood up and ran after him.

José Luis had told us that he, Lauro, and *profesor* Merla attended the movies regularly. Andrés and I decided to join them instead of staying at the hotel by ourselves. *Doña* Susana asked us to have dinner early because she and her maids would close the kitchen to go to the movies, too.

The sun was going down when a voice on a loudspeaker resounded all over town.

"Only ten songs away for the start of the *El Charro Negro* movie," a masculine voice informed. "Be sure you don't miss the *premier* of this sensational movie."

"Whaaat? Is he kidding? That movie is so old!" I told José Luis, laughing. "How can it be a *premier*?"

"Well, it's a *premier* here, because it's the first time they exhibit it," José Luis explained. He smiled and shrugged.

The sound of a song filled the late afternoon air. When it finished, the same voice announced, "Nine more songs before starting tonight's show."

A second song was played. "Only eight more songs to go." The loudspeaker thus communicated the countdown.

In between, the announcer let people know about the next new releases: *The Revenge of the Charro Negro*, *The Return of the Charro Negro*, and *The Son of the Charro Negro*.

Profesor Merla and Lauro came by the house, and when we heard, "There are only five songs left before tonight's show begins," we went as a group to the movie theater. On our way, I saw many people carrying chairs. José Luis said they were going to the movies, too, and wanted to be sure they had a place to sit. He explained that we didn't need to take any because he and the other teachers always sat in a balcony that had seats.

The theater was an old mid-sized building, with balconies on the sides. In the center on the floor, there were some benches and a large space for the people who carried their own chairs. It had a second floor with seats. We called it the gallery, and it covered only a quarter of the area. This place was not only used as a cinema. Festivals and school graduations were also held there, as well as political presentations. Having its own generator avoided electrical interruptions that would have ruined events.

There were a lot of people, but the theater wasn't full. Some of the balconies were still empty. We, the five teachers, occupied one on the right side. It had a good view.

José Luis offered some information about the people in the other balconies. "All those girls in the balcony across from us are the Berrones. They are very gentle girls. One of them, Irma, is our student. In the next balcony is *don* Peregrino, the friendly pharmacist, with all his family and some foreign relatives. The young guy waving at us is his son Paco. He and his sister Socorrito attend the middle school. In the next one, the couple with all those teenagers looking over here, are *doña* María Eguía *y don* Max Rodríguez. They have a store in the next block."

I remembered that three boys and a girl of such a family would be our students. I greeted them with a nod, to which they responded with some smiles. The young girl waved a hand slightly.

The theater wasn't full yet. "I guess people are not crazy about the *premier* of this movie," I told Lauro.

He looked at me, and waving his index finger, he said, "I bet you the priest said at the end of the Mass, 'This is a movie good for all the family,' or not?"

"How do you know?" I asked. Indeed, I had attended Mass in the morning, and the priest had said just that.

"Well, any time the priest advises the people that they should not go to see so-and-so movie, the theater gets packed. Of course! Everybody wants to know why the priest doesn't want them to see it. However, when he says that 'the movie is good for all the family,' people think it must be boring, and they don't come."

Andrés and I found this explanation amusing. Even more amusing was the curiosity of the people around us. Andrés and I were the newcomers, so everyone wanted to give us a good look. Some people glanced at us discreetly; others elbowed each other and observed us openly. Several craned their necks so they could see us. We pretended not to notice.

Finally, the lights dimmed, and the *Charro Negro* appeared on the large screen. I was surprised that I paid attention to the movie. When it finished, many people applauded, happy that the *Charro Negro* had won the fight against the bad guys and also won the girl's heart.

After the lights came on, several persons came over to say hello, and *profesor* Merla introduced Andrés and me to them.

"Did any of your family come with you?" a young woman asked me, giving me a sidelong glance.

Before I could answer, an older woman interrupted. "Are you here by yourself?" She had an almost accusatory tone of voice. She stared at me, raising an eyebrow.

"No and yes," I said. "I was supposed to come with two lady teachers, but they changed their minds at the last minute, and *profesor* Andrés took their place. Unfortunately, nobody in my family could come with me." I realized I was almost apologizing.

"Sorry to interrupt," *profesor* Merla said, tipping his hat, "but we have to get up early tomorrow. Good night, ladies."

He took me by the elbow and guided me toward the exit door. The two women stood behind with sarcastic expressions on their faces.

"Thanks, *profesor* Merla." Fortunately, he had noticed my discomfort.

"Listen, *señorita* Socorrito, you don't have to answer any malicious questions. Don't pay attention to people like that."

Later I reproached myself that I had offered explanations to those spiteful women. Their questions had taken me by surprise. To this point, I'd lived a sheltered life with people who were always kind, but I was now in another environment and would have to learn to defend myself, and the sooner the better. The year was 1958, and there were the same old taboos. I was a young *señorita*, and I was by myself. Those were two great targets for poisonous darts. Something I had heard before came to my mind. "In a small town, they either love you or they hate you. There are no middle terms."

I swore to myself that those people would love me—in time—if they gave me the chance; however, at that moment, my personal life was none of their business.

CHAPTER TEN

THE FIRST DAY OF SCHOOL

The next day, Monday, the school year began. I could hardly wait to start this new phase of my life. I wore one of my new dresses and high-heeled shoes and paid extra attention to fixing my hair and makeup. I wanted to make a good impression on my new students.

I joined Andrés and José Luis in the dining room for breakfast. There wasn't a choice of menu. *Doña* Susana and Teresa made the same for everyone. That day we had scrambled eggs with chorizo and small potatoes on the side, plus Mexican sweetbread and coffee. I thought I wasn't hungry, but once the aroma of the onions and chorizo reached us, we couldn't say no to the food on our plates. We thanked the owner and Teresa and went back to our rooms to finish getting ready. We were on our way out when *profesor* Merla and Lauro came by the house. All of the male teachers wore jackets and ties. After a brief exchange of comments, the five of us headed toward school. The day was bright and warm.

We arrived at the old house temporarily converted into a school. I was surprised to see that some students were already there. Young people started filling up the courtyard little by little. I watched the reunions, hugs, and handshakes amid expressions of joy. The sound of their voices and laughter filled up not only the space between the walls of the school, but also in my heart. These youngsters weren't strangers anymore. They were my new family, and I felt at home again. My heart jumped with happiness.

As we waited in the office for the start of classes, Lauro and José Luis shared some discipline tips with Andrés and me. They were going to be of great help, since both us had worked only with elementary school children before.

The *director* checked the large clock on the wall. The time was 8:30 sharp. "Well, it's time to start. Good luck to all of you and remember that we are here to support each other." The male teachers put on their jackets.

From the door, *profesor* Merla sounded his whistle, and the students took their places in the center of the courtyard. When everybody was quiet, the *director* removed the Mexican flag from its stand, and the five of us stepped outside of his office. We all saluted the flag and sang the National Anthem. When the ceremony finished, *profesor* Merla gave the flag to Lauro and proceeded to introduce Andrés and me to the students.

"These are your new teachers." After mentioning our names, he continued, "Make them feel welcome in our school by being on your best behavior and studying hard."

The students stood in straight rows listening intently. Some of them smiled in a friendly way. Others were serious, as if they were analyzing us. The rest just looked at us with curiosity.

From the back of one of the lines, somebody raised an arm. I saw Horacio's familiar face behind the waving hand. I smiled, remembering he promised to be there for me if I needed him.

Once the presentation finished, the students walked in an orderly manner to their respective classrooms, and we got ready to start our lessons.

The middle school program was divided into first, second, and third levels—the equivalent of seventh, eighth, and ninth grades in the US. My first lesson was Human Geography, second level. I knew Horacio was in this class, and I trusted that he would behave well.

I remembered *doña* Susana's warning to her grandson at some point. "If I receive the slightest complaint," she had said sternly, "you can be sure that I'll hit you with a big log."

"C'mon, Grandma. I'll behave. You'll be proud of me. You'll see," Horacio promised.

"Hmm," *doña* Susana murmured, cocking her head and raising an eyebrow.

As I entered the classroom, all of the students rose to their feet. This was a common custom in the schools as a sign of respect for the teacher or any adult stepping inside.

"*¡Buenos días, clase!*". I placed my books on top of the desk.

"*¡Buenos dias, maestra!*", they answered in chorus.

"*¡Por favor, siéntense!*", I said in a friendly tone.

They immediately sat.

There was a welcoming message on the blackboard. "*¡Bienvenidos, Profesora Socorrito y Profesor Andrés!*".

As I faced the group, Horacio's smile clearly betrayed the author of such a welcome.

"*¡Gracias, clase!*", I said in general, although looking directly at Horacio. "But no more messages because I will need to make use of the blackboard."

Horacio continued smiling while he opened his Human Geography book like the rest of his classmates.

At roll call, each student responded *"¡presente!"*. I was writing down who was sitting next to whom. José Luis and Lauro had already named the troublesome kids in the class. We were just getting started, but if there were any problems, I would make new seating arrangements. At that moment, I wanted them to be happy seated next to their friends.

The rest of the day was almost the same in the other classes. I would teach all the girls Home Economics, including crocheting, embroidering, sewing, and handcrafting. With the exception of crocheting, I felt confident. My mom had taught me how to make dress patterns and how to use the Singer sewing machine, too. I knew a lot of beautiful stitches because I had learned to embroider pillowcases, bedspreads, and tablecloths in elementary school.

I had already planned some strategies to make the classes more interesting to the students. My goal was to motivate them to pursue a university career or, at least, to learn a trade. To accomplish this, they would be class participants instead of observers. I would teach them to solve problems and convince them that they could succeed if they studied hard.

The arrival of a new guest at our hotel brought an addition to our small family. Manuel Gutiérrez, a lawyer, came to work as a public order minister. His wife and two children stayed in Monterrey. Manuel was of medium height, slightly husky, with a light complexion. He had straight hair and a well-shaven face. He wore eyeglasses all the time and suits frequently. Manuel, who people called the *Ministerio Público*, Public Ministry, was very amiable, and slightly older than the rest of us. His main job was to supervise punishable acts such as death in unusual circumstances. Later, he would investigate it and promote public criminal actions if warranted. We got used to hearing a policeman knocking on the front door at odd hours of the night requesting his presence.

Life at the hotel became a pleasant routine. Manuel and we teachers ate together, went to the movies twice a week, and played cards in José Luis's room late afternoons. There, we listened to his radio and recounted the daily events. We also talked about our families back home and about our future plans. As we got to know each other, our appreciation of and respect toward one another grew.

We understood that eventually we would take different paths, but at that moment, we had only each other, and that was the best way to survive our loneliness so far away from our homes, families, and friends.

CHAPTER ELEVEN

DEALING WITH TABOOS

One afternoon on my way home, I stayed behind the other teachers to talk with a small group of girls. After several weeks in town, I was trying to get acquainted with my new students. The day was bright, and a light breeze gently moved the leaves of the trees. We walked at a slow pace. I was in no rush to bury myself in my room for the rest of the afternoon. As we crossed the main plaza, I heard a female voice calling me.

"Maestra Socorro, ¿Me permite un momento?"

Someone was requesting a moment from me. I turned around and saw a woman approaching us. The sound of her high heels resounded rhythmically on the hard pavement. I had never seen that person before, but apparently the girls knew her. They looked at her with a frown and muttered something.

"I would like to talk to you," the woman said. She crossed her arms and stared at the girls, as if dismissing them with her dark eyes, but the girls didn't flinch. Instead, they got closer to me as if protecting me from something. I found this reaction strange but couldn't ask them the reason at the moment.

I told the girls to continue walking, which they did reluctantly. They waited at the corner, covering their mouths as they talked to each other. I waved them on, and they finally left. I then gave my full attention to the lady in front of me. She was very pretty. Her black hair was fixed in a chignon. The tight skirt and white blouse with ruffles showed off her nice figure. She looked modern. I figured she was a few years older than me.

"Hello! I'm ..." She gave me her name, looking at me as if I should know her.

"*¡Mucho gusto! Socorro Camero, a sus órdenes*", I replied with a confused expression.

She finally explained that she was the sister of one of my students.

"I just returned to Doctor Arroyo and found out we have new teachers in town." She gave a friendly smile. "As a welcome, I'm extending you and the rest of the teachers an invitation to my home for coffee and pastries. You just choose any afternoon and send me a message with my brother."

"That's so kind of you." I smiled back to her.

She seemed to be a sophisticated woman. The soft wind carried the sweet fragrance she wore. *It must be an expensive perfume. She wouldn't wear a cheap one, for sure. One day I will be able to afford perfume like that, one that leaves a nice trail.*

"I'm looking forward to meeting each one of you," she said. "Oh, and the invitation includes the lawyer who lives in your house, too."

I promised to give her an answer in one or two days after checking with the others. After a short chat, we said goodbye, and I headed home feeling happy. I missed my friends Mari Paz and Licha a lot, so I thought that if we got along, maybe this lady could be my new female friend in town.

The main plaza was only one block from *doña* Susana's hotel. I noticed two women talking outside a house. They whispered something to each other, while looking at me. I nodded at them with a smile, but they hardly answered. *I'll just ignore them. I better get used to their ways.*

As I walked into the house, I saw *doña* Susana in the middle of the hall with her hands on her waist. She was wearing her apron, a sign that she had just stepped out of the kitchen. She was tapping the floor with the heel of her shoe. The severity of her face was exacerbated by one raised eyebrow. The stray curls on her forehead were wet with perspiration. I saw her eyes and felt the approach of a storm. Claudia stood close by, very attentive, and biting her nails. *Uh-oh! I believe that doña Susana is waiting for Horacio. Perhaps he has done one of his famous pranks.*

Duque was lying lazily on the floor. He raised his big head, looked at his mistress, and ran to lie down elsewhere. He fixed his yellow eyes on her. Suddenly *doña* Susana came to meet me.

"*¡Señorita!*" she said, raising her raspy voice, "the old man, *don* Juan, already came to talk to me. One of his customers stopped by his store to let him know you were talking to …" *Doña* Susana then mentioned the name of the woman I had just met. "He said you were with her in the middle of the plaza."

I opened my mouth and stared at her. I couldn't believe it. She was upset with me, not with Horacio!

"Excuse me? Yes, I talked to her. What's wrong with that?"

"Don't you understand? Everybody could see you." She shook her head.

"What do you mean by 'everybody could see me,' *doña* Susana? I really don't understand," I said in a strained voice.

"Well, *don* Juan was very disturbed. He even closed the store to come to tell me. He said you are new in town, and you don't know who that woman is, but it's not good for you to befriend her."

The more she talked, the more upset I felt about her ex-husband's intrusion. I held my emotions in check and my jaws clenched. I looked at her through half-closed eyes. *Who do they believe they are, telling me who I should or should not talk to?*

"That woman is divorced! To be seen with her is bad for your reputation."

Isn't she divorced, too? People call don Juan her ex-husband. I thought they would be divorced, but maybe they just live apart.

While I was trying to contain my anger, *doña* Susana continued. "The old man emphatically said I should warn you, so it won't happen again."

By that time, José Luis and Andrés had come out of their bedrooms. They stood next to their doors, listening with expressions of surprise. Andrés held his chin pensively, and José Luis stood, frowning deeply, with his hands in the pockets of his jacket.

My pulse was racing, and my face was burning. I didn't know whether to continue feeling angry or just laugh. I had talked with that woman for no more than ten minutes, but the news had already spread like fire in a cornfield!

I tried to be openminded about this new situation and finally accepted that *doña* Susana and *don* Juan were trying to protect me in the only way they understood.

"Well, *gracias, doña Susanita.*" It was the first time I had used her first name in diminutive, and I noticed her stern face melt into a gentle smile. "Please tell *don* Juan not to worry, and that I thank him for his concern."

"You don't need that kind of friendship," she pointed out in a more cordial voice. "My daughter, Nena, will be back very soon from Monterrey, and you two will get along very well." After saying that, she went back to the kitchen with a smile of satisfaction on her face.

"What was all that about?" José Luis asked.

Andrés took a step forward. "What happened, Socorrito? You look upset."

I told them what had happened and how much *doña* Susana's scolding had bothered me.

"Listen, Socorrito, I understand your displeasure. Unfortunately, we live in a small town, and if we want to stay out of trouble, you and the rest of us have to follow this society's standards," José Luis explained in a conciliatory voice.

"Being a divorced woman doesn't make her a bad person. Nobody knows the circumstances," I protested. "Besides, she seems very nice and polite."

"Believe me, I have lived here longer than you, therefore I know what I'm talking about," José Luis said.

Even though he was one year younger than Andrés and me, José Luis always behaved like an older brother, giving us wise suggestions. I recognized he spoke from experience, so I promised to follow his advice.

We decided we would accept her invitation to go for coffee, but I realized that afterward, I couldn't accept any more invitations from her. That made me extremely sad. I wondered if the attractive woman would have any friends. If she didn't because of the townspeople's taboos, I thought she would be a lot happier living in a big city. That way, her opportunities would be greater to find another husband and new friends.

"Regrettably, Socorrito," José Luis said, "we live in a small place—where everybody finds out about the lives of others."

"Yes, the *crystal box*. My mom advised me about that before I left home," I answered with a sigh.

Some days later, we attended the *merienda*, a mid-afternoon light dinner. Even though it was a casual affair, we dressed formally for the occasion. For Manuel, Andrés, and me, this was our first social visit in Doctor Arroyo.

The *merienda* consisted of frothy Mexican hot chocolate served in porcelain cups and delicious pastries made by the lady of the house and her divorced daughter. The sight of the pastries on the silver trays and the aroma of the hot chocolate whetted our appetite. Our student was there, too, keeping us company. At the end, all of the pastries were gone.

We spent a pleasant afternoon and retired after almost two hours. The ladies invited us to come back, but sadly, I knew that would never happen.

José Luis's advice about living by the town's rules made me reconsider my way of thinking. Besides, not knowing how long I would be working there, I should stay on good terms with the townspeople. Once I accepted this, it was easier for me to abide by some traditions that would have been unacceptable elsewhere.

I never imagined how soon I would start learning the real meaning of living in a *crystal box*.

CHAPTER TWELVE

THE BURIED GOAT CONTEST

The festivities for the celebration of Mexican Independence Day on September 16 came with excitement and patriotic fervor. I received an invitation from the town's municipal office to present a medal to the winner of one of the contests open to the public. That would be my first time to participate officially. This made me feel very special.

For such an occasion, I put on a white Mexican dress made of *tira bordada*. My mom had patiently sewn together twenty-centimeter-wide embroidered cotton strips until she had enough material to make my pretty dress. I also wore high-heeled white sandals; a pair of large, Mexican gold-filigree earrings; and a red Mexican *rebozo*, which is a long shawl with a silk fringe.

I arrived in the company of the other teachers and Manuel, the lawyer, to the designated place. One of the organizers presented me with a colorful corsage and escorted me to my seat on a platform. There were around nine other young women wearing nice clothes and the same kind of corsages. All of them held a ribbon with a medal in their hands. I didn't recognize anyone, so I said *"¡Hola!"* in general and sat to wait for instructions. From the corner of my eye, I noticed that some of these women glanced at me but kept their distance. Two of them whispered to each other, half covering their mouths. *I can imagine what's on their minds. How do I dare to arrive by myself with four men? It must be too much for the town's standard. Well, if they resent it, it's their problem, not mine.*

I wasn't concerned about people's opinion. They didn't know me yet. But there wasn't any doubt in my mind that I would earn their trust and respect once they got to know me better.

I was aware of many eyes fixed on me and tried to keep a composed expression, but deep inside I felt isolated. A few minutes later, I heard somebody calling my name.

"Maestra, maestra Socorrito!" It was Horacio, and he was with several of his classmates. They were trying to get my attention by tapping on the high platform where I sat.

"Hi, boys!" I said, smiling at them. They waved and smiled back to me. Their presence made me feel better. *I am not completely alone in this town. I have all of them, and they are the important persons in my current life.*

From a loudspeaker came the sound of a patriotic tune, the *"Marcha Zacatecas."* Several children and adults enthusiastically waved Mexican flags. Others rode their bicycles that sported ribbons with the national colors of green, white, and red. Many women and little girls wore traditional Mexican dresses representing various states. They were a cheerful crowd.

We were in an open field under a pristine blue sky. The day was comfortably warm when the participants—all of them men on horseback—started lining up. In front of them stood a long wooden bar. From this high horizontal bar hung several cords with a medium-sized metal ring at the end. To win one of the ten medals, the contestants had to place a stick with a ribbon inside the metal loop while riding their horses at full speed. The task wasn't easy because they had to stretch to reach the constantly moving rings. The men tried several times while the crowd cheered when one of them accomplished the objective and laughed every time one missed the target. When there were nine winners, and only one opportunity to win a medal remained, the tension in the rest of the contestants mounted. The tenth winner was the one who took the longest to qualify. At the end, ten triumphant horsemen proudly wore the blue ribbons with medals that the other women and I had placed around their necks.

The persons in charge thanked us for our attendance and everyone started to leave. My students waved and left, too. I said goodbye with a nod to some of the women, but even though they did the same, none said a word to me.

As I came down from the platform, the teachers and Manuel joined me.

"There's another contest bigger than this," Lauro said. He pointed to the men who were arriving on horseback. Most of them were in groups of six or more.

José Luis stopped walking and stared at us with his brow furrowed. "I don't know if we should stay, especially Socorrito. That show can be a little barbaric," he said.

"Yes, you might be right," Lauro said. "Let's go back to the plaza."

But Manuel, Andrés, and I said that we wanted to watch that contest. We were coming from the city, therefore all of this was a novelty for us. Besides, it couldn't be that bad if women and children were present, too.

Lauro shrugged, and José Luis made a gesture of resignation. So, we headed to where the other contest would take place. We looked for a place to sit. In the center of an open large area, the horsemen formed two large teams on opposite sides. Their horses scratched the ground with their hooves and moved nervously from one side to the other while the men restrained them, holding the reins tightly in their hands. Contestants and animals waited impatiently to get in action. Here and there, a horse reared, but his rider controlled him by forcing him to turn in tight circles. The uneven sound of the horses' hooves, their neighs, the horsemen's loud voices, and the noise of the spectators produced a powerful cacophony.

Suddenly my sight focused on a live little goat, half buried in the middle of the field. Only the head and the four tied-up legs of the animal were visible. With all of the noise, it was hard to hear the heartbreaking bleating of the terrified goat, but the sight of the little animal was enough to make me feel uneasy.

With a knot on my stomach, I asked Lauro, "What kind of tournament is this? Why is that poor animal there?"

"¡*Es La Chiva Enterrada!* The Buried Goat," he said. "The team that pulls it out of there is the winner, if they can keep it for some time. You'll see."

The sudden silence of the crowd told me that the contest was about to start. All eyes locked on a man at the center of the field. He wore jeans and cowboy boots. He had a microphone in one hand and a black cowboy hat in the other.

"He's the referee," José Luis whispered.

"Ready ... Set ... Go!" the referee yelled, hitting the ground with his hat.

One man from each team on opposite sides came galloping at full speed toward the buried animal. The sound of the horses' hooves mixed with the beating of my heart. Bending dangerously to the side of their horses, the men tried to grab the goat by his legs while raising a cloud of dust. The teams took turns repeatedly, but their efforts were in vain. There was lots of shouting from the fans in support of their favorites and a general sound of disappointment when they failed. Finally, one of the most daring and skillful riders pulled the goat from the mound. A roar from the public rose in the air. Within seconds, the rider, protected by his team, ran in a certain direction while his opponents tried to snatch the goat from him, amidst much hard shoving and yelling. We saw them disappear in the distance.

"What happens now?" I asked José Luis, seeing that people stayed there.

"If the first team is able to reach their destination with the goat, they will be the winners."

He didn't have time to continue his explanation because suddenly the crowd yelled again. The horses were coming back, indicating the opponents had been able to steal the goat. They came back and crossed in front of the cheering crowd, galloping fast. Members of the first team followed them closely and tried to retrieve the goat. They left a big cloud of dust behind, and the sound of the horses' hooves diminished little by little until it was completely gone.

"We better go now," José Luis said. "You won't want to see what might happen next."

"What might happen?" Andrés and I asked in unison.

"Sometimes they disembowel the poor animal when the men pull it in different directions," Lauro explained.

"Are you serious?" My heart beat faster.

Lauro said, "Quite serious."

Andrés and I looked at each other with wide eyes. Such a possibility was enough to make us leave the place in a hurry. *I don't want to watch such a barbaric thing. I'm so sorry for the little goat.*

"I will never again attend one of these competitions," I said as we left.

The following day, some of my students were talking about the *Chiva Enterrada* contest before the beginning of class.

"If Dimas García had been present, no doubt he'd have been the winner. He has the best horses in the region," one of them said.

"Too bad he didn't come. I'm sure he would have won," another added.

Several students agreed. This aroused my curiosity.

"Who is Dimas García?" I asked.

"Whoa! He is a very famous man in these areas. Everyone here knows him," one of the students stated.

"When Dimas is in town, he goes inside the bar with his mare, and both of them get drunk," added another student. He smiled, proud of the information.

"Many people fear him," a girl who was usually silent said. "He's bad!"

"He gets into fights easily and kidnaps girls," another girl added, looking around.

The boys laughed, noticing the girls' apprehension.

"You better be careful, *maestra*, because if Dimas likes you, he could kidnap you on his mare," another girl advised me with wide eyes and a straight face.

I laughed. Either my students were trying to scare me—they had lots of imagination—or they had seen too many *Charro Negro* movies lately.

"You'll meet him soon," another student said. "He will be here for the town's fair."

"Hmm. When will that event take place?" I asked.

"It will be the first week of December," the same youngster answered.

The town's fair was still more than two months away. For now, we had a class to attend, and I soon forgot the silly conversation about kidnappings and drunken mares. What madness!

CHAPTER THIRTEEN

REGARDLESS OF CONSEQUENCES

Sometime during the following weeks, *profesor* Merla started talking to us about the possibility of having our own school building. The number of students was growing, and we concurred that soon, it would be impossible to find a building large enough to accommodate all of them.

The *director* shared his ideas with us about the way to make this dream a reality. We gave him some suggestions. Having a building was important for all of us, but even more for *profesor* Merla, who had dedicated many years of his life just to bring middle school education to Doctor Arroyo. I wondered how many people would really appreciate all of his dedication to this endeavor.

I knew that he had previously started a middle school, but the studies of that first school were not recognized. In his extraordinary effort to educate the young people of Doctor Arroyo, he had to work for a year without pay. That spoke volumes about how much he loved his profession.

The government of the state through *La Secretaría de Educación Pública de Nuevo León* had barely authorized the creation of the middle school in 1955. The evening classes began with *profesor* Merla as the school's principal and two teachers. By 1956, there were already five teachers and a custodian, and classes were held morning and afternoon. The number of students had grown, and the school continued to move from one place to another. Andrés and I came to replace two previous teachers: *profesor* César Tamayo and *profesora* Esperanza Martínez.

Now, we were there, in 1958, trying to make *profesor* Merla's dream a reality. We all wanted the youngsters from Doctor Arroyo to be successful. Having a permanent building was necessary to achieve this purpose. We agreed that we would pursue this project after our return from Christmas vacation.

Meanwhile, I looked forward to my mom's letters. Whenever I saw an envelope with her beautiful, small handwriting, I read it right away, always hungry for news from my family. My mom's words conveyed not only her love for me, but also her hope that I would work close to home the following year. From time to time, my dad wrote to me also, but it was harder for him to do it, because he worked fourteen hours a day.

My boyfriend's letters started arriving, too. Martín had joined the US Air Force two years before, so we had a long-distance relationship. Special circumstances had prevented him from coming to see me in Monterrey, where we had met. I dreamed often that one day he would surprise me by arriving in Doctor Arroyo wearing his uniform. Meanwhile, I had to be happy with his letters and his picture on top of my dresser. His big smile gave me comfort, but it also made me feel nostalgic. I would have loved to have a normal courtship, seeing each other every day and sharing with him all the things that other couples in love enjoyed.

My friends Mari Paz and Licha wrote to me now and then. I missed them a lot. I learned that Mari Paz used to cry over my absence. Licha hadn't accepted a job outside Monterrey, so she missed her opportunity to work for the State of Nuevo León. For that reason, she had to search for a job on her own.

So far, my only friends in Doctor Arroyo were the teachers and Manuel, the lawyer. The loneliness made us especially appreciate our friendship in which every one of us found mutual support. Attending Mass on Sundays was my spiritual comfort. Andrés stopped going to church, but I continued attending by myself.

One Sunday, coming back from church, I found *profesor* Merla talking to Andrés and José Luis in the restaurant. He interrupted his conversation when he saw me.

"Good morning, *profesor* Merla. How are you doing?" I asked him cheerfully.

"Good morning, *señorita*," he answered coldly. He tapped the table and ignored my question. His attitude puzzled me. We had talked and laughed the day before. He said something to José Luis and Andrés. Then, he looked directly at me and said, "*Señorita* Esperanza was a team member. She was always in solidarity with the rest of us."

I knew Esperanza was the teacher who I replaced, but *profesor* Merla's remark was incomprehensible to me. Confused, I asked him, "Excuse me, *profesor*. I don't understand your comment. Why are you saying this?"

"Because we never attended mass nor did she," he said, raising an eyebrow. Then he rested his back on the chair and looked at me like he was waiting for an answer.

He didn't invite me to sit down, so I stood in front of him feeling my cheeks burning. What I had just heard was incredible! I bit my lower lip and thought carefully about my answer.

I decided it was better to let the *director* and the rest of the teachers know where I stood in my Christian beliefs. I felt my hands shaking and held them together, trying to hide my nervousness. I breathed deeply. Then, I said, "With all of the respect that you deserve, *profesor* Merla, I have to tell you this. As my school principal, you have all the right to set regulations or correct me about my job, if deserved. However, going to church is part of my private life, and since my parents are not here, I decide what's best for me. My religion is not part of my obligation to my job, nor does it interfere with it, and for this reason, it is not even a matter of discussion. I'm sorry."

The teachers' faces began to blur, and I fought back my tears. I didn't want to cry in front of them.

It was obvious that Andrés and José Luis observed the scene with some tension. José Luis cleared his throat and his frown deepened. Andrés crossed his arms, and half closed his eyes. None of us liked to provoke our principal's anger, but this time it had been unavoidable. There was a long uncomfortable silence.

Angry lines appeared around *profesor* Merla's slightly trembling lips. He put aside his cup of coffee and got up from his chair. Then he put on his straw hat twisted to one side—one of his idiosyncrasies when he was angry. He gave me a cold look that made me shiver.

"I'll see you tomorrow," he said. He pushed his chair in and stormed out of the restaurant.

Shaking, but at the same time proud that I had expressed my feelings, I told José Luis and Andrés, "I'm sorry, but I had to defend my convictions."

Andrés smiled shyly and shrugged. He stayed silent, and I wondered if he had disapproved of my words.

José Luis, on the other hand, tried to calm me down. "Don't worry, Socorrito. *Profesor* Merla will get over it soon. Tomorrow will be a new day."

"I hope so." I sighed. I hoped José Luis's words would come true. However, I felt that something was broken in my heart.

CHAPTER FOURTEEN

A GATHERING WITH TALENT ...
AND MALICE

As José Luis said, Monday was a new day, and *profesor* Merla had already overcome his displeasure. As usual, he had come early for coffee. Before leaving, he woke us up by knocking on our bedroom doors. I got up right away and heard José Luis moving in his room. We had to knock two or three extra times on Andrés's door to wake him up. He was a heavy sleeper, so he had a hard time getting up. On several occasions, shaving hastily at the last minute had cost him cuts. It made us laugh to see him later with a small patch over the wound. He only managed a shy smile. Lauro ate with *profesor* Merla, so we only saw him at work and at nighttime when he came to visit with us. From time to time, both of them came to eat at the restaurant.

That afternoon, the *director* informed us that *don* Ramón Perales and his wife had invited us to their home the following Saturday to a *tertulia*—a social gathering with refreshments. Their son, Homero, was one of our students.

He and Horacio had a very close friendship. Homero was a smart and friendly boy who loved to make people laugh, especially in class. For this reason, he was frequently in trouble.

The Perales family ran a business and were influential in the community. They lived in a two-story house, right across from the main plaza. Their business was on the first floor.

The day of the *tertulia*, we arrived when the lights from the electric plant had just come on. All of us dressed formally, as we always did on special occasions. The men wore a jacket and tie, and I had a white pique dress with buttonhole neck.

"Welcome to our home," *don* Ramón said, inviting us with a wave of his hand to come into the house.

"Thank you for inviting us," *profesor* Merla replied on behalf of all.

Don Ramón gave each one of us a firm handshake and asked us to follow him upstairs to their large living room. *Señora* Perales and several persons who accompanied her stood up when we went into the room.

Don Ramón introduced Manuel, Andrés, and me to the other guests. There were two middle-aged women who were elementary school teachers. One was heavy and the other tall. Next to them sat an attractive widow named Ofelia and her sister Toñita, a *simpática* and loquacious lady. Also there was Father Rangel, who was very sociable and well-liked by people.

Señora Perales passed around some refreshments and small and tasty canapés. We sat in a circle and had a light conversation.

After a while, the hostess said, "I'm so glad all of you came so we can get to know each other better. What better opportunity than this to show your talents?"

The other teachers and I exchanged glances. *What's this? It didn't occur to me we would be asked to show our skills. I thought we were going to listen to some special guest. That is the concept that I had of a tertulia.*

From the expressions on their faces, Manuel and the other teachers apparently thought the same.

Señora Perales approached the two elementary teachers first, but they just giggled and declined to do anything. "Maybe some other time," one of them said.

Faced with that refusal, her attention turned to another guest. "Toñita, we would love for you to recite one of those beautiful poems you know."

She accepted immediately. "I'll be glad to declaim for all of you a poem in honor of St. Francis of Assisi, *'Los Motivos del Lobo'!*"

In those years, the art of declamation was very popular, and it was frequently manifested in friendly gatherings and even formal events. It began to decline during the 1970s. Today it survives mainly thanks to school activities. It is a difficult art, since it requires histrionics and good handling of rhythm and nuance.

Toñita stood up, and in a clear voice interpreted the beautiful poetry of Rubén Darío. The story of the terrible wolf that came to behave like a docile lamb thanks to San Francisco was recited with great emotion. As an experienced declaimer, Toñita used her body expressions and varied and dramatic nuances of voice to convey her feelings. Undoubtedly, the emotion she projected reached us deeply because in the end, she received a long ovation from all those present.

The parade of talents was just starting.

"*Profesor* Lauro, it's your turn. Are you going to sing us something?"

Lauro, who had a beautiful voice, played the guitar and sang a *tango*. He did it with ease, like someone used to performing in front of an audience. To sing this musical genre, tango, requires a special tone of voice—vigorous and dramatic at the same time to tell the story in the song with the sound of a soul's lament. Lauro had all of these traits. We all listened to his performance with pleasure.

After the warm applause for his performance faded, *señora* Perales looked around to choose the next person. The rest of us who hadn't participated yet moved nervously in our seats. José Luis frowned more than usual. He was a private person, and this wasn't his cup of tea.

"I think we should leave now," he whispered, covering his mouth with his hand. "Pass it around."

It was too late for me. Just when I was going to pass José Luis's message, I heard *señora* Perales's voice.

"So, what are you going to delight us with, *profesora* Camero?"

The hostess's question froze me. "Oh, I'm not good at doing anything in public other than teaching," I said. I knew some poems, but after Toñita's performance I did not dare to declaim. *And I certainly won't be dancing in the middle of the room.*

"We're sure you can do something," the heavy teacher said. She gave me a condescending sneer while waiting for my answer.

I felt all eyes on me and blushed.

Father Rangel joked, trying to cheer me up. "Don't tell us you don't sing in the shower."

I decided on a song that I liked to sing with my mother at home. She dedicated it to me with affection for the reference to the tone of my skin. Now, intimately, I would dedicate it to my mother.

I breathed deeply and announced, "Okay, I'll try to sing '*Morenita Mía*.'"

Because this is a very popular Mexican song, almost everybody started singing with me, so I didn't worry too much about being out of tune at some point. I relaxed, and at the end, everyone applauded enthusiastically, maybe celebrating themselves for their own participation. I felt glad I chose that song. The last thing I wanted at that time was to give the two teachers a reason to ridicule me later. My mother's prayers were undoubtedly with me.

Luckily for everyone, *señora* Perales decided that was enough participation for the night. Afterward we mingled with the other guests. I was talking to Father Rangel when the two teachers approached me.

"So, *profesora* Camero, how do you like working here?" The heavier teacher looked at me with a raised brow. "Do you enjoy being by yourself?"

I didn't have time to answer.

"Do you know *profesora* Esperanza Martínez? She's *profesor* Lauro's girlfriend," interrupted the taller teacher. She stared at me. Her head tilted with a sardonic smile on her face. The two of them completely ignored Father Rangel's presence. He, on the other hand, stared at them with a puzzled expression.

There was obvious malice in the women's questions. They smiled at each other, pleased to make me feel uncomfortable. Then they crossed their arms, waiting for my answer.

My mom's advice came to my head, "*Hijita,* don't forget, you can disarm your worst enemy with kindness." I had to try it.

"I love my job, and everyone in town has been kind to me, but I do miss my family because we are very close. I also miss my friends back in Monterrey because other than my coworkers, I don't know anyone here."

"Hmm!" mumbled the heavier teacher who held her chin, pensive, and looked at me with piercing eyes.

Without letting her intimidate me, I continued, "It must be hard for you to understand because you have the fortune that you don't have to work away from home like me. Also, you're surrounded with people you've known for a lifetime. Thank you for asking!"

Then, I turned to the taller teacher. "And regarding the second question, no, I don't know *profesora* Esperanza, but I have heard her name. I think it must be hard for *profesor* Lauro and her to be apart."

"What about *profesora* Lupita Martínez. Do you know her?" the same teacher asked me. She elbowed her friend, who had turned her attention to Father Rangel.

"I don't recognize her name. Is she Esperanza's sister?"

Somebody called Father Rangel, who gave me a pat on the shoulder as he left.

"No, no relation," said the tall teacher. "They came here at the same time, but *profesora* Lupita came as principal of the elementary school. She was way too young for that position, if you ask me." There was a scornful tone in her voice.

"She certainly was," the heavier teacher said. "Too bad she had to leave before the end of the year."

"How come?" I asked.

"She got sick and never came back." The taller teacher smirked and shrugged after she said this, and then, both of them walked away to talk to somebody else.

'Pueblo chico, infierno grande'. "Small town, big hell," my mother had said. She was so right. I just prayed that people like those two women would stay away from me.

The *tertulia* lasted for another hour. Everybody started to leave at the same time.

"We had a great time. Again, thank you for inviting us," *profesor* Merla told *señor y señora* Perales.

Each one of us complimented them about their hospitality, their house, the food, and the ambience.

The hosts smiled widely. They knew the *tertulia* had been a success. They stayed by the door, waving goodbye to their guests.

Lauro told us good night and left in a different direction from ours. He whistled a tune as he walked away. I enjoyed the soft cool breeze of the starry night as I strolled home in between Andrés and Manuel.

"It would be great if Lauro would live with us, too," Manuel said. Andrés and I agreed.

I wanted to learn more about Lupita Martínez, but José Luis and *profesor* Merla were chatting all the way home. As soon as we arrived, we said good night to each other, and everybody went to bed.

I fell asleep thinking that somebody eventually would tell me about *maestra* Lupita. I was sure most of the townspeople would know a lot about her, as they did about everything else.

At the end of the day, we were living in a *crystal box*.

CHAPTER FIFTEEN

MY NEW FEMALE FRIEND

Life in Doctor Arroyo became a smooth routine. From Monday to Friday we worked four hours in the morning. Then we went home for an early dinner and sometimes to take a short nap. Afterward, students and teachers returned to school for our afternoon shift. This schedule was completely different from that of the last school where I worked as student teacher in Monterrey, where we labored a five-hour straight shift.

At nighttime, usually around seven, we had the *merienda*, which was something light like coffee, milk, or hot chocolate and sweet bread. When we had something heavier like tacos or meat and vegetables, it was a *cena*. This was more infrequent because we had our heavy dinner earlier in the day. Afterward we played cards in José Luis's room, where we talked about the daily events or shared personal stories. We went as a group to the movies twice a week. As for me, I attended Mass on Sunday morning and the movies in the evening. *Profesor* Merla hadn't made any more comments about my religious practice, which convinced me that I was right to express my feelings about it. Being away from my family for the first time in my life, I found lots of comfort in going to church, and I wasn't willing to deprive myself of that or compromise my beliefs under any circumstances.

Some of the students came to visit us from time to time. They told us about themselves and their families, and through them, we learned about other people, too. Little by little, we became acquainted with the townspeople and their customs. We learned the nicknames of many of them—hilarious, generally. Teresa's husband was called *Juan Cazuelas*, referring to the fact that he sold clay pots. *Juan, El Salivoso*, received this name because he spat all the time, and there were several more *Juanes* in the town, with their respective nicknames to differentiate them. There was also *Pedrito y Medio*, "Pete and a Half," who was a very tall man. Another very popular man in town was *José Mentiras*, "José Lies." It's easy to imagine why he earned this nickname. Finally, one of my students was called *Sergio El Guapo*, Handsome Sergio, due to his attractive appearance. Yes, I knew more people but was still missing a female friend with whom to share women's issues and personal things—a good friend like the ones I left in Monterrey.

One afternoon, as we came back from work, *doña* Susana came out of the kitchen wiping her hands on her apron. There was a happy expression on her wrinkled face and some wet curls stuck to her sweaty forehead. Her scalp was still showing the black dye she had used on her hair the day before.

"*Señorita*," she said smiling and showing a gold tooth, "*¡Tengo una sorpresa para usted!*".

I was curious about what surprise she had for me. As she moved to the side, a younger woman stepped out of the kitchen. "*¡Ésta es mi hija, Nena!* She just came back from her vacation in Monterrey."

Doña Susana had told me a lot about her daughter, and I was eager to meet her.

"Cleotilde López Portillo," she introduced herself with a shadow of a smile. She extended her hand to me, studying me carefully.

"Oh, *usted es la famosa* Nena Portillo. I'm so happy to finally meet you." I shook her hand. "I'm Socorro Camero. It's nice to have another girl around here. I hope we'll become good friends."

"I'm sure we will," she answered with half a smile. "I was getting ready to sit down for dinner. Would you like to join me?"

Nena was so serious that I didn't know if she was just being polite or if the invitation was spontaneous.

"Go ahead and join her," José Luis said. He had come to say hello to Nena and to introduce Andrés to her.

"Okay, Nena. I'll be right back," I said. "Please tell Teresa I'll be eating with you."

I rushed to leave my belongings in my room and wash my hands. Afterward I went back to join my new friend. The maids had already set a table for the two of us, and Nena was waiting for me to start eating.

Nena was a girl of medium height, although she looked taller because she walked or sat very straight. She was thin, with pale white skin; her short hair was dyed and curled. The only makeup she wore was a clear lipstick. I knew through her mom that she was older than I was.

"I have lived with my father since he and my mother split," she told me. "I didn't want him to be alone. Anyway, my mother has Horacio and the maids to keep her company. My father and I have a small clothing store in the next block. We come for breakfast and dinner daily, so in a way, I see my mother every day."

Nena also explained to me that Horacio was one of two sons of a deceased brother of hers. Horacio's oldest brother lived in México City with their mother. Horacio visited them every year during the summer.

"Horacio and I don't get along," Nena said, frowning and observing her well-groomed hands. "I think my mother has spoiled him too much."

"Well, so far he has behaved well in school," I said. "He's been very polite to the other teachers and especially to me. Horacio even told me to let him know if someone bothers me, and he will take care of putting him in his place. Imagine!"

"Hmm," Nena murmured, raising an eyebrow.

We talked for quite some time until her father, *don* Juan, came for dinner. He slammed the swinging doors and picked a table far from ours. He glared at us.

"My dad isn't too happy that he had to close the store in order to come," Nena said, giggling, amused at her father's displeasure. She left right away, but not before promising that we would continue with our conversation later.

From that day on, my life in Doctor Arroyo changed. I had dinner with Nena almost every day. She had grown accustomed to my company, and we laughed easily. On Sundays, we attended Mass together and during the week, we would go for a walk to the main square after the *cena*. There was always something to talk about.

"My mom told me you were amiable and easy to get along with, but I wasn't sure until I met you," she said. "By the way, do you know *maestra* Esperanza and *maestra* Lupita Martínez? They came to work in Doctor Arroyo at the same time."

"No, I don't know Lupita or Esperanza. In fact, I heard Lupita's name for the first time at a gathering at the Perales family's home. There were two elementary school teachers there, and one of them asked me if I knew her."

"Really?" Nena said. She raised an eyebrow and shook her head.

I told her about the conversation that had taken place the day of the *tertulia* and how later on some of my students told me that *maestra* Lupita had a nervous breakdown because of the way some teachers treated her.

"They told me that some teachers didn't like Lupita because she came assigned as the school principal and she was very young and inexperienced."

"She was younger that any of the teachers, for sure," Nena said. "We didn't have a friendship, but I met her. She was very nice, and yes, she had to leave before school was over. She was a sweet person, and the students loved her a lot."

"That's so sad. I can't believe that she had to endure such abuse from some of her staff," I said, remembering some of the incidents the students had mentioned. *I hope one day I can meet Lupita to corroborate some of the stories I've heard.*

Nena sighed deeply, then said, "You just don't know how lucky you are working at the middle school with male teachers."

"You're right. I'm very lucky to be working under these conditions and especially having you as my friend."

She smiled and squeezed my arm. I felt really blessed with her friendship.

Sometime later, Nena told me that the Berrones' older girls, Chelo and Eva, wanted to meet me. We were invited to play *Canasta Uruguaya* at their home. José Luis had told Andrés and me before that their father, *don* Amancio, was the most important man in town. His maids, who had taken care of the family forever, still called him *Niño* Amancio, and his sisters—who were old ladies—*las Niñas*. And they celebrated their birthdays with piñata parties. I found these customs charming and amusing.

The Berrones family lived in a large comfortable house next to their store. This was located in a corner facing plaza Juárez. When the *rancheros* came shopping in Doctor Arroyo, they tied their horses outside the store. It looked like a set of an Old West movie.

Irma, one of the younger Berrones sisters, attended our school. Another two, Alicia and Petrita, were still in elementary school. All of them were kind, polite girls. I liked all of them, especially Eva, who was around my age and still single. Chelo, one of the oldest sisters, was married to the town's telegraphist. She was older than me. They also had some other siblings living in Mexico City. What I admired most about this large family was its simplicity; they were not pretentious at all.

When Nena introduced me to Chelo and Eva, I felt a little bit shy, but Irma and Alicia took care to give me confidence.

"I'm so glad you came to visit us." Alicia added a hug to her words. She was a very sweet girl.

"*¡Maestra, por favor siéntase en casa!*", Irma said, patting my arm. I thought it was very sweet of Irma to tell me to feel at home.

"Thank you for making me feel welcome," I told both girls.

We went into a large living room. There was a sofa and some cushion chairs. Several family pictures were displayed on the walls around the room. There were some vases with colorful flowers on top of small stands. Their sweet aroma wafted through all the place. We sat around a large coffee table where two decks of cards awaited us.

"I don't know if Nena mentioned to you that I've never played *Canasta Uruguaya* before, but if you teach me, I will have no problem," I told them.

The Berrones girls patiently explained the game rules to me. With such good teachers, I learned it fast. We played several rounds among gales of laughter every time we were close to winning. I really enjoyed this game and couldn't wait to try it again.

Later on, we had a delicious lunch of Mexican *antojitos*, like *flautas, quesadillas*, and *guacamole* amid lively conversations. I felt as if we had known each other for a long time. Before leaving, Nena and I promised to return soon.

After the first visit, we got together frequently. We played cards or danced with a record player. We had lots of fun at these gatherings. When any of us went on vacation to México City, San Luis Potosí, or Monterrey, we brought back the latest fashion styles and new songs and dance moves to share with the others. Being only twenty years old, despite living in a small town, this was still very important to me, as I was a city girl.

I belong to a dancing generation that executed each rhythm with its characteristic steps. We lived in a very quiet Mexico, and dancing, not only in the salons but also in our own houses, was a collective diversion with which we cultivated social relationships and got out of our routines.

My circle of friends was growing, and I was acquiring new ways to have fun. However, my priority continued to be my students, for whom I had a responsibility with both the school and the townspeople.

The middle school now had an important role in Doctor Arroyo's society. Parents and citizens were able to see how much our school had grown when the group of proud students took part in the parade on November 20.

Parade: Lilia Nava front, Sergio Sánchez behind her. Photo provided by Profa. Lilia Nava.

I loved to see them in their uniforms. The boys wore navy-blue pants and white shirts. The girls wore white pleated skirts, short navy-blue jackets with gold buttons and shoulder pads with gold fringe, black shoes, and white socks. In front of all marched the standard-bearer and her *escolta*, made up of two girls and two boys. Two of them were Lilia Nava and Sergio Sánchez, *el Guapo*.

Behind them, the *banda de guerra*, the drum and bugle corps, perfectly marked the steps of the contingent of our school with the beating of its drums and the sound of its trumpets. Horacio was part of it, and his grandmother, *doña* Susana, smiled with satisfaction when she saw him pass by playing his trumpet.

Our youngsters represented the bright future of a developing town.

CHAPTER SIXTEEN

THE VILLAIN: TRUTH OR MYTH?

My new female friends had given my life new meaning too. I was having lots of fun with them. Soon, we would enjoy together one of the town's most significant celebrations.

One Friday afternoon, I noticed a lot of activity at the main plaza. I saw large trucks distributing lumber among some of the people present. Several of them were already using it to build different-sized stands around the plaza. That explained the divisions I had seen marked on the floor with whitewash. They were the spaces assigned to these participants.

That afternoon, I asked Nena about it. "Nena, what's going on at the plaza?"

"We are getting ready for the annual town's fair," she said. "The people you saw are the ones who will be selling food or having some kind of entertainment, like the *lotería*."

"A town's fair? That's fantastic. When will it start?"

"The first of December. The fair, which many people call *la Función*, is in honor of the *Virgen de la Purísima Concepción*, the town's patroness."

"I can hardly wait. I'm sure it's going to be a lot of fun."

"There is also a *novena* of pilgrimages for the Virgin, from November 30 to December 8. This is followed by another four days of pilgrimages, from December 9 to December 12, in honor of the Virgin of Guadalupe."

"Ah, of course. After all, the Virgin of Guadalupe is the Patroness of México."

Nena explained to me that during the *novena*, two groups of pilgrimages take brand-new wax candles to church every day. One group comes from some ranch near Doctor Arroyo, and the other is organized by a town lady. During the pilgrimage, the participants sing and pray all the way to the church, usually accompanied by a town band. All the large candles or tapers brought to the church as an offering to the Virgin will be used in religious services throughout the year. Afterward there is a Mass for each group.

"And the pilgrimages to the Virgin of Guadalupe?"

"Those are from the ninth to the twelfth, and they are run by men. Likewise, there are two daily pilgrimages to the church, but both are local. Here, in addition to the wax candles, the children come with typical costumes, offering flowers to the Virgin of Guadalupe. If the host can afford it, it will include groups of *matachines*. The pilgrimages are accompanied by rockets and the joyous peals of the church bells. It really is a great time of the year," continued Nena. "Many families from Doctor Arroyo who work in the United States will start arriving soon. Every year they come home to attend these festivities."

"Will they leave town at the end of the celebrations?"

"Not at all. They'll stay for the *Posadas*," Nena said. "You know that this is one of our great religious traditions in México."

Nena told me that the visitors would stay not only for the *Posadas* and the New Year's parties, but for Kings Day, *Día de los Santos Reyes*, on January 6. In reality, most of them would stay throughout December and January—partying most of the time. Afterward they would go back to their jobs in the States.

"It's an exciting season because it breaks the town's monotony. Just wait, you'll see many new faces and lots of fancy cars," she said. "It's quite a sight!"

"Where do all these families come from?" I asked.

"Their cars mostly have plates from Illinois, California, Oklahoma, and Texas."

"Hmm. Just wait to hear all of their noise in the usually quiet streets," *doña* Susana said, grumbling as she brought us a new plate of food.

"Yes, Mom," Nena laughed, "but you and the whole town will be very attentive to see what cars the visitors will bring this year. Maybe because they seem to change them frequently."

"Hmm," repeated *doña* Susana before going into the kitchen.

"Your mom doesn't look very enthusiastic about these foreigners," I said before savoring a spoonful of the rich flavor of the meatball soup. The aroma of fresh cilantro and cumin was delightful. Still, I spiced it with more hot sauce and lemon.

"'Lots of noise and lots of visitors,' she says, but she'll be the first one looking out to see who came." Nena chuckled.

"By the way, there are still quite a few people I don't know, so how do I know who the foreigners are?"

Nena told me that I would recognize them right away because they dressed and behaved differently from the local people, especially the youngsters. She said that even though many of them had acquired an accent, they hadn't forgotten their roots and romances in Doctor Arroyo.

"Well, now, I'm not only excited but curious, too," I said.

Nena stared into space for a couple of minutes. Then, exhaling deeply, she said, "The one nobody wants to see is Dimas García, who always comes around these dates."

"Who is Dimas García?" I asked her, remembering what the students had said weeks before.

"He is the region's bad boy, like in the movies. Unfortunately, there is a feud going on between his family and another family in town."

"How is that?" I said, intrigued with what sounded like a Western film.

She told me the story that was circulating in the town: Some years ago, a dance had been held to celebrate the New Year. It was already the first minutes of the first of January, when Dimas had an altercation with a young man. Relatives on both sides got involved. They took out their weapons and suddenly there was an exchange of bullets. When it was all over, there were six bodies lying on the ground—three from each family.

Nena paused again, as she collected her thoughts. "Since then, both families have been trying to take revenge on each other. Because their relatives died *de mala muerte*, each family had been stealing crosses from the graves of their rivals for a long time."

I shivered when Nena said they died 'in a seedy way.' I wanted to know more. "And what do they want the crosses for?"

"According to superstition, the relatives of a victim carry the stolen cross and bury it in front of the door of their house. The murderer's family will try to rescue that cross and it will be the opportunity for the victim's relatives to take revenge. In the case of the relatives of Dimas and the other family, after constantly replacing the wood crosses in the cemetery, each family finally replaced them with others made of cement; for now, they remain intact," she explained.

"Oh, my God! I hope Dimas forgets to come," I said.

"He won't forget. You'll see. He always arrives with a bunch of friends and gets into the bar with his horse. There are lots of stories about his *parrandas* or drunkenness. They say that when he's drunk, he gives beer to his horse. I don't know how true these stories are, but people believe them."

"But do you believe them? You've lived here all your life, so you should know if people are telling the truth or exaggerating."

Instead of answering, she just shrugged her shoulders.

Teresa had been listening to our conversation while she picked up dishes from the tables. She approached us to make her contribution. "Do you know that last year Dimas got furious for some reason and used his whip to smash several of the electric connections at the fair?"

"And what did the police do?" I asked her.

"They kept him detained for some hours, until he paid for the damages, and then he was out. And that's not all. People claim he has kidnapped four or five girls, but he goes around free as the wind."

"What are you saying, Teresa? I can't believe something like this could happen in the 50s! Simply for stealing cows they imprison those responsible. Maybe people are making up these stories about that man."

"I wish we knew," Nena said, shrugging her shoulders again.

So, maybe what my students said about Dimas is true, and I didn't believe them.

"What does he look like?" I asked her. In my mind, I already had an image of him. Being a villain, he had to be somebody ugly and grotesque, with big scars on his face.

"He's tall and good-looking. You will identify him immediately, even if he's in a large group of men. He has a strong presence."

"Wow, really?"

"Really. Oh, I hope he doesn't put his eyes on you, because he just might carry you off on his mare to his ranch," she said.

I don't know what the expression on my face was, but it made my friend laugh.

"Oh, be quiet, Nena, and knock on wood!" I said. I felt something cold run down my spine. Even if it was just rumors, I remembered the saying, *'Cuando el rio suena, agua lleva,'* which literally means,

'When the river sounds, water carries.' Anyway, I hoped not to come across this heinous character. I wouldn't know how to react.

Well, I found this out, sooner than I had expected.

One afternoon, as I entered the dining room, I noticed four men sitting around one of the tables. One of them had his back to the door. I could see only his big shoulders and his head with short black hair. At the sound of my high heels on the tile floor, he turned around. He stood up from his chair, and I knew immediately who he was— Dimas García.

Nena had described him perfectly: he was tall, good-looking, and with a strong presence. I felt as if somebody had hit me in the stomach, leaving me without air.

"¡Buenas tardes, señorita!", he said, smiling and courteous. The other three only greeted me with a nod.

"¡Buenas tardes, señores!", I answered in general. Too late to run and hide!

Nena had told me the day before that she would be late for dinner and not to wait for her. I walked toward the table designated for us, the teachers. My legs felt weak and shaky.

Dimas elbowed one of the men and changed places with him. Even though he wasn't facing me directly, I knew he could see me. I kept my eyes on my placemat, hoping that the teachers would show up for dinner soon. I felt my forehead start to perspire, but I didn't dare to dry it.

I was ready to ask Claudia to call them when José Luis and Andrés came through the hall door. I sighed in relief.

"*¡Buenas tardes, señores!*", José Luis and Andrés said to the men. They answered the greeting back as was customary.

I noticed José Luis had recognized Dimas immediately. As he sat down, he asked me in a whisper, "Do you know who that tall man is?"

"I do. He's Dimas García," I whispered back, holding my hands nervously.

Andrés looked discreetly in Dimas' direction.

By that time, the maids already knew the man and his friends were there. They looked for excuses to come into the restaurant, paying more attention to him than to the food they were putting in front of us. Teresa was in charge of Dimas's table, and she did her job with a grave expression. José Luis, Andrés, and I talked in a low voice, glancing often to the four guys who talked animatedly.

When the men finished eating, they stood up, picked up their hats, and walked toward the restaurant's main door.

"*¡Maestros, con permiso!*", Dimas said, stopping briefly by our table and respectfully raising his hat, an action that was repeated by his three companions.

"*¡Hasta luego!*", we said. They went through the swinging doors, and we saw them standing outside for few seconds. Soon they disappeared from our sight. I heard the rhythmical sound of their boots as they strolled on the sidewalk in the direction of the pool hall and cantina.

Very soon, everybody knew Dimas García was in town.

"*¡Hola!*" Nena said next time I saw her. "Have you heard that Dimas García is in town?"

"I already met him. He came to eat at the restaurant. I saw him, and he talked to me. He's exactly as you described." Then I told her all that had happened. "You put fear into me when you told me about Dimas. I could hardly eat, knowing that he was just a few steps away."

Nena laughed to the point of crying. She wiped her tears and laughed again.

As usual, Nena and I went for a night walk around the main plaza. Several small stands were already decorated. The merry-go-round was almost finished. A person inspected that the carousel horses were well adjusted. Another connected the sound system. Everything else seemed to be in place.

"I wonder what kind of fair we'll have this year," Nena said. "People from Matehuala and many other communities come to Doctor Arroyo for this celebration. Unfortunately, every year somebody dies. Last year, five persons were murdered around the area. Still, there is lots of fun."

Upon hearing this, I understood why no one wanted to teach in Doctor Arroyo, but I was there, with the firm decision to be happy practicing my profession. Besides, we would be going home for Christmas vacation in less than a month. I was eager to see my family and share all my experiences in this town with them. Hopefully, Doctor Arroyo would be my home only for a year.

At least, I hoped so.

CHAPTER SEVENTEEN

THE TOWN FAIR AND A LINK TO MY PAST

It was the last day of November. Within a few hours, the annual fair would begin. The excitement could be felt throughout the town.

The stalls around the main plaza were ornamented with multicolor crepe paper flowers and strips. Large posters advertised the menu items and prices. The merry-go-round was in place, clean and shiny, ready to be mounted. Some children wanted to know how long they had to wait to enjoy the ride. A man told them to come back the following day. Behind him, another person tested the sound system.

On the plaza's south side, another popular ride, *La Ola*, "The Wave," was being installed in a hurry. This was a platform like the carousel's, but it was more elevated. Instead of wooden horses, it had a single bench all around for people to sit. The bench faced outward and the platform moved up and down like a wave as it spun to the sound of music. To mount it, one had to climb a wooden ladder with several rungs. This mechanical ride belonged to the Castilleja family.

"It will be finished tonight," said Pepe Castilleja. His brothers Vicente and little Pedro were helping too.

Some onlookers decided to give them a hand. With the extra help, everybody knew *La Ola* would thrill them soon.

Eva and Nena told me they had new dresses made for the fair's celebration. They gave me their seamstress' name and address in case I wanted to have some clothes sewn. I decided to wear what I had instead of spending money in new clothes. We would go home in three weeks, so I needed to save what was left of my paycheck to buy some Christmas presents for my family. Every month I had sent half of my salary to my mom; consequently, after paying for my room and board, I didn't have much left.

That afternoon, Nena and I chatted while waiting for our dinner. The aroma coming from the kitchen increased our appetites.

"We are hungry, Mom," called Nena.

"We are coming. We are coming," answered *doña* Susana from inside the kitchen.

She and Teresa came from the kitchen with two steaming bowls of beef soup that they placed in front of us. We squeezed our lemons in the *caldo* and put a bunch of fresh *cilantro* in it. I added a couple of spoons of hot sauce in mine. The beef, carrots, potatoes, cabbage, and corn on the cob filled the bowl to the rim. It looked colorful and delicious and made my mouth water.

Doña Susana, who stood by the table, cleared her throat a couple of times and rubbed her hands on her apron. Then she said, "Do you know that the Nava family arrived in town last night, just in time for the beginning of the fair?"

"How did you already find out, Mom?" Nena asked.

Doña Susana placed her arms over our table and bent over. "One of my customers told me this morning. He was on the bus when the

Nava family's car passed by them. According to him, at the beginning nobody knew who it was, but when the people inside rolled down the windows to wave, the passengers on the bus recognized them."

"News sure runs fast in this town." Nena shook her head.

Doña Susana shrugged and went back into the kitchen.

"Well, Nena, like in any other small town, we are living in a *crystal box*," I said, chuckling. "Now let's finish eating, and tomorrow we can also see the newcomers."

Life was certainly not boring around me.

The next morning, a loud noise startled me. I opened my eyes and raised my head from the softness of my pillow, trying to find out what was happening. Then I realized the sound was coming from a speaker on the street. *Could these be don José Mentiras' famous loudspeakers that some students had told me about?*

A masculine voice said, "And now, with lots of love, we dedicate this song to the Virgin, *'Las Mañanitas'*!"

The words of the traditional Spanish language birthday song traveled through the thin air, probably waking up everybody in town. I looked at the clock. It was just past six o'clock. It was the first day of the fair, but I didn't expect it would start that early.

I tried to go back to sleep, but after *"Las Mañanitas,"* there was one song after another. Some were dedicated to the Virgin and others to friends, especially between *compadres* or *comadres*. Men and women participated.

The choice of songs ranged from serious to romantic and sometimes even hilarious, like the song about a man who gave two pesos to his wife Bartola and hoped that with that money she would pay "the rent, the telephone, and the electricity." And the ungrateful husband still hoped that she had money left over for something else!

All of the town's hotels were full. At breakfast time, *doña* Susana told Nena and me that she had rented one of the last two available rooms to a teacher, who was a friend of José Luis and Lauro.

"And where is he, Mom?" Nena asked, looking around.

"He arrived early and is in his room taking a nap."

"Is he handsome?" Nena asked. She looked at me and started giggling.

"Hmm, you'll have to wait to meet him. Then you'll tell me," *doña* Susana answered, shrugging.

"He's tall and quite handsome," Teresa said while she picked up some dirty dishes from one of the tables.

Nena looked again at the door and then at her watch and sighed. "You have to tell me how he looks later, *maestra*. Now I have to go, or my father will be angry." She winked at me as she left.

"That old man gets angry about everything!" *doña* Susana grumbled.

I stayed in the dining room keeping company with José Luis, who was eating alone. I accepted a cup of aromatic fresh coffee that Teresa offered me. We talked for a little bit, and just before I asked him about his friend, the new guest, my eyes got big when I saw a man enter the dining room. I recognized his tall frame, his blue eyes, and his shy smile.

"Santiago Cantú! What are you doing here?" I stood up smiling from ear to ear.

"Hi, *Socorrito.* Surprised to see me?" He advanced and gave me a light hug.

"Do you know each other?" José Luis asked, frowning when he saw my reaction.

"Of course, we know each other well. We are old friends. Santiago was my classmate at the teachers' university, the Normal School," I answered.

Santiago nodded and smiled. Then he told us he was teaching in a town several miles away from Dr. Arroyo. He said he had heard about my assignment there. That explained why he wasn't surprised to see me.

"Are you still writing to your boyfriend in the Air Force?" he asked.

"I'm still doing it, Santiago." All of my classmates knew about my relationship with Martín because they had to know why I couldn't accept a date with anyone. They understood it, and when they asked me about him, I used to tell them of the places where he was at the time.

"I'm so glad to see you again, Socorrito," Santiago said. "There will be another friend to visit when I come into town, which will be often."

"I'm delighted to know you'll come back often," I told him sincerely. Santiago was a link to my happy student days in Monterrey.

That afternoon, Nena came to get me around seven o'clock. The weather was pleasant, but we carried light wraps to wear later in case it got cold. We headed toward the main plaza where Eva and her sisters Irma and Alicia already waited for us. We all wore new outfits and took extra time fixing our hair and makeup. My friends loved the royal blue, faux suede dress I was wearing. The week before the fair, I had received a package from my mother with this dress and a red one of the same material, a white coat that I could wear with both, and a pair of red shoes. It was extraordinary how my mother always seemed to guess my needs. I was moved to think of what she would deprive herself of to give me this beautiful gift.

After a short chat, we started walking around. There were several small gatherings of boys and girls from my school. I greeted them from afar and they waved back. Some of the girls ran to hug me. I spotted Horacio with some pretty girls I'd never seen before. They dressed differently from the town girls, and I deduced that they were newcomers. Apparently, they weren't Nena's or Eva's friends, because they just nodded at each other from a distance.

We continued walking and approached the merry-go-round. Children of all ages laughed with joy when the different animals they mounted went up and down. When the music stopped, most of the children dismounted their animals to let others ride. However, there were a couple of them who refused to come down. Their parents gave up and paid for a second round. Afterward we headed to a big, bustling stall.

We tried our luck at the popular *lotería*, a game similar to bingo. The game is played on rectangular cards with sixteen figures on them. One person calls out on the microphone each figure, and the players who have it mark it on their card with a grain of corn. The winner is the person who fills up the card first or matches four figures in the center, horizontally or across. The winning person must yell *"Loteria!"* at the top of his lungs. This is to stop the caller from naming another figure, which could give the prize to somebody else. Irma and Alicia won a couple of prizes. After four games, we convinced ourselves that it wasn't a lucky day for the rest of us, so we left the unlucky cards and continued with the *paseo*.

The aroma that came from the food stalls was irresistible, and we opted to sit down and eat some *antojitos* accompanied by lemonade. *Antojitos* are specialties of the region, like *flautas*, made with corn tortillas filled with meat, rolled thinly, fried, and served with sour cream and spicy *guacamole*. *Antojitos* also include *taquitos*, which are tortillas folded and fried, filled with chicken or beef, and garnished with avocado, lettuce, and tomato. There were also *gorditas*, that are round and thicker than a pancake with different kinds of fillings. These *antojitos* are usually served with *aguas frescas*, like *limonada*, *horchata*, *jamaica*, or *tamarindo*.

Once we satisfied our hungry palates and stomachs, we went to the side of the square chosen for the dance. This was in front of the municipal office, and the atmosphere was already at its peak. We found a place to sit and almost immediately we saw Andrés and Manuel. As soon as they noticed our presence, Andrés invited me to dance, and Manuel invited Nena, who accepted shyly. After a couple of songs, I went to sit down. I was talking to my friends when one of my older students walked toward me. I froze. It didn't occur to me that they would invite me to dance! Fortunately, Santiago appeared at that moment, and smiling, extended his hand to me. I gladly agreed to dance with him. My student turned around with a gesture of frustration.

"Thanks, Santiago. You just saved me!"

"How did I do that? I didn't see you in any kind of danger." He feigned astonishment.

I told him about my student's intention to invite me to dance. I didn't want to embarrass him by declining his invitation. Santiago just smiled, and we changed the subject.

At the end of the song, we went to meet Nena and Eva. I made the introductions. I had already explained to my friends that Santiago and I had been classmates in the *Escuela Normal*. He acknowledged the introduction with a shy smile. He had always been this way. Then we returned to the center of the dance floor.

We talked about our jobs and all of the latest news about Martín. Santiago was so tall that he had to bend over to talk to me. I thought for sure both of us would have a sore neck later. I noticed several people whispering when we went by. I realized it was a novelty to see me talking to a new man in town. After we had danced to three songs, I asked him to take me back to my chair.

My friends and I decided we had enough for the first day, so, we went back home. Before going to bed, I looked for Horacio.

"*Hola*, Horacio," I said when I saw him coming out of the kitchen. "Because you offered to help me, I have to ask you a big favor."

"Did anybody bother you? Who was it? Do you want me to beat him?" he said, rolling up his sleeves.

"Of course not, Horacio; calm down." I laughed. "I'd never ask you to fight someone. What I would like for you to do is to tell my students never to invite me to dance. As long as I'm their teacher, we have to keep a distance, and I don't want to embarrass anybody by saying no. Will you do it for me, please?"

"*Profesora*, you can count on me." Horacio's solemnity made me laugh.

"I know I can, Horacio. And thank you again. It was an excellent day. Good night."

"It was for me, too," he said, winking an eye. "Good night, *profesora*."

The boy walked away, whistling happily.

CHAPTER EIGHTEEN

THE FAIR GRAND FINALE

The town fair was in full swing. Every day began early morning with music from the loudspeakers. People expressed their feelings more openly through songs. The dedications became bolder and bolder. I was sure that, like me, the rest of people in Doctor Arroyo were paying increased attention to their meaning.

Most dedications were romantic, but sometimes they talked about a broken heart and, because more than likely we knew the person and the story behind the song, many of us felt sorry for the suffering soul. "*¡Pobrecito!*", we used to say, referring to the man in question.

A secret admirer could not be missing, that is the shy lover who dedicated songs to a town lady. Townspeople loved this type of melodies.

"And now," a man's voice said at the microphone, "for *señorita*— we paid attention to the name—the song *'Amor Indio,'* from a secret admirer."

The guessing game started. People talked about the dedications in whispers, and in many cases, the supposedly secret admirers were ridiculed aloud. I didn't realize that we, the teachers, participated in the game, too, trying to guess the anonymous person.

The rest of the days of the fair were almost a repetition of what we had done on the first. My friends and I strolled around the crowded plaza, enjoying meeting people we knew.

We stopped for a few minutes to see some respectable grownups riding the merry-go-round and having fun like little kids. Of course, they did it with the excuse that they had to take care of their child.

The music from the merry-go-round and from the Castilleja's *Ola* ride filled the air, mixing with the noises of the cheerful crowd. Here and there, someone yelled, trying to attract people's attention to their food booths. This wasn't necessary because the delicious aroma coming from them enticed dozens of hungry customers. We usually left this pleasure for later on, so, we continued with our *paseo* around the plaza.

We couldn't resist playing *lotería*. We liked the excitement of almost winning and the frustration of somebody else doing so. After deciding that enough was enough, we left the *lotería* booth looking for a new place to eat Mexican *antojitos*. Afterward, we attended the crowded fair's daily dance.

Many of the people who gathered there didn't go to dance. They just wanted to see who was there, who talked to whom, and what everybody else was wearing. It was the place to see and where others could see you. Some people arrived early, carrying their own chairs. They looked for the perfect spot to watch the dancing area and also to glance at the people in the plaza.

Observing the dancing couples, one could identify which people were from Doctor Arroyo and which were from other towns. Some danced with their right arm hanging down very stiffly and swayed their bodies from side to side. Others moved their right arm and right leg front and back with *gusto*, while others did small jumps and shrugged their shoulders. These styles were funny to us who had grown up in the city and danced in a very different way, so we tried to imitate them.

I loved to dance, and Andrés was a frequent partner, but even more so Santiago, who in his shyness did not invite other girls, even though I encouraged him. Maybe he had more confidence with me. After all, we had been classmates and friends for a long time.

At the fair's dance, I saw José Luis and his girlfriend together for the first time. She was a good-looking girl around the same height as José Luis. She had straight black hair and dressed nicely. While they talked, she looked at us frequently. I thought maybe she wanted to meet us, but José Luis didn't introduce her to us, and we didn't approach them either.

During the fair, there were a couple of brief fights that the police controlled without any problem. In one of them a couple of bottles flew over our heads, but luckily no one was hurt. The disruptive persons were taken to jail to cool off. I saw Dimas García and his friends only twice but knew he spent a lot of time in the *cantina*. A lot of people worried that he would cause trouble under the influence of alcohol. The *cantina*, which was also a billiard hall, kept some doors open, and from the street you could see the interior. Because it was on the same block where we lived, I wondered if one day I'd see Dimas inside with his horse, as the legend said.

So far, nothing bad had happened in town, so everybody was certain that the fair would end without incident. This peace was short-lived. One afternoon, almost at the end of it, a frantic policeman came in a jeep looking for Manuel. We were having dinner. Manuel stood up as soon as he recognized the policeman. After talking with him in private, he apologized for having to leave without finishing his dinner.

"Qué pasa, abogado?" Andrés asked. "What's going on, lawyer?"

We all waited for his answer because we realized something serious had happened to force him to leave in such a rush.

"There is a dead man in *don* Peregrino's drugstore," he said. He put his jacket on while following the policeman. The two of them got in the jeep and left in a hurry.

We looked at each other, not knowing what to say. We decided not to speculate, but to wait to hear any news directly from Manuel. Eventually, we continued with our conversation.

Manuel returned after a couple of hours. He told us that someone had walked a man to the door of the pharmacy and then left in haste. The man was mumbling and stumbling all over the place. *Doña* Magdalena, *don* Peregrino's wife, thought that the man was drunk, so she ordered him to leave. There being no answer, she threatened him, saying she would call the police. At that moment, the man fell over the counter with his arms extended. *Doña* Magdalena saw that he had a knife stuck in his back. Frightened, she screamed for help. Some people heard her, so they went looking for a doctor and the police. When help arrived, the man was dead.

The lawyer added that they had located some witnesses and felt sure they would find the killer soon. The fair was becoming complicated.

The culminating day of the fair finally arrived on December 8, the feast of the Virgin of the Immaculate Conception. This was the last day of the fair. As on previous mornings, the sound of music from the loudspeakers resounded very early all over town.

The deep voice of a man announced, "So-and-so makes ten dedications of '*Las Mañanitas*' song to the Virgin." From then on, "*Las Mañanitas*" was played repeatedly because many people wanted to congratulate the Virgin on her day. Someone occasionally requested another type of song.

At midmorning, there was a special Mass, which I attended with my friends. The image of the Virgin of the Immaculate Conception , the town patroness, looked beautiful, with a new silk dress and her recently polished crown. Fresh flowers and new candles decorated the altar. The aromas of roses, carnations, and wax spread to all the corners of the church.

Church at night in Doctor Arroyo.
Photo provided by Rodolfo Contreras.

The building was completely full, especially with all the foreign people who were visiting. Every time one of these outsiders entered, it became the center of blatant attention from some, concealed from others. The foreigners seemed oblivious to this curiosity and took their places without concern.

Women covered their heads with a veil or lace *mantilla* as a sign of respect. Some of them held them discreetly over their mouths to hide the fact that they were whispering something to the person sitting next to them. When someone arrived late, some parishioners elbowed their neighbor to draw attention to the unpunctual. Two or three persons knelt in the center of the aisle with their arms extended. At this point, I didn't know if it was out of devotion or if they wanted to have a better view of what was going on. Father Rangel gave an emotional sermon. When Mass was over, some people rushed outside and waited by the door for a closer look at the people who had come from other places.

Interior of La Purísima Concepción. Photo provided by Matilde Briones.

The party had already started on the main plaza. Several young men sat on the benches facing the church, waiting for their girlfriends. As soon as they saw them coming, they left the group to meet the young ladies. Their friends then patted them on the back, laughing, hooting, and wishing them good luck.

Plaza de Armas in Doctor Arroyo

The day was sunny and beautiful, so Nena, Eva, her sisters, and I decided to stay in the plaza for a couple of hours. Then we would go home to eat, rest, and change clothes for the nighttime diversions. We all wanted to look our best for the last day of the fair.

"Let's have some ice cream first," Eva said. She sent Irma and Alicia ahead to hold a table that a family had just vacated.

The ice cream parlor was a small place right across from the main plaza and very close to the church. We sat at a table next to its open door. As we savored our banana splits, we observed the people walking around.

I enjoyed seeing unfamiliar faces around. There were some new couples, so it didn't surprise me to see Horacio walking with a pretty young girl I had never seen before. She was talking in a lively manner to him, and he looked at her and smiled. Horacio pretended not to notice our presence but had to turn to see us when Eva's sisters called him by name.

"*¡Hola*, Horacio!" they shouted. "*¡Preséntala!* Hi, Horacio, introduce her to us!"

He smiled and tipped down his brown cowboy hat, but he continued walking with his new girlfriend who gave us a cold look. Irma and Alicia laughed, amused the girl didn't like that they had called to Horacio.

"Let's play *lotería*," I suggested when we finished our ice cream.

The *lotería* game booth was packed with people. We decided to wait for a place to sit.

The man who was running the game yelled over the microphone, "The one who sang to San Pedro ... The rooster!"

"The poor people's blanket ... The sun!" he continued.

This way of naming lottery figures, with detours or metaphors, is very common in México. The degree of humor depends on the ingenuity of the animator.

The players placed corn kernels on top of the pictures that matched the names called.

The man continued yelling, "The one that shines at night ... The moon!"

"I have it. I have it!" yelled some of the players, placing a corn kernel on their card.

The announcer continued with the star, the rose, the crown, the soldier ...

Eventually, somebody yelled "*¡loteríaaa!*"

The rest of the players protested in loud voices because they almost had it. The winning card was read aloud. All of the matches were right, so the lucky winner had his choice of prizes on a long table in the center.

On it there were multiple gifts such as decorations for the house, sets of glasses, jugs, lamps, tablecloths, stuffed animals, and many others.

When finally some people left their places, my friends and I sat to play. We also screamed every time we were close to a win, but we never made it. We left, laughing at our bad luck.

"Well, after all, you know the saying, 'unfortunate in the game, fortunate in love, and vice versa,'" Eva said philosophically.

"I hope you are right," I said, laughing at her comment. "Now let's go home and get ready for tonight."

Every girl would be wearing her prettiest dress for the occasion. I couldn't wait to wear my new red dress, made of imitation suede material, with the white overcoat that my mom had sewn for me with so much love. I would also wear my almost-new red shoes.

I say almost because somebody else had already put them on.

Some days back, as I went into my room, I found Claudia with a broom in her hand trying on my new shoes. As soon as she saw me, she took them off. Her face turned pale.

"I just wanted to know what they looked like," she said with quavering voice. "Please, don't tell *doña* Susana because she will punish me."

I was furious at her, but I felt worried that *doña* Susana would really punish her. "Claudia, I told you before not to come into my room. Teresa will clean it. She is the only one who has my permission to enter when I'm not here."

"Okay, I won't come anymore," she answered in a sheepish voice that made me forget my aggravation. She put her face against the broom's handle.

"I won't tell *doña* Susana this time, but if you ever touch my things again or if you come into my room without my permission, I'll have to let her know."

She just signaled her acceptance of my statement with her head and ran out of the bedroom when she heard *doña* Susana calling her.

"What were you doing in *señorita's* room?" *doña* Susana asked her, shaking a finger.

Claudia looked at me with wide eyes and bit her lower lip.

"She just wanted to see my new shoes, *doña* Susana," I told her while I put them away.

"Okay, then, but don't let her be too familiar," she said. After warning me of this, she returned to the kitchen.

Claudia came back with the broom still in her hand. She looked back to make sure *doña* Susana wasn't there.

"Yes, Claudia? Did you forget something?"

"Can I have them when you get tired of them?" Claudia whispered.

I grabbed my old sandals and showed them to her. "Are you talking about these?"

"No, of course not. I'm talking about your beautiful red shoes!"

I couldn't believe her nerve. I tried to find the right words. "Claudia, you'll have to grow up first and learn to clean your nose before you can wear heels," I whispered back.

She looked at me with wide eyes and scratched her head, trying to digest what I said. "Then I'll learn soon so I can have your red shoes," she said with a big grin.

I sighed and closed my bedroom door.

CHAPTER NINETEEN

ON THE EVE OF HOLIDAYS

The town's fair ended, and we were back in classes. Two or three days were needed for the students to settle down. Even my friends and I kept talking about all of the fun we had experienced during the fair, especially on the last day. Each one of us had looked prettier that night, with our new dresses and nice hairdos. We all got many compliments and danced a lot. Everybody had seemed to stay until the end of the festivity.

When the music ended, the *lotería* booth went silent, the merry-go-round and the *Ola* stopped, and little by little the booths closed. Only then did people begin to empty the square. The fair had been great.

There was only one week left before returning home for Christmas vacation. Our students had difficulty concentrating, so we pushed them hard to study. They would take their midterm examinations before leaving.

My fellow teachers and I took care of formulating the questionnaires that would show the knowledge the students had acquired. The results of these were crucial, not only to the students but also to us. One of *profesor* Merla's favorite sayings was, "When we grade a student, we are grading ourselves because a test will show how well or how badly we taught a subject." I was eager to know my own results.

On the day of the examinations, every teacher dictated the questionnaire they had written up. We didn't have a copy machine or the money to do them any other way. The students had to write both the questions and answers. This required a lot of our time because every test had to be graded, recorded, and returned to the students.

It was easy to spot which students had studied and which ones depended on their luck—or their ability to copy a classmate's answers. The first ones would start writing their answers as soon as the teacher finished dictating the questions. Those students were the same ones who always participated in class and did their homework.

In my case, the few who didn't study for the test started wiggling in their seats or leaned on their desks, trying to see what others were writing. In turn, they made sure that I did not observe them, pretending to be thoughtful. Some reached for a paper hidden inside of their socks or under their sleeves. When I saw them checking the palm of their hand, I knew it was not to guess their future. Surely there was data written there. The number of tricks they used was vast, some of them very ingenious. Occasionally some were obvious, like the boys who always wore tee shirts and then, all of a sudden, they showed up wearing a shirt and tie. I knew there were notes inside it.

The easiest way to prevent cheating was to move such students to the front seats where any attempt to copy would be more than obvious. Some of them returned their papers with only a couple of answers. After getting a zero, they really had to study hard to take a second test if I decided to give them another chance.

The last day of classes finally came. We wished all of our students a happy holiday, and right away we left school, eager to go home the following day. We still had to finish packing.

"Would you believe that it's almost four months since we last saw our families?" I asked Andrés that afternoon after dinner.

"Sometimes it seems longer than that," he said. "I miss my mom. As I told you before, if she could come to live with me, we could rent a house, and you could move in with us. You would be like my sister."

"Thank you, Andrés. I won't forget your offer. Now we better hurry up to finish packing or we'll have to wait another day for the bus."

We thought we were finished, but to our surprise, many students came by the house in the late afternoon with presents. They brought fresh cheeses, chorizos, marmalades, prickly pears and other fruits, embroidered or crocheted items, and much more. Some parents sent *tacos* and *tortas* for all of us to share during our trip back to Monterrey.

"How in the world am I going to carry all of these things with me?" I said, staring at all of the presents.

"Don't worry, *señorita*," Teresa answered. "I'll get you a couple of boxes, and we can fit everything in them."

A few minutes later, she came back with two medium-sized boxes. She put everything inside and tied them with a strong cord.

"Ready," she said, smiling with satisfaction.

"Thank you, Teresa. You saved me from leaving these things behind. My family will really enjoy them."

We were so eager for the trip home that nobody slept much that night. Manuel, Lauro, José Luis, Andrés, and I took the bus at five o'clock in the morning. We transferred to another one in Matehuala, and by early afternoon, we saw in the distance the magnificent Saddle Mountain or *Cerro de la Silla*. My heart leapt with happiness. We were in Monterrey. The final minutes to the bus terminal seemed extremely long. I couldn't wait to see my loved ones.

When we arrived, I identified them from afar. They were trying to see if the bus that was pulling in was the one that was bringing me home. I opened the window and waved at them. As soon as they saw me, they waved back. I heard Julie and Norma yelling my name while they jumped up and down. My brothers waited next my parents. There were big smiles on all of their faces. As they waited for the bus door to open, my mom pulled to the front of the group. She grasped her hands together and stared at the closed door. Since I was sitting in front, I would be the first one to step down. I knew she was eager to hug and kiss me, just as I wanted to kiss her.

Inside the bus, the teachers, the lawyer, and I wished each other Merry Christmas and a Happy New Year. We left the bus in a hurry. After an emotional encounter, first with my mother and then with the rest of the family, I went home with all of them.

Besides the presents I carried with me, I had lots of stories to share with them. Two weeks' vacation seemed like a long time, but the days would fly by fast. I would make every second count. I found it wonderful to be back with my family, my friends, and familiar surroundings. The city lights and the Christmas music filled my heart with content.

CHAPTER TWENTY

VISITING FAMILY AND FRIENDS

The Christmas of 1958 meant a lot to me. The time I spent with my family made me forget the loneliness I had endured being away from them. Dinner time was as I had it embedded in my memory: My mother, smiling and singing while making dinner; my father, sitting at the head of the table, reading the newspaper, waiting for everything to be ready; and the rest of us, engaged in lively conversation spiced with laughter. This was the part of the day that I considered the happiest.

Sharing my bed with my two sisters contrasted with my lonely nights in Doctor Arroyo. I wasn't bothered that Norma and Julie talked and giggled until they fell asleep. Norma always snuggled next to me, trying to warm her small thin body. I knew she missed me as much as I had her, but hopefully, I would get a job in the city next September.

The sparkle in my mom's eyes and her beaming face told me she was elated to have me home. However, I worried when Norma told me my mom had cried a lot because of my absence. All day I kept thinking about it. I still had another six months before I could go home again. There was nothing I could do to change that fact.

The next day I asked Héctor and Cayito about this. I didn't ask Javier, the oldest of the boys, because he spent a lot of time in the library locked up in his books and frequently ignored what was happening around him.

My brothers told me it was true. My mother cried a lot in the first few weeks after I left.

"Mom missed you a lot, and this naturally worried us," Héctor said. "I agreed with Cayo and Norma to spend more time with her to distract her with our talk, but it wasn't enough. Then something occurred to me. As you know, Mom has always been interested in different kinds of contests."

Effectively. For some years, my mother had participated in radio contests, not only local but even from México City. With ingenuity and talent, she had won many prizes, in money at times, and in merchandise at others. With these contributions, she helped my father in the family finances.

"We knew that Mom was interested in a live program in the studio theater of a radio station," Héctor continued.

Norma put her two cents. "It's called 'Do You Know Your City?' They ask questions about the history of Monterrey."

Héctor explained to me that it was a weekly program. It was broadcast live at night, with an audience in the studio theater. They decided to attend it with my mom. In each program several contestants took turns. The challenge was to answer up to four questions, each one more valuable than the last. If the contestant was wrong, he was disqualified, and they asked the public.

"So, Mom began to soak up the history of Nuevo León," Cayito said.

"Mom knew a lot, but she didn't dare to go up the stage," Héctor continued. "But she did answer several times from her seat. In order not to attract attention, she even whispered to me an answer on more than one occasion, and I won the partial prize."

"But one time, before the program started, the announcer invited Mom to compete on stage and she shyly accepted." Cayito seemed eager to get to the end of the story.

Héctor continued "And despite the fact that university students had participated—and even professionals, no one had managed to reach the fourth question before. Mom was the first to do it!"

"They all applauded her standing up!" Norma said.

The smile on their faces told me how proud they were of my mother. And I was too. She was so smart and special.

"Mom still misses you," Cayito concluded, "but now she has something else on her mind to distract herself because we continue to attend."

I sighed. Hearing that good news and knowing how responsible my siblings were with her, took a great weight off my shoulders.

Licha, Mari Paz, and I continued with the friendship we had before I went to Doctor Arroyo. There was so much to talk about. Mari Paz was one of the 180 Normal School students who had been retained. She would have to wait until the following May to graduate.

Licha had found a job at *Colegio Israelita*. She knew it would be impossible to get a position working for the State, at least during the actual government administration.

My friends couldn't comprehend the circumstances under which I was working—living away from family and friends in a small town with no roads, no water, and no electricity. I was sure they expected me to tire of it and decide to return to the city soon. They seemed to forget the fact that I was there because I needed to help my family financially.

"Socorro, I just don't understand. How can you stand to live in a place like that? It must be so boring!" Mari Paz said raising an eyebrow.

"You have always lived in the city. Do you realize all that you are missing? No movies, no dances, no reunions." There was a somber tone in Licha's voice as she shook her head.

"Oh, but we do attend the movies. I have already seen all of the *Charro Negro* series."

"*¡'El Charro Negro'!*. Are you kidding? Nobody sees those movies anymore," Mari Paz said, laughing aloud.

"In Doctor Arroyo we do, and it isn't that bad. We even have a bad boy in town like in the movies." I told them about Dimas, and they listened to the details with their eyes wide open. I knew Mari Paz was very apprehensive, so I changed the subject.

"I have attended some dances, too. Let me show you some new steps." I stood up and showed them the way the people danced in Doctor Arroyo, shrugging their shoulders while they danced or with the right arm stiff, pointing to the floor.

My friends laughed watching me dance, and they took turns practicing the new steps with me.

"Well, believe it or not, I'm never bored." I explained to them what my hobbies were together with the other teachers, and how much I enjoyed teaching teenagers, which was a new experience for me. Licha and Mari Paz found it very interesting because their work experience had been only with young children.

"Do you know that I have students who are almost my age? I even had to forbid them from inviting me to dance as long as I'm their teacher."

I clarified to them the reason for this measure and how I had asked Horacio to deliver the message to his classmates.

"Well, it looks like Horacio is going to be a big help to you," Licha said.

"He will. He even offered 'to take care of business,' as he said, 'if anybody bothered me.' And I don't doubt he would do it if I would ask him, but that will never happen. I'm pretty safe with his dog, Duque. Horacio instructed him to watch over me, and the dog now sleeps right outside of my bedroom. He lifts his big head and growls whenever anybody walks nearby. Poor Andrés and José Luis, they have to go around the dog when they come out of their rooms."

"At least you're well protected," Mari Paz said.

"I'm very relaxed and, besides, I don't have to get up for work when it is dark or commute by bus like I used to."

Mari Paz and I laughed, remembering the way we had gone to work the previous year.

"Poor Socorro! By the time the bus got to her house, it was always completely full. Every seat taken, and the rest of the passengers traveled tight like sardines," Mari Paz commented to Licha.

"Yes. Luckily, the driver knew I was a teacher and invariably stopped in the middle of the block to pick Ernesto and me up, but so briefly that we had to jump inside the minute he opened the door."

"The driver did it to avoid all the people standing on the corner," said Mari Paz. "Or maybe to be charming to you," she added, laughing.

"Remember how I traveled daily, standing on the lowest step, with the bus door open most of the time? Thank God that Ernesto could sneak in among the passengers and that I never fell!" I shuddered at that possibility.

"Yes, I remember. I was luckier because I got on the bus before you two and usually found an empty seat," Mari Paz said.

"The worst thing for me was that I had to get off the bus every time it stopped to let people get off." The memory still bothered me.

I felt glad that my mom had never seen this and that I didn't have to do it in Doctor Arroyo.

Licha, Mari Paz, and I attended the Normal School's Christmas Dance at *Círculo Mercantil*. One of the best orchestras from México would perform. We were excited knowing we would see many of our old classmates there. For sure, we would all be curious to find out how everybody else was doing.

One of the first people we saw was Margarita Romero, who was a friend of ours. We heard that she had been assigned a teaching position in China, a municipality of Nuevo León. Besides Doctor Arroyo, China was the other place where teachers didn't want to work. Both towns had the reputation of being unsafe.

Margarita explained to us that some weeks after she arrived, a man there had asked her to be his girlfriend. She rejected him. She did not tell us her reasons. After that, on several occasions, somebody had shot at the house where she lived alone. Margarita was sure it was the same man, but she couldn't prove it. She reported the incidents to the police, but they hadn't done anything. Supposedly there weren't any witnesses, but she knew the man was very influential and that people were afraid of him.

"I'm fine right now, but the months I've worked there have been a nightmare. I'm not even sure if I'll go back, my nerves are shot." Her eyes clouded with tears. *Now I understand the reasons why no one wants to take a job there. At least I am lucky to have good coworkers and the townspeople treat me well in general.*

We tried to distract her with our talk. I briefly told her about my job, and she was glad that at least I was doing well. The music from the orchestra was very inviting, so we danced a lot. We spent part of the long night visiting with our old friends. Everybody was trading interesting stories. Some were happy, but not so those colleagues who did not get a job.

Only a few of them, like Licha, had found a teaching position in some private school. But not everybody wanted to work in that system. They paid lower wages than the public schools, and private schools' parents had a lot of power. Teachers had to make every decision very carefully.

I felt lucky not to have to work under such circumstances. *Profesor* Merla always backed us up on discipline. He would never take the side of a parent against us, and if we thought a student needed to be retained, he never questioned our decision.

In public schools, several of the parents of our students would come to see us and say phrases like: "*Maestra*, you are like a mother to my child. If he breaks your discipline, if he is disrespectful or doesn't want to pay attention, you have my permission to hit him with a ruler or with a stick. Don't hesitate because I won't be angry. And when he gets home, I'll be sure to give him a second round with my belt."

These always sounded like excessive measures to me. I assured the parents that their teenager and I would understand each other without having to go to such extremes. However, I thanked them for their unconditional help, which was extremely valuable.

In those years, parents supported teachers in everything, and their children knew it.

CHAPTER TWENTY-ONE

CHRISTMAS HOLIDAYS AT HOME

December has always been my favorite time of the year. Christmas music filled every corner of Monterrey with joy. Public buildings, plazas, and stores showcased Nativity scenes and seasonal decorations. Wide-eyed children and adults paused in front of store windows to admire the ingenious electronic Christmas displays. The mountains near the city glowed at night with Christmas messages, and the lights from hundreds of homes on their slopes made them look like a giant Nativity scene.

The cold weather did not stop hordes of people looking for presents to bring joy to their loved ones. Children waited impatiently for the presents that Baby Jesus would leave for them on the night of the twenty-fourth.

Working adults also eagerly awaited their *aguinaldo*—the Christmas bonus from the companies where they labored.

According to tradition, the *novena* of Posadas would begin on December 16. By then, Norma and Cayito had already turned a dry branch into a miniature tree. They had obtained it in the neighboring Río Santa Catarina and painted it white using lime. When it dried, they placed it on some cardboard boxes.

Julie and Ernesto looked for small stones shaped like balls. They wrapped them with eye-catching metallic foil wrappers or red and green cellophane. Cayito and Norma placed these handmade spheres and many colored bows on the humble tree. Later, the four of them hung strips of metallic paper from the branches and angel hair to simulate snow.

Once the dry branch had been transformed into a colorful and unusual Christmas tree, my siblings continued with the task of designing the Nativity scene. They covered several boxes with brown wrapping paper. With the same paper they imitated hills and rocks. But it looked lifeless.

"What are you going to cover that wrapping paper with? It still needs something." The four of them looked at me silently. We all knew what was missing: *paixtle* or dry hay, moss and ... money. Seeing the hope on their faces, I decided I couldn't let them down.

"I'll give you some money; see what you can buy with this." The joy they showed made me forget that now I would need to adjust my budget.

They returned giggling from the market with the *paixtle* and moss. Soon the Nativity had a lush ground, spread with Mexican clay figurines, survivors of many Christmases. In a prominent place was the Mystery: José and María, waiting with their eyes fixed on the manger, still empty. They shared the stable with a mule that had lost an ear and an ox without horns, which lay on the ground waiting patiently. The three Wise Men, with their gifts, were ready to go up to worship the One who was to be born.

Above the stable, a silver star hung from a branch, and under it, an angel with a white robe, indicated the place chosen for the birth of Jesus. Far from there, on the mountain, there was a cave with a one-arm hermit, and in a lower part, another cave with the devil;

strips of red cellophane on the lights near him looked like flames. Several shepherds, sheep, and ducks completed the scene. Most Mexican Nativities showed these figures.

Strips of aluminum foil turned into a waterfall that fell into a lake, made from a broken mirror. Small twigs became a bridge, and a cylindrical container resembled a well. Cayito and Norma decorated several boxes with doors and windows and turned them into little houses. Under the protective mantle of the Christmas tree, the humble Nativity was filled with color and life.

"How does it look?" Norma asked with a smile.

Ernesto and Julie were satisfied with their collaboration.

"Like the ones on display in the stores. Are you sure you did it by yourselves?" I asked.

"The four of us did it alone," Ernesto assured me, smiling at the compliment.

"Then, all of you are already hired to do it next year," said my mom.

My four siblings smiled with pride.

Finally, the first day of Posadas arrived. Everything was ready to start the *novena de Posadas*, the Spanish term for the nine days of these festivities. The only thing missing was to buy the *bolo*: oranges, sugar canes, peanuts, and candies that would be put inside paper bags and distributed to the attendees. My mom went shopping at the market with Cayito in the morning.

She told me that after making all her payments with what Dad gave her the day before, she had set money aside for about five *Posadas*.

"And the rest, *madrecita*?"

"Don't worry, *hijita*. Some lady neighbors have already said that they want to take over a *Posada*. You'll see, God will provide, and we will have our nine *Posadas*."

That night our home was overflowing with guests. Most were neighboring children, my siblings' friends. Some came accompanied by their mothers. Except for my father, who was working quite late in those days of many sales, the rest of our family was there. The chairs and furniture in the living room were occupied by the adults. The kids sat on some blankets on the floor.

Once my mother managed to quiet the general hubbub, she guided the prayer of the Holy Rosary and the intercalated songs:

"Humble pilgrims, Jesús, Mary and Joseph,

Humildes Peregrinos, Jesús, María y José

My soul I give with them, my heart too,

Mi alma doy con ellos, mi corazón también,

To Bethlehem! To Bethlehem! My heart also."

¡A Belén!, ¡A Belén! Mi corazón también.

When we finished praying the Rosary, we all went out to the patio. The budget for the day was enough to buy only a box of twenty candles that were distributed among the ladies and the older children. Two by two we circled the courtyard singing *'la Letanía.'* With the candles lit, it looked like a ring of light. To each invocation of my mother, in honor of the Virgin Mary, we answered *"Ora pro nobis!"* Several of the children responded instead, *"Oooooora por dónde?"*. This "now where?" was followed by giggles. I had to keep from laughing to help my mother keep order.

Then came the request for *Posada*. In this part, which is sung with alternating verses, we divided ourselves into two groups. The people on the patio accompanied the images of Joseph and Mary, requesting *posada*; the other half, inside the house, repeatedly denied them lodging without consideration.

Finally, the Holy Pilgrims were given shelter and allowed to enter. They were placed carefully in the Nativity to await the *Posada* the next day. The evening ended with the gift of the bag with the *bolo*, enough for everyone to leave happy and wish to return the next day.

Thus, passed the next eight Posadas.

On Christmas Eve, the twenty-fourth, I traveled early to Laredo, Texas, to get gifts for my family. I bought a cute doll for my little sister Julie, and some friction cars for Ernesto. Those little cars ran really fast, so Ernesto would love them for sure. I bought sweaters, gloves, hats, and scarves for the rest of the family.

The merchandise is much cheaper in Laredo, which is why many people from México go shopping on the other side of the border, especially at Christmas, and particularly on the Eve, when everything is half price.

As usual, it was a war of nerves going through Customs. We all knew that Mexican Customs, the *aduanales*, often seized merchandise, with any silly excuse, even at Christmas. I had spent most of my Christmas bonus, and I was afraid that Customs would keep the toys because "no children were with me," one of their excuses.

This time, the Customs agent, *el aduanal*, got on the bus and asked for a fixed amount per person, "so you don't have to waste time going through Customs," he said, smiling cynically. We gave him the *mordida*. It was preferable to pay that extortion to having to give him the merchandise. I sighed. I had only enough money left to buy my ticket back to Doctor Arroyo. But it was worth it, knowing that my gifts would put smiles on my family's faces. I returned to Monterrey in the middle of the afternoon. After putting everything in my closet I rested for a while. I was ready for the prayer at the last *Posada*.

Everything happened as on the previous nights, but this time, after the Holy Pilgrims were admitted inside the Inn, we continued with the *Acostada*.

With great care and devotion, my mother brought the small figure of the Baby Jesus, lying in the center of a scarf.

Then she invited a neighbor to each hold one end of the scarf, like a hammock. In our tradition this is considered an honor, so the surprised neighbor happily accepted.

"¡Muchas gracias, Petrita!", said the lady. "How good that now we will be *comadres*."

With songs about His birth, we all lulled Baby Jesus while we lit sparklers. Immediately, my mother placed the figurine on a tray that contained many sweet candies called *colaciones*, in high demand during that season. One by one, the attendees adored the Baby Jesus, giving him a kiss and picking up a sweet. Once this was finished, the new *comadre* placed the figurine of the Newborn in the manger that had been empty the days before this celebration.

That night was the climax of the *Posadas novena* and it had to end with something special. We went out to the street where my brother Javier, from the roof of the house, was holding a long rope that was tied at its other end to a nearby pole; from it swung a *piñata* in the shape of a dice. Norma and Cayito had made it with a simple cardboard box that they later adorned with white tissue paper and black circles that indicated the numbers on each side. It was rudimentary, but it looked great. The girls first and the boys later took turns hitting the *piñata* with a broomstick. Javier, from his position, amused himself raising and lowering it by means of the rope to the frustration of the children. When it was finally broken, a cascade of sweets spilled all over the floor. Between struggles, shoves, and laughter, everyone hurried to collect what they could. Afterward, the guests received their *bolo*, the little bag with goodies, then wished us a merry Christmas and went back to their homes.

As soon as my father arrived from work, we enjoyed the delicious *buñuelos* and *tamales* that my mother prepared for the occasion. We chatted animatedly, commenting on the incidents of the day. Finally we wished each other a merry Christmas too and retired to our rooms.

When I calculated that everyone was sleeping, I approached the Nativity. There weren't stockings hanging like in the United States; instead, on the floor was a shoe of each member of my family, waiting.

A few hours later, the best gift I received was the satisfaction of seeing my loved ones happy with what they found.

On the last day of the year, I attended a neighbor's party for a while. I was having a lot of fun but like in the Cinderella story, I had to go home before midnight. In my case, it was to await the arrival of the new year, an unshakable tradition on my mother's side of the family. My friends Mari Paz and Licha knew this, and that was why neither of us made any attempt to meet that day. Also, we had already shared time and attended some parties together and, although I was happy to see them, my greatest desire was to enjoy the celebrations with my own family.

As usual, we went out into the street, warmly dressed, amid great excitement. We enjoyed the cold of that night and the clear sky, full of stars. When the bells of the nearby Cathedral announced midnight, my mother lit a candle "to see which side the year 1959 would enter," she said. We found out after the wind moved the flame in a certain direction. I still don't know what difference knowing this made, but I've continued the tradition with my own family anyway.

"Happy New Year! Happy New Year!" We all began to scream as we hugged and kissed and expressed our good wishes for the New Year.

With a kiss and her blessing, my mother whispered in my ear, "May you come home soon, *hijita*, and may you always be very happy."

My siblings asked permission to stay outside for another ten minutes, watching the neighbors throw some *buscapiés*, small rockets that are ignited and thrown to the ground producing a zigzag that makes spectators run in all directions.

Mom told them only ten minutes while we heated dinner. Dad came into the house too.

After this time, Mom asked me to call my siblings; the food was ready. Just as I walked out the door, I could see Cayito setting fire to each corner of a newspaper page. The fire approached from all sides to a small mound of gray dust in the center of the newspaper. I realized what it was—gunpowder!

"Watch out, Cayito!" I managed to yell at him. He just saw me and waved his hand, to indicate that I should not worry.

All my brothers were watching from afar, but Cayito remained about six feet from the burning paper.

In that minute the fire reached the gunpowder, and we heard a sound similar to that of a match being lit, but amplified many times. Simultaneously, a great mushroom of fire rose up, like a tiny atomic bomb, and produced a very bright light. The smell of burning powder spread around us.

While I was petrified, my siblings applauded the show. Not so Cayito.

He turned in all directions and to our amazement began to say, "I don't see! I do not see! I cannot see anything!"

Dad and Mom came out at that moment. The three of us ran to help him, although we didn't know what to do. Someone came and poured a glass of water on Cayito's face, although he didn't know why either. Two or three minutes later he calmed down.

"Already—I'm already seeing. That light blinded me!"

Héctor and Javier began to imitate Cayito. "I don't see, I don't see!" And they pretended to stumble.

"It's not funny, this could have had fatal repercussions," my dad scolded them.

"I want you all inside," Mom said. "It's over!"

"Where did you get that gunpowder, Cayo?" My father frowned deeply.

There we learned that Cayito had bought gunpowder from a classmate. The boy's father was a pyrotechnician, so the boy sold my brother the equivalent of a fist, without major problem.

"But don't worry, Dad, I already learned. Next time I will not stay near the gunpowder," Cayito concluded, very satisfied with the success of his exhibition.

"Whaaat? Don't even think about it. Neither near, nor far!" My father shook his head and frowned. "This stubborn boy!"

I never laid a hand on Cayito, but that day I wanted to spank him a couple of times because of the scare he gave us. Thank God no misfortune happened.

I sighed. After all, 1959 had started well for us. I wondered if Martín was working that night or celebrating the New Year with his friends. *Is he thinking of me like I think of him?*

This thought made me nostalgic. For three years, Martín had promised to come; many times I had to defend our relationship against those who made malicious comments when he was unable to do so for one reason or another.

At the end of my vacation, my whole family accompanied me to the bus station to say goodbye. This time the separation would not be as difficult for me as the first time, I believed.

How wrong I was! When I turned around to say goodbye and saw their drooping faces, it felt like my heart was clenched into a cold fist.

CHAPTER TWENTY-TWO

WHO SLEPT IN MY BED?

Returning from my Christmas vacation, I met my fellow teachers at the bus station in Matehuala. We greeted each other with affection. We were like a small family, and now we were heading to our second home in Doctor Arroyo.

As we boarded the old bus, I noticed how respectful the townspeople were. They had left the front seats empty. They clearly gave us those places. Andrés and I occupied the ones on the left side, and Lauro and José Luis sat by the door. Chepa, the driver, started a brief talk, looking at us through his rearview mirror.

"Did you have a nice vacation?" he asked.

"Yes. It was wonderful to be home again," I said.

"Only the days went by fast, and before we knew it, we are back," Andrés added.

"Anything new, Chepa?" Lauro asked.

"No, nothing important happened while you were away." Chepa looked at us again through the mirror, then fixed his eyes on the narrow road.

The weather was cold, and there was no heat inside the bus. We tried to keep warm rubbing our hands and keeping our coats closed.

While most of them slept, Andrés and I talked of everything we had done on our vacations. By seven o'clock, we saw the church's tower in the horizon. That was a most welcome sight. A few minutes later, the bus pulled into town. This time, the trip to Doctor Arroyo took us only four hours, instead of twelve like the first time.

As usual, there were a lot of curious people in the main plaza waiting for the bus to arrive. Some of them rose from their benches to get a better view. This time, all of us were covered with dust from head to toe because it hadn't rained. We tried to clean up a little, but that was almost impossible. That ghostly look was funny. We would have preferred that people didn't see us like that, but there was nothing we could do other than walk home quickly.

As we left the bus, Horacio greeted us, smiling widely. He was wearing his now familiar black leather jacket. Next to him was his dog Duque, wagging his tail from side to side. José, one of my most faithful students, Jorge, Ernesto, Matilde, Josefina, and some others were there, too. All of them volunteered to carry our belongings home. The people who had been waiting for the arrival of the bus began to disperse once their curiosity was satisfied.

We also saw Claudia, *doña* Susana's little maid. She jumped and clapped when she spotted us. So much enthusiasm made me smile. She pulled up her blue jacket to cover her nose and mouth from the cold and waited with attentive eyes until the last passenger descended from the bus. Then, she ran ahead of us to let the owner know we had arrived. When we entered the hotel, we heard Claudia telling *doña* Susana that "a couple of salesmen had come into town also."

The little girl enjoyed finding out who got off the bus, especially when the travelers were outsiders. I still don't know how she managed to find out what these people were doing in Doctor Arroyo. Probably she asked Chepa or the other passengers about it.

Doña Susana knew we would arrive that day, so she had kept dinner warm for us. She greeted us with the shadow of a smile on her wrinkled face. Teresa and the rest of the maids greeted us with friendly expressions. After we freshened up a bit, we ate and shared with each other the highlights of our vacation. *Profesor* Merla came by the house to say hello. As he drank a cup of black coffee, he broke down the agenda for the second school semester.

"The most important project we have is the acquisition of funds for the students' graduation. We'll have two fundraising dances with a D.J., and refreshments will be sold in both instances," he said. "Now we have to decide when we'll do this." *Profesor* Merla showed us his calendar, and after some proposals, we chose the dates for the events.

"The money will be used to pay for leasing the theater for the graduation ceremony, and paying the orchestra's fee for the dance," he continued after he finished writing the dates. "I have already contacted one popular orchestra in Matehuala. The contract will take effect when we deposit some earnest money on it."

Afterward he shared with us his plan for another important project, to call for a meeting with parents and authorities to create a committee for the construction of our new school.

"If everything we need is approved, it's probable that the building will be finished in time to start the next school term," he said.

We smiled optimistically. Having our own building was something we all wanted.

That was only few months away, but knowing *profesor* Merla's strong hand and firm determination, we knew he would be able to carry out such a project. With all of these plans ahead of us, we were excited and eager to start as soon as possible.

Profesor Merla left after José Luis stood up and announced he was tired and would go to sleep early. The rest of us decided to do the same. We all were exhausted because we had started our trip early that morning. Besides, the trip from Matehuala to Doctor Arroyo down that bumpy road had left us battered.

I went to my room to get ready for bed. After lowering the flame of my kerosene lamp and saying a couple of prayers, I finally laid down. Sleep overcame over me almost immediately. However, an itch all over my body woke me up with a start. *Surely, it's the dust from the road.* Because of the late arrival, nobody had been able to bathe. The air was too cold. We just washed and cleaned up as best as we could. We would have to wait for the maids to warm up water the following day.

The itching got worse. It was too much. I decided to get up to check under the covers. I raised the flame of my lamp. The smell of the kerosene floated in the room. I pulled the covers up and recoiled in horror. Several fat red bugs were running over the white sheets. A chill ran up and down my body.

I quickly placed the lamp on the table and removed my nightgown in a rush. After throwing it in a corner of the room, I put on a clean one and a robe. Then I called Teresa to my room, which was just across from hers. I was shaking with cold and disgust when she came to see me. She was already wearing her nightgown and had put a coat on top of it.

"What's wrong, *señorita*?" she asked, with alarm.

"Teresa, I'm sorry to wake you up, but please look in my bed! I was itching like crazy and found there are bugs there."

She pulled up the sheets, and raising her eyebrows she said, *¡Ay, mi Dios!* "Oh, my God! They're bedbugs. I'll change the sheets right away, *señorita*. Don't worry."

Claudia, who always appeared when least expected, came from behind Teresa. She bent over my bed to look and said, "Uh-oh, I think the man who slept in this room while you were gone left those *chinches*."

Thinking I hadn't heard correctly, I put a hand on Claudia's shoulder and asked her, "What are you saying, Claudia? Repeat what you said, please."

She fell silent. She realized she had said too much and ran away without answering. I looked at Teresa in disbelief. I expected a denial from her, but she just looked embarrassed.

"Teresa, what did Claudia mean? Did someone sleep in my room?"

"*¡Ay, señorita!* I'm sorry. *Doña* Susana rented your room to a customer when you were gone." She looked at me and then looked down.

I opened my mouth in disbelief and my body shook with anger. I was leaving to look for *doña* Susana when she appeared. Claudia surely went to warn her, and now she was watching behind the door.

"What's going on?" *doña* Susana asked in a raspy voice. She pulled a black wool shawl over her long flannel nightgown.

"*La señorita* found *chinches* in her bed," Teresa said bashfully.

"*Doña* Susana, did you rent my room when I wasn't here?" I asked her, breathing heavily.

She didn't hesitate for a second to answer. "Yes, I did, but only for a couple of days. I have known this man for a long time, and he couldn't find a place to stay. So, I gave him accommodation in this room. I knew your things would be safe," she said.

"What's going on, Socorrito?" José Luis said, coming from behind *doña* Susana, who was blocking the door.

She moved a little and I saw that Andrés and Santiago were with him, too. Because my bedroom was between Andrés's and José Luis's, they had heard all the commotion and came to check on me. They had a worried expression. I explained to them what had happened, but I was so upset that I could hardly talk. At the same time, I was sorry that the entire house had been awakened.

A stranger had been admitted in the privacy of my bedroom—a man. *Had he been looking at my clothes or reading my letters?* The more I thought about it, the angrier I felt. What made it worse was that *doña* Susana didn't see a problem in her decision.

"It was only for two days, and I'm sure you aren't missing anything," she said, shrugging unapologetically.

I felt my temples throb. "You did not have the right to let anybody use my bedroom," I said. "I pay you for the personal use of my room. Right now, it's very late, but I'll look for another place tomorrow." Tears rolled down my cheeks. I held my hands tightly, trying to stop them shaking.

"*Doña* Susanita, how could you do such a thing?" José Luis said. "Socorrito has reason to feel angry. I'm sure you would be very upset if somebody stayed in your room without your permission." His frown deepened.

"Tsk, tsk," Andrés said. He held his chin and shook his head in disapproval.

Santiago stared at *doña* Susana with half-closed eyes and shook his head, too.

"Well, I'm sorry, *señorita*. Teresa will change the sheets and the blanket so you can go back to sleep. Tomorrow we'll spray the mattress." She turned around ready to leave.

"*Doña* Susana, I think you don't understand. Those ugly *chinches* have already sucked my blood! I won't sleep on that bed again. The mattress and the entire bedroom are infested with them." I felt tired, sleepy, angry, and frustrated with the whole situation. The worse part was that she acted as if she were listening to the complaints of a spoiled child. I rubbed my arms and felt some welts caused by the bedbugs. More tears poured from my eyes.

"Here, wipe your tears." Santiago handed me a box of tissues.

Doña Susana looked around and saw the disapproval in everyone's eyes. She thought for a moment, and then she said in an inappropriately serene voice, "Well, in that case, if you wish to change rooms, you can have the one next to mine. It's larger than this, and I just bought a new mattress for the bed."

I was so upset that I didn't answer right away. Everyone stared at me.

"Take it, Socorrito," José Luis said. "I'm sure this will never happen again. Isn't that so, *doña* Susanita?" His tone of voice sounded like a warning. He crossed his arms and looked at her, waiting for an answer.

I didn't have a choice. I didn't want to stay by myself in any of the other hotels where people supposedly saw ghosts.

"I'll take it, but if something like this happens again, I will move out immediately."

She didn't answer. Instead, she told Teresa to take care of me. Afterward she went back to bed, followed by Claudia, who slept on a small cot in *doña* Susana's bedroom.

The new room was slightly larger than mine. Teresa went to get clean sheets and covers for the new mattress. While she made the bed, everybody helped me move my few belongings out of my old bedroom. I would check them carefully in the daylight. Then Teresa would help me hang my clothes after shaking them on the patio.

I thanked them all and offered my apologies for waking them up. They told me not to worry about it, and then everybody went back to their rooms.

The events of the evening had dispelled my sleep. However, exhaustion eventually defeated me, and I fell into a deep sleep as soon as I lay down.

The following day, after breakfast, Santiago got ready to continue his trip to the small town where he worked.

"I'll be back soon so you won't miss me." He had a big smile and a spark in his eyes.

José Luis, Lauro, and Andrés joked with him.

"Don't rush to come back, Santiago. We'll still be here."

"Time to start working, my friend."

"Hey, Santiago, you better not visit us too often or your students won't learn anything."

When it was my turn, I shook his hand and said, "Santiago, I hope the townspeople and your students may still recognize you."

Santiago smiled slyly. He put his few belongings on his bike and left, waving his hand. We waved back. We stayed by the front door until we didn't see him anymore.

"He is more isolated than we are here in Doctor Arroyo," José Luis said.

"No wonder he wasn't in any hurry to leave. Here he was among friends," I said.

I looked forward to Santiago's next visit. To me, he was a link to a very happy past.

CHAPTER TWENTY-THREE

SHARED SECRETS

My return to Doctor Arroyo didn't start well. First was the problem with the bed bugs, then, the disappointment that none of my friends were in town. Nena was visiting relatives in Monterrey. Eva and her sisters were in México City. They had family there, so every year they spent Christmas and New Year's festivities away from Doctor Arroyo. I didn't know when they would return but hoped it would be before long.

I longed to go back to work and see my students again. Some of them, like Ernesto, Jorge, José, Vicente, and Lupe Nava, came to welcome us back.

Little by little, I learned more about them. Ernesto, for instance, had three other siblings attending our school: Pepe, who was in the same class as Ernesto, and Roberto and Minerva, who were in the first level. Their parents and grandparents were businesspeople, and they had some of the best-stocked stores in town. I mention this family in particular because later on our lives would be closely linked. Josefina, Lilia, Lupita, Matilde, Irma, and Minerva visited me often, too. Their company made me feel less lonely.

There were things I couldn't change, but there were others that required my immediate attention, like making my new room look less cold and impersonal.

I opened my suitcases and pulled out a few things I had brought from Monterrey to decorate it. When I finished, I looked around and smiled with satisfaction. The narrow table now had a pleated cover to the floor that my mom sewed for me. It was a pink cotton print with small red roses. On top of it was a picture of Martín wearing his blue Air Force uniform. I would have loved to place a picture of my family, too, but at the moment, we didn't have any. The rectangular mirror above the table had a ruffle around it made of the same printed material. My clothes, which hung on the wall, were out of sight behind a pink-colored curtain. I hid my two suitcases under the table's cover.

A rocking chair and a white handwashing bowl in the corner of the room completed the simple décor. This was going to be my castle for some time. My mother's presence was there in what she had made for me. That gave me a lot of comfort.

I sighed looking at the faded bedspread. I wanted to buy a new one before coming back, but I had spent my *aguinaldo* on the presents for my family. Now, I would have to wait several months to do it—at least I thought so.

A few days after moving to my new bedroom, *doña* Susana, in a conciliatory gesture, replaced my old bedspread with a new one. Maybe Teresa had suggested it because it complemented the color of the table's cover perfectly. It was a nice detail on *doña* Susana's part that made me happy. I decided to thank her immediately.

I went to her bedroom, which was right by the hotel's entrance. *Doña* Susana was lying on her bed, her back propped on several pillows. She kept the door open in order to see the dining room across the hall. In this way, she could check on the maids and customers from a distance while she rested. As I stood in her doorway, she invited me to enter.

A musty odor filled the large, shadowy bedroom. The small windows to the street were shut. The only light came from some small blinking votive candles. There were offerings to the many saints whose framed prints she had on her wall and on small shelves. Pictures of people long gone inside dark oval frames looked menacing with the effect of lights dancing on them. I had the sensation of a spider crawling up my back.

"Tell me, *señorita*, what can I do for you?" *doña* Susana asked while getting up.

"*¡Oh, nada, doña Susana!* I only came to say thank you for my new bedspread. It's very pretty. I'm sorry if I disturbed you."

"*¡Para servirla!*". "You're welcome," she said with a smile of satisfaction. "And no, you didn't disturb me. I have to see if the girls finished making dinner."

Lowering her voice, she added, "Ah, and before I forget, I have to ask you a couple of favors. Please don't tell Nena why you moved to another room. She will be furious with me if she finds out the real reason."

"Don't worry. I'll just tell her I liked the room I have now much better."

"And please, that the other guests don't find out I bought a new bedspread for you. They will be asking me for a new one, too."

"I'll tell them I bought it, *doña* Susana," I said giggling. "Thanks again."

"Don't mention it." She brushed her hair slightly and put on her apron. I left her bedroom, and she followed me. Then she headed into the dining room to attend her customers.

As I went into my room, I heard José Luis's voice. "*Doña* Susana, I heard that you bought a new bedspread for Socorrito's bed. How come I have the same old one?"

I turned around to see him standing at the kitchen door, his arms across his chest and the characteristic frown on his face. He smiled and winked at me.

Doña Susana's voice came out loud and menacing, "Hmm. I just know who opened her big mouth. Clauuudia, damn kid! Come here right now, and don't hide! I'm going to find you wherever you are and give you a spanking with the broom! Big mouth kid!"

The secret was very short-lived. This made me remember how I learned another *secreto*.

 Placing my head against the back of the rocking chair, I listened to the singing of the caged *jilgueros* and *censontles*, the Spanish names for the goldfinches and Mexican mockingbirds on the patio. I heard a masterly concert with a diverse repertoire of trills. I wondered if their song was one of joy or a cry for freedom.

In this peaceful environment, I reflected on the privileges I enjoyed being the only young female in the house. My new pink bedspread and wooden rocking chair were two of them.

I paid attention to the common noises rising from the kitchen: the clattering of pots and pans and a familiar patting sound. Somebody was making *tortillas* on the *comal*, a round disk made of thick clay. The air began to smell of toasted corn. The aroma signaled my brain that soon it would be time for dinner.

Listening to the rhythmic sound patting of the maids making *tortillas* I remembered a conversation I had with Ernesto and Jorge.

One afternoon, when they came to visit me, Jorge asked, "*Maestra*, do you know how some parents find out if their son's girlfriend is ready to get married?"

I gave him several answers, none of them correct. "I give up; what do they do?"

"Well, when their son tells them he wants to marry a girl, they invite her to eat at their home. Then the boy's parents ask her to help warm up the *tortillas*. They pay a lot of attention to see how she does it. If the girl turns the tortillas back and forth too many times, they say she isn't ready to get married."

"Why? What is she supposed to do?" I asked him. Jorge and Ernesto exchanged glances between them and smiled. I felt my cheeks flushing. *They must be thinking "poor lady, she's not ready to get married either!"*

"Warming up *tortillas* is an art, *maestra*," Jorge explained patiently. "The girl must place them on the hot *comal* and then wait for the right time to turn them over twice. If she does it correctly, the *tortillas* will puff up. She should never do it more than two times." Jorge had a very serious expression as if he had shared a big secret.

"Does Lilia know how to warm up *tortillas*?" Ernesto asked Jorge with a sardonic giggle.

Jorge's face reddened, and I found it amusing.

"I should ask you the same about Amparo," Jorge said quickly.

Amparo was one of the Berrones girls, and I knew she was Ernesto's girlfriend. I had met her once. She was a very pretty girl, and she was younger than Eva. I guess she and Ernesto had a long-distance relationship because she lived in México City with other siblings.

"Yes, Ernesto, tell us about it." I settled in my rocking chair and crossed my hands ready to listen. Jorge and I grinned and stared at Ernesto who wiggled in his seat as his ears reddened.

"We better go," he said, standing in a hurry and heading toward the door.

Jorge laughed and went after him. They left, pushing each other playfully.

I had learned something new—the secret of warming the tortillas correctly.

I would made sure to practice just in case my future in-laws asked me to do it.

CHAPTER TWENTY-FOUR

TROUBLESOME NOMINATION

The return of the students to school was a happy event. Given that everyone knew each other, it was like a big family reunion. Some of them had spent their vacations out of town. They were on time for the first day of school. I was glad to notice Irma Berrones with a group of students. That meant her sister Eva, my friend, was back, too.

There were many hugs and laughs among the youngsters. When *profesor* Merla blew his whistle, the noise level went down. Talking became whispers, then the students became silent. His mere presence commanded respect. The students lined up in the center of the courtyard, ready for Monday morning's pledge to the flag. An *escolta*, a group of five youngsters, brought the flag from the principal's office. They paraded with it until they faced the rows of students. Then, we all sang the Mexican National Anthem. We saluted the flag, placing our right hands across the chest, with the palm down. When it finished, the students stayed at attention until the flag left the courtyard. Afterward, they marched to their respective classrooms.

We knew the kids always had lots of questions the first day of school, and it was fine to answer them, as long as we didn't waste the full hour. After roll call, we talked briefly about our vacation. At their age, the teens knew many tricks to disrupt the class routine.

However, most of us teachers had mastered the art of avoiding those situations, so the classes ran smoothly.

Before the end of the day, *profesor* Merla and Lauro came by the third-level classroom where I was teaching *Historia de Nuevo León*, our state's history. The entire class stood up, as it was a usual show of respect. The *director* walked to the front of the class, while Lauro stayed in the back of the classroom.

"Please sit down." *Profesor* Merla indicated with both hands to do so. "*Señorita* Socorrito, please excuse me for interrupting your class, but I need to talk to the students."

I assured him it wasn't a problem, so he proceeded to talk about his plans for the graduation. His eyes shone, and a smile lit up his face while he talked. The students listened attentively. They had a thousand questions and several raised their hands. He answered them patiently.

"Will we wear suits?"

"Can we have sponsors?"

"Are we going to have a dance with an orchestra?"

The *profesor* answered "yes" to all of their previous questions. Each affirmative answer made them react with enthusiasm.

"Are we having a graduation Mass?" one of the girls asked shyly.

Profesor Merla rubbed the sides of his mouth. The class went silent.

"We'll talk about that later," he said without committing, to avoid further conversation on religion. He proceeded to explain about the fundraising dances. Then he told the students to form a committee.

"The next important thing is to select one of the teachers as the person who'll manage all the money collected from the dances."

Ernesto Rodríguez raised his hand. "I nominate *maestra Camero* for that position."

"I second the nomination," Jorge Martínez, Ernesto's best friend, said.

This nomination came unexpectedly. I was standing in front of the class next to the *director*. Surprised, I turned my head to look at him and saw that his eyes were half closed and his lower lip was trembling.

"Excuse me, pupils. I suppose you don't know that *profesor* Merla managed the money before. I think he should do it again." I felt mortified, thinking they had not been aware of this fact.

Profesor Merla crossed his arms and waited. Lauro, who observed everything from the back of the room, cleared his throat nervously. I felt a knot in my stomach and rubbed my arms because I felt a chill.

There was complete silence in the classroom. Some girls wiggled nervously in their seats, but not a single voice seconded my suggestion.

I turned to see Ernesto and Jorge, who sat on one side of the classroom. I begged them with my eyes to rectify their proposal. *Profesor* Merla looked at them, too. They didn't blink, not even once. They were tapping nonchalantly on their desks, and I realized they were ignoring us on purpose.

"It's very clear they trust you," the *director* said. He looked at me with blazing eyes. "Those who are in favor of *señorita* Socorro, raise your hand," he solicited with a raspy voice.

To my horror, every student in the classroom raised his hand without hesitation.

"Congratulations, *señorita* Socorro, you are in charge. Good luck," he said with an icy voice before storming out of the classroom followed by *profesor* Lauro.

The students and I were mute, shocked by *profesor* Merla's reaction. We looked at each other. Finally, I said, "Kids, thank you for your trust, but as you saw, the *director's* feelings were hurt. I wish you would reconsider and let him manage the graduation money. After all, he's the principal."

"*Maestra*, we want you to take care of the money. We decided this unanimously," Jorge indicated.

"As the *director* said, we trust you," Ernesto added with a wicked smile.

"But why?"

They didn't answer.

"Okay, if all of you chose me, I'll do it. But I know *profesor* Merla won't let me forget it."

I didn't know then how prophetic my words would be.

After being elected to manage the students' graduation funds, I was left with the task of dealing with the *director's* incomprehensible reaction. Before leaving school, I went into his office to try to smooth things over with him.

"Excuse me, *profesor* Merla, I hope you are not angry at me for what happened in—"

"Don't bother to explain, *señorita*. The students chose you, and that's it. It is clear that they trust only you. They didn't nominate anybody else, so the rest of us are not worthy of their trust."

What does he mean with 'the rest of us'? Is he trying to find sympathy from the other teachers?

Lauro, who had been a silent observer of the incident in the classroom, motioned to me to say nothing. "You don't have to apologize," he whispered. "*¡Ya se le pasará!* He'll get over it."

"Thanks," I muttered, trying to hold back the tears.

The other teachers and I picked up our belongings and got ready to retire. On the way out, Andrés elbowed me softly. He signaled with his head to look at the *director's* hat. Instead of the usual way he wore it, it was turned toward one side. He did this whenever something bothered him.

At dinner time, I felt stressed, thinking that if he came to visit us like he often did, I would have to look at him and probably listen to his unwanted comments. Fortunately, he came in when we were leaving the table. I was glad we had already finished eating. José Luis, always chivalrous, kept him company, while Andrés and I preferred to go to our rooms. *Profesor* Merla scarcely acknowledged us as we excused ourselves and headed to the exit.

In the following weeks, the *director* looked for ways to show me his displeasure, never recognizing that I was not to blame. In one of these occasions, Andrés noticed how much it had affected me. He reached me when I was about to enter my bedroom. "Don't pay attention, Socorrito. You know how he is. He takes everything personally, but he'll get over it soon, you'll see." He patted me on the shoulder and smiled.

"I hope so," I said looking at him gratefully. I thought how fortunate I was that he had taken an assignment that six months ago some female teachers had rejected. Andrés had a big heart and was a kind, fair, and loyal friend. Undoubtedly, I knew I could always count on him.

CHAPTER TWENTY-FIVE

LET'S TALK ABOUT GHOSTS

Manuel, the lawyer, returned from his vacation in Monterrey toward the weekend. He was part of our small family; therefore we were delighted to see him again. He was quiet at dinner time, so we teased him about already being homesick, which he didn't deny. Manuel was the only one in our group who was married. I figured it was hard for him to be away from his family. I tried to cheer him up, telling him about the latest news in town. Soon he was as talkative as ever.

In the late afternoon, I got together with the teachers and him to talk and play cards in José Luis's room. As usual, an atmosphere of camaraderie prevailed. Several occurrences made us laugh while we played. I felt glad that we all got along so well. Besides, being the only woman in the group had its advantages. One of them was feeling protected in many ways.

"Have you ever fired a gun, Socorrito?" Manuel suddenly asked.

"A gun? No, Manuel. Other than target shooting at fairs—which I enjoy a lot—I've never fired a real one. Why do you ask?"

"Well, I was thinking that you should get one. In fact, all of you should have a gun," he said. "It's important that you have something to defend yourselves with, if necessary, but first, you have to learn how to use it."

I smiled, thinking about the big stick that *doña* Susana gave me to secure my bedroom door. Besides, I had Duque, the big scary-looking black dog—Horacio's pet.

"I'll tell you something. Let's go target shooting one of these days. I'll take a couple of guns," proposed Manuel.

We were thrilled with the prospect of learning how to shoot. We asked Manuel a lot of questions, which he answered patiently. We agreed to practice outside of town the following weekend.

"I'm sure you aren't a fearful person, Socorrito," Manuel said.

"Well, sometimes I can feel fear like anyone else. However, even in unusual situations I try to reason calmly."

"Talking about unusual things, did you hear an owl's hoot last night? It seemed to me that the sound was coming from in front of my room." Andrés waited for us to answer while rubbing his chin.

"Quite so!" I answered, "but it wasn't the first time. It has happened before."

"I heard it, too," José Luis said.

"I'm sure there was an owl standing on one of the branches of the fig tree," Andrés said. He seemed very pensive when he made this comment.

There were so many superstitions about owls that many people were apprehensive whenever they heard their hoot.

"I'd be more afraid of seeing a ghost under the fig tree than finding a poor owl," Lauro said, chuckling and looking at us with an amused expression.

"Well, provided that the ghost is a pretty girl, I wouldn't mind," José Luis said with narrowed eyes.

His comment made us laugh, because he didn't usually joke.

"Yes, a lady ghost wearing a white chemise," added Andrés. Chemise dresses inspired by the fashions of the 1920s were a very popular style at the time.

Everybody laughed but Manuel. He kept looking furtively outside. He moved away from the door and didn't participate in the conversation. José Luis winked at me and pointed at Manuel with a gesture. We continued to play cards and pretended not to notice Manuel's nervousness.

"Does anybody need to go to the bathroom?" Manuel asked tensely.

Everybody said a loud "No!" We all laughed at the spontaneous synchrony.

"Why don't you ask Teresa or Claudia to keep you company, Manuel?" someone suggested to him. "Nobody needs to use the bathroom now."

"I always call Teresa if I need to go at nighttime," I said. That was true. I did it mostly to be sure her husband, Juan, wouldn't show up suddenly like the first time that I saw him. The big man with bell-bottomed denim overalls and a big straw hat gave me chills.

Finally, Andrés picked up a kerosene lamp and accompanied Manuel. As I mentioned before, the bathroom was an adobe room at the end of the patio. Instead of a door, it had a curtain that people pulled when they entered. High on the back wall there was a rectangular opening without a window. On dark nights, the bathroom was a very spooky place to go. I couldn't avoid thinking about ghosts, spiders, snakes—and Juan.

One time before then, I needed to use the bathroom when it was already dark. Noticing that Teresa and the other maids were busy, I grabbed my kerosene lamp and went by myself. There was an eerie silence in that part of the house. As I entered the bathroom and lowered the curtain, strange noises came from behind the wall. I looked up to the window. *My God, someone will enter through there at any minute.* My heart started beating loudly, but I couldn't move. Suddenly, I heard a loud thump on the wall! Overcome by panic, I rushed out of the place. A few seconds later, I heard a braying. It was a donkey that had kicked the wall!

Teresa saw me at that moment and came to keep me company. With a nervous laugh, I told her what had happened in the bathroom. She told me there was a corral behind that wall and the animals roamed freely in it. After that I promised to myself that I would go to the bathroom at nighttime only in the company of one of the maids.

As the days went by, we noticed that Manuel got tense whenever we joked about ghosts, so the more he tried to change the conversation, the more we talked about it.

Since *La Llorona*, or the Weeping Woman, is one of the most popular myths in Mexican culture, we brought up all the terrible stories we had heard about her. Thus, we remembered the legend of the beautiful woman who drowned her small children in order to be with the man she loved. When the ungrateful man left her, she killed herself and was denied entrance to heaven because she didn't have her children. In that way, she was sent back to Earth. Since then—

hundreds of years ago—her lament is heard, *"Aaay, mis hijos!* Aww, my children!"* as she runs to search in empty streets, under bridges and branches of trees, close to rivers. Some say to have seen her wearing a white dress and her long hair all disheveled.

We took turns talking about people's encounters with *La Llorona.* Every story was more terrifying than the previous one, until we started getting almost as nervous as Manuel.

"Horacio, please come here," Andrés said one day when he saw him go by.

"What do you need, *profesor* Andrés?" the boy said, standing by the door.

"We want to know if you have ever seen a ghost of a lady who appears under the fig tree?" Andrés asked with a wicked smile and a wink.

As usual, we were all in José Luis's room playing cards. We giggled because by that time we had tacitly decided that the nonexistent ghost was female.

"Only a couple of times, but she is harmless," he answered with a straight face, playing along with us.

We were all paying attention to Manuel's reaction to Horacio's words.

"Have you ever asked her what she wants?" I told him. "People say that spirits want to communicate, when they need help."

"No, I'm afraid she might start crying," Horacio answered, instinctively linking her to *La Llorona* stories.

"Crying? What kind of crying?" Andrés asked mischievously.

"*¡Aaaaaay, mis hijos!*" Horacio said, making a long and painful crying sound. If we hadn't understood the joke, that gloomy lament would have caused us goose bumps.

We all giggled, with the exception of the lawyer who found no humor in our stories. For us, it was ironic that his job required he would go to see the cadavers of people who had died under mysterious circumstances, and yet, conversation about a ghost was enough to change the color of his skin.

Manuel asked *doña* Susana to move him to another room. We didn't ask him the reason, but we guessed it. He got a bedroom next to Andrés's. Meanwhile, we continued thinking of other ghost stories to share.

Finally, we stopped doing it. We would not have liked if Manuel ended up moving to another hotel where he was sure there would be no ghosts—nor would he listen to legends about them.

CHAPTER TWENTY-SIX

THE NEW FOREIGNERS

"There's a new guy in town. Have you met him?" Nena asked me one afternoon.

"Not yet. Who is he?"

"All I know is that he is a chemist. I think he's making tests on the well's water. He stopped by the store and talked to my father," Nena said. "Unfortunately, I wasn't there."

Nena's words aroused my curiosity.

Two days later, a tall, handsome, and athletic man arrived with José Luis at the restaurant. Andrés and I were getting ready to sit down for dinner.

"Hey, guys, I want you to meet Alberto. He's a chemist, and he'll be staying several days at the hotel across the plaza."

Andrés and I introduced ourselves to the newcomer.

"Alberto, we were getting ready to eat. Would you like to join us?" I asked.

"It would be my pleasure. I already tried the food from the other hotel. Let's see if it compares to the one here," he answered, rubbing his hands.

We occupied our regular places, leaving a space open for *profesor* Merla, who would eat with us that day and would arrive at any moment. The maids came and went, pretending to be cleaning the empty tables. They observed the newcomer discreetly. Claudia ran to *doña* Susana's room to wake her up from her afternoon nap and probably to tell her about the foreigner. A few minutes later, the owner appeared in the dining room, tying her apron and fixing her hair. She looked with curiosity at Alberto; then she asked, "Are all of you eating?"

"Yes, we are," I answered, "but we'll wait for *profesor* Merla. By the way, this is Alberto, *doña* Susana."

"*¡Mucho gusto!*", she replied with a slight inclination of her head.

"*¡Igualmente, doña* Susana! Yes. I want to try your food," Alberto said amicably.

"Hmm. You'll see that my food is tastier than at the other hotel," *doña* Susana assured him, heading toward the kitchen.

We looked at each other and smiled at her comment.

"So, tell us, Alberto, what are you doing in this place, so far from civilization?" Andrés asked.

At that moment, *profesor* Merla came into the dining room. We introduced Alberto to him. The *director* seemed to be analyzing him. He hardly talked to him, just listened. Either the chemist didn't notice it or decided to ignore it all together. He kept telling us about his job and his experiences in town.

Soon, Teresa and another helper served us a delicious *guisado de puerco*, which Alberto praised to the owner's satisfaction. The pork meat was so tender that it almost melted in the mouth. We could smell the garlic and cumin in the savory tomato sauce. The Mexican rice and refried beans with chorizo complemented the aromatic dish.

Profesor Merla left right after dinner, but Alberto stayed to play cards with us at José Luis's invitation. Lauro joined the group at the usual time.

From that day on, Alberto came to visit us or to eat with us anytime he was in town. He was a new face and one more friend in Doctor Arroyo. He was pleasant, an enjoyable companion who made us laugh constantly.

He wasn't the only one to come to town to break the routine. In those days, a young, good-looking doctor came to work at the new clinic. Of course, many of the single girls tried to catch his attention at the dances or any other place where the doctor was present. The entire town knew who he talked to, who flirted with him, who gave him presents, and who made special dishes for him. He was a new member in the *crystal box.*

Finally, *doña* Ofelia Eguía, the attractive widow who we met at the Perales' *tertulia* was the lucky one, and later on, she ended up marrying him. This lady had two children. One of them was our student. She was also the Rodríguez children's aunt. Occasionally Minerva told us stories about the jealousy some people felt toward her aunt. *Doña* Ofelia never paid attention to the people's comments, and in the end, she won the big prize. They made a great couple.

Sometime later, three civil engineers came to town to begin planning the construction of a paved road between Matehuala and Doctor Arroyo. Soon, the three of them started coming to our hotel to visit. I found it amusing when Nena told me some of the young women felt jealous that I was talking to these men.

"So, what am I supposed to do?" I asked. "I live in this place. It's not my fault if they come by, and I'm not going to hide in my room when they show up. Let them talk!"

"Okay, *maestra*, don't get upset. Tell me what you all talk about. Are they single? How long will they stay here?" Nena asked.

"Listen, that's a lot of questions," I said, laughing. "You are almost as bad as those other girls. Well, from what I heard, all of them are single, so put up your antennae before other girls do it."

"And what about you?" Nena said.

"You know I have a boyfriend, even if he is far away. I'm hoping he'll come to see me this year. It's becoming an old story that he can't come. Patience has a limit." *If he just would come to see me, I would know how committed he really is to this long-distance relationship.*

"Well, you'll have to introduce me to the engineers first. You know that Eva would like to meet them, too."

"The only bad thing is that they come only at night, after they have finished working, and had dinner at their hotel. More than likely, you are already *en los brazos de Morfeo*, at that time."

Nena laughed at my comment about her being asleep in Morpheus' arms. She said she would look for an opportunity to stop by soon. "In the meantime, don't introduce them to anyone else. Remember, I'm first." She winked an eye and squeezed my arm.

"I might start charging you for introducing you to every guy that comes to visit," I said. "I bet you I would get rich fast."

The arrival of the civil engineers also added variety to our everyday living in a small town. All of us who were foreigners tended to form a private small circle. Thus, Manuel the lawyer, my fellow teachers, and I became acquainted with the engineers soon after their arrival. They established a pattern of coming by our place two or three times a week. We always had a good time in which we discussed ideas and experiences, and since they traveled back and forth to Monterrey, they kept us well informed of the latest news of the big city.

The engineers were actively involved in politics, especially Fernando Parás, who was the nephew of one of the ex-governors of Nuevo León. He proposed that we attend a political rally in Monterrey. There, each one of us would present a *ponencia*, a petition that would be studied later by a committee. We would present it verbally or in writing if there wasn't opportunity to travel to Monterrey.

I wasn't interested in getting involved in politics. I only wanted to do a good job as a teacher and told Fernando so. He suggested I try it at least once, so I decided to do it just for the experience. I don't remember the subject of my presentation, but after participating, I realized without a doubt that politics wasn't for me.

Besides the thrill of meeting new friends, in this case the engineers and Alberto the chemist, we continued enjoying the company of Santiago, who always stayed at *doña* Susana's hotel. I was the only woman among all these men, and although I often stayed in my room to give them the freedom to talk about men's things, someone invariably came looking for me.

"C'mon, Socorrito, we are waiting for you," was the usual expression from any of the teachers, Manuel, or Alberto.

Many people might have been curious about what transpired in our gatherings, but since the doors of the rooms were always open, and *doña* Susana or Teresa were usually close, I knew nobody could point a finger at me regarding my conduct. I never forgot the fact that we lived in a *crystal box*, and the walls had eyes and ears. What people could observe was the affectionate camaraderie full of respect among all of us. I never heard anyone swearing or telling obscene jokes. We did, however, laugh a lot, most of the time telling stories related to the students or talking about personal incidents that occurred to us.

One of those anecdotes was the occasion when we went to eat roasted pumpkins and corn on the cob at a nearby ranch.

Manuel the lawyer had accepted the invitation and he extended it to us. He also informed us he would take a couple of guns to practice shooting.

We were excited about the outing. *Profesor* Merla said he would attend, too.

"You should have a small gun, Socorrito. I told you before you need to have something to defend yourself if necessary."

"Well, thanks for the advice, Manuel, but with all of you keeping an eye on me, I don't think I'll ever need one," I excused myself.

"Undoubtedly you are well cared for, Socorrito, not only by all of us, but also by that ugly dog, Duque," Manuel said.

"Indeed," I said shaking my head and sighing.

The day of the outing, we started our travel to the ranch early. The sky had a pinkish tone, announcing the sun, and the air was cool but nice. As we arrived, a breeze brought the smell of roasted corn up to us.

Next to a large white house, there was an arched entrance, where the owner and his family were already waiting for us.

"*¡Bienvenidos a mi rancho!*", was the friendly reception from the owner.

Manuel made the necessary introductions, and the rancher and his family shook hands with us. Several children giggled and hid behind their parents while two dogs smelled our shoes and clothes with curiosity.

"Now please follow me," the owner said. He guided us into an orchard full of trees. His children skipped playfully ahead of us, followed by the barking dogs.

"These *elotes* are ready. Please try some while we wait for the *calabazas*." The host pointed to a large tray full of recently roasted corn on the cob.

We removed their leaves carefully because they were still quite hot. We spread fresh butter, salt, and *chile piquín* on them. Soon, we enjoyed the flavor and crispiness of each kernel of corn.

Manuel asked the owner for permission to practice with the guns while we waited for the *calabazas*, which were roasting in a large pit covered with cactus leaves.

"*¡Mi casa es su casa!*", said the owner. "Go ahead, please."

We thanked him and followed a man who took us to another part of the orchard. Manuel set up a target. After a short explanation on safety and the use of the weapon, we took turns practicing. It was a strange experience to feel for the first time the cold metal of the gun in my hand. Pointing toward the target, I thought about all the damage such a small object could cause. That feeling reaffirmed that I didn't want to have a gun in my room. I found it too much responsibility.

Anyway, we had a lot of fun and laughed every time we missed our target. We stopped when the owner called us to eat the roasted pumpkins.

At the pit, the cactus leaves had already been removed and the roasted pumpkins were on the side, on top of a big container.

"You'll like it," said the owner, pointing at them. A man handed us a large plate. He then cut the steaming pumpkins in half and gave each of us one half. My mouth watered as I put the fork down on the warm pumpkin and saw the bright orange flesh peel off easily. When I brought the fork to my lips, the owner came up to me and asked, "*Señorita*, would you like to eat your pumpkin with fresh milk?"

That reminded me of my years in San Luis Potosí when I was growing up. We always had *calabaza con leche*, pumpkin with milk, on November 2, the Day of the Dead.

"I would love to. That's the way I used to eat it in San Luís when I was a little girl," I said.

The owner made a hand signal for me to follow him.

"I think I would like to eat it like that, too," Andrés said. He followed us, holding his half-pumpkin with both hands.

I saw the owner's wife coming with a ceramic pitcher in her hand, which I supposed was full of warm milk. I wet my lips with my tongue, already savoring that delicacy in advance.

"Milk for the pumpkins," the rancher's wife announced, showing us the pitcher.

"*La señorita* likes it fresh," the owner said, bending next to a cow. He held the cow's udder on top of my pumpkin and squeezed the milk several times while I gaped at him. I heard Andrés chuckling behind my back.

"Here it is, fresh as you like it," the owner said, very satisfied, as he gave it back to me.

"Tha-thank you," I stammered, taking it from his hands. "Your turn, Andrés," I said, turning around. Now I would laugh at my friend! Instead, I saw him next to the owner's wife receiving milk from her jug.

"Chicken!" I mumbled as I passed him, and he laughed.

"Mooo, mooo!" he said, laughing louder as he followed me back.

"What's all this about?" José Luis asked, coming to meet us as he ate his pumpkin.

"That Socorrito wanted fresh milk, and she got it—straight from the cow!" Andrés explained, continuing to laugh with tears in his eyes.

By then, the rest of the group was around, everyone laughing at my situation. I stood there with my pumpkin, not knowing what to do. Just then, the owner came with a spoon in his hand.

"I'm sorry I forgot to give you a spoon. Please, please, don't be shy. Eat your *calabaza* before the milk gets cold. Let me know if you need some more."

"Go ahead, Socorrito, or the milk will get cold," Andrés said, chuckling.

In response, I glared at him.

The owner encouraged me with his head, and I saw all the eyes on me. There was an amused expression on all of the faces.

I took the first spoonful. To my surprise, it tasted wonderful. Before I knew it, I had finished it.

"Well, what did you think?" asked the host.

"Delicious. Thanks!" was my sincere answer.

"I'm so glad. I imagine it brought back your childhood memories."

"It sure did," I assured him.

The owner said something to his wife and went away.

A few minutes later he came back smiling. "Since you liked it so much, *señorita*, here is your other half," he said. He handed me the pumpkin with warm milk and a clean spoon.

I looked at him with surprise. In the distance, we heard a cow mooing, "Moo, moo."

Everyone laughed. I did too.

CHAPTER TWENTY-SEVEN

A SUCCESSFUL DANCE AND
A GREAT SECRET

The first dance to raise funds for graduation was a resounding success. The event took place in a large open court next to the theater. A group of enthusiastic students had taken care of advertising the dance, even in places as far away as Matehuala.

Profesor Merla was an excellent organizer. He was attentive to all the details, regardless of his hurt feelings after the students chose me, and not him, to handle the money. He hired police to take care of the peace and order during the event and kept supervising to ensure that everything would go smoothly.

José Luis, well-groomed as always, kept a vigilant eye on everything and everyone from a distance. He was serious and quiet, but always polite. The students and townspeople liked him and respected him. Lauro, with his good looks and charismatic personality, was surrounded by several of the attendees, while Andrés, with his friendly and gentle disposition, and I, mingled with the people.

Nena, Eva, and her sisters were back in town. I was sure they would attend the dance, so I had reserved some places, and we sat together. All of us wore new dresses and had new haircuts. As usual, we had returned from vacation with all that was fashionable in the city.

The place was full, wall-to-wall. Nobody wanted to miss this public event. The D.J.s were the same owners of the theater. They had a good sound system and a varied collection of popular records. The polkas were the dancers' favorite tunes. Whenever one started, the men ran to invite their favorite ladies. The two D.J.s were brothers, and they took turns enjoying the event. Antonio, the tallest of them, invited me to the dance floor a couple of times. I also danced with Santiago who was back in town for the occasion. My friends laughed at the fact that even though I was wearing high heels, my dance partners had to bend over to dance with me.

"Those men will be hunchbacked if they continue with you as a partner," they teased.

"I'll ask them to dance with you so they can straighten their backs."

"Don't you dare," Nena said. She was the most formal of the three of us.

Horacio, Homero, Sergio *El Guapo*, Ernesto, and Napoleón—another very popular student—formed a lively group with some young ladies. It was nice to see them having fun. Several of them were already dating. There was a particular couple—Jorge Martínez and Lilia Nava—who I thought one day would end up married because they had much in common. They came from very religious families and both were very serious, kind, and studious, and they seemed quite committed to each other.

My faithful student José preferred to sit next to me and my friends. He volunteered to keep an eye on our coats and purses while we danced. He felt very proud to be in charge of this, even though I had suggested to him several times to join the rest of his classmates. I was concerned that he preferred to be there instead of mingling with people his own age. He said he enjoyed watching others have fun. The next melody was a polka, and all of us were invited to the dance floor. I noticed Horacio and Homero approached him.

"José, what are you doing just sitting there? Look at all those girls! I'm sure they are dying for you to invite them," Horacio said. He and Homero were carrying some Cokes for their partners.

"Look, that girl is pointing at you. Surely, she wants to dance," continued Horacio signaling with his head to one of the girls who was waving at them.

"I'm fine here, and I don't care if somebody wants to dance with me or not," José answered. He looked with disdain at the two grinning boys in front of him. "You are just jealous because you can't be trusted to take care of anything of value."

Horacio and Homero broke into a big laugh. "Look José, then we are going to send some girls so that they invite you," Horacio warned him. The two boys left when Andrés and I returned to our seats.

"What's going on, José? Were your friends bothering you?" I asked him. He told me what had transpired between him and Horacio.

"I just ignore them. I think that they are just envious because all of you trusted me with your things," he said, shrugging.

After sitting and talking to my friends for a little bit, I went to look for the rest of the teachers. I observed several girls talking to José. They must have talked about some personal matter because they made him move a little bit away from Nena and Eva. One girl, Josefina, placed her hand on José's shoulder and started explaining something to him in whispers. José listened attentively while looking in the direction of where the teachers and I were. Some of the girls turned around from time to time, too. They seemed to talk in whispers but with a lot of excitement. They finally left, and José went back to his chair.

After a while, the dance finished, and my friends waved goodbye to me from a distance.

Profesor Merla counted the amount of money collected that night. My coworkers and I waited on the side, eager to find out if we made some profit. He took out the money we owed for the D.J. and for the rent of the place. Then, he let us know what our profit was. We did very well. We all smiled and congratulated each other.

"The kids will be very happy when you let them know how much we made," I told *profesor* Merla.

"Inform them yourself. In the end, they trusted you with their money, didn't they?" There was a trace of resentment in his words.

I could see from the faces of my teacher friends that they did not approve of the *director's* comment. He knew the students had chosen me freely, yet, he had taken it as a personal offense. I didn't say anything and returned to pick up my things from José. Minerva, Josefina, and some other girls were keeping him company, but they left right away when I arrived.

"Thank you so much, José. What were you talking about with the girls? They left in such a hurry."

"Oh, they need me for something that for now I can't tell you about," he said.

I looked at him with curiosity, but he only said good night to me and left hastily.

On the first day of classes after the fundraising dance, I gave the third-level students a report of the earnings. They were very impressed when they heard the amount we had made. They got euphoric and promised the next dance would be even better.

"Listen, kids, you better study hard from now to the end of school year; otherwise, instead of graduating, you'll still be sitting here next year, planning some extra dances."

"Don't worry, *maestra*, all of us will be walking on the stage to receive our diplomas," assured Jorge.

There were several exclamations from the rest of his classmates in support of his words.

"For the record, it's a promise. Now, open your books. Let's get started with today's lesson."

Around the middle of the week, I saw José talking to Josefina, Minerva, and some other girls during recess. Then, all of them went to talk to Horacio. He listened carefully, and I saw him nod his head agreeing with something they said. The strange thing was that they scurried away when Andrés and I approached the group.

"I wonder what the kids are up to." Andrés frowned when he saw Horacio talking to several students.

"I'm sure it's nothing bad if José is in the group. You know he doesn't follow the others," I said. However, I remembered what the kid told me the day of the dance, so I became really curious.

"Listen, José." I approached him at the first opportunity I saw him alone. "May I know why the girls are talking to you so much?"

"It's not for me to say," he replied, looking uncomfortably at Josefina and Irma who observed us from the distance, "but it's nothing bad, I swear."

"Okay, if you say so, I believe you. I know you'd never do anything to disappoint me."

"I won't. You can be sure of that. Now please excuse me. Josefina is calling me."

He left in a hurry. Andrés joined me while I walked to pick up my purse to go home.

"Did you find out what the conspiracy is about?" he asked.

"No, I couldn't find out, but something's definitely up."

One early afternoon in February, I was sitting in my rocking chair reading a book and enjoying the sound of a light rain when *doña* Susana sent Teresa looking for me. It intrigued me, as this was unusual. I followed Teresa to the kitchen where the lady was wiping her hands on her apron. Her face was red from the heat of the burning charcoal on the *fogón*, a hearth full of clay pots of many sizes and shapes. A mix of aromas filled the kitchen, stimulating the appetite and reminding us it was almost dinner time.

"*Señorita*, I have something to tell you! Teresa, stay alert and be sure that nobody comes!" ordered *doña* Susana. She looked so serious that I felt alarmed.

"This is supposed to be a secret, so if Horacio finds out I told anyone, he's going to be angry," she whispered with much mystery.

A secret? Is it related to those mysterious conversations among the students?

"What's going on?" I asked. "Please don't keep me in suspense."

"Well, as you know, tomorrow is *profesor* Andrés's birthday. Some students plan to serenade him with the '*Mañanitas.*' Josefina and José will pick up several girls at their homes because they aren't allowed to walk alone so early in the morning. Then, they'll meet with some boys in the plaza, and all of them will be here around 5:30 in the morning. Horacio will open the front door for them. The custom here is that the birthday person receives the group with hot chocolate and sweet bread. Since it's a surprise, we can't tell *profesor* Andrés about it, thus I want your approval to order these things. I'll give him the bill later." She smiled at the conclusion of her explanation.

"But of course, *doña* Susana. Thank you for telling me. So, how much bread do you think we should buy?"

"I think two big baskets will be enough. According to Horacio, around twenty-five students will come. I already have enough milk to make the chocolate. The milkman brought it this afternoon. I'll just confirm with the bakery next door the amount of bread that we'll need."

So, that was the kids' great secret! They wanted it to be a complete surprise. I remembered that some weeks back they had asked about our birthdays. I told them mine was on June 27, during summer vacation. They agreed that, in that case, they would transfer my Saint's feast day to May 13 and celebrate then instead of my birthday.

Teresa came into the kitchen in a hurry. "*Profesor* Andrés is looking for you, *señorita*," she said.

Doña Susana placed a finger over her closed lips, and understanding the signal, I answered her with a nod. Then I poured some black coffee in a cup and walked out of the kitchen.

"*Hola*, Andrés, Teresa said you were looking for me."

"Yeah. I thought it would be fun to walk in this light rain, and I wanted to know if you would like to keep me company."

"Of course. Just let me finish this cup of coffee, and I'll be ready as soon as I get my umbrella."

"I think I'll have some black coffee, too," he said. He went into the kitchen and came back with a steaming cup of coffee.

After we finished, Andrés suggested that we visit the *aljibes*, which were on the north side of town. We saw them when José Luis guided us in a tour of the whole place. We had learned that since there weren't any rivers or lakes around, the water from the three *aljibes* scarcely met the needs of the townspeople and that the water carriers sold it house to house.

The sidewalks were narrow, and there wasn't any traffic, so Andrés and I walked in the middle of the cobblestone street. We protected ourselves from the light drizzle with our umbrellas. Thin streams ran along the sides of the street. As we joked and carried on our conversation, we observed some people peering out their doors after we had passed in front of their homes. At a signal from me, Andrés and I turned our heads suddenly to look back at them. Every time we did this, they tried to hide quickly, which amused us. We knew people were wondering what we were doing walking in the rain.

"Tomorrow will be my first birthday away from home," Andrés said, kicking an empty can into a puddle. "I feel a little bit homesick, and that's why I asked you to take a walk with me. Thank you for coming."

"I'm glad you asked me, Andrés. You know we promised we would support each other on the day we rode the bus together for the first time," I said, remembering when we met. "Tell me the way you celebrate your birthday back home."

Andrés told me his mom always made *mole* for him and a cake. I knew *doña* Susana would make *mole* for him. This is the traditional dish for special celebrations. Making it from scratch requires grinding different kinds of *chiles*, roasted peanuts, and several spices on a *metate*, an elongated hard, porous flat stone. This is a hard job, especially if one had to kneel on the floor to do it.

"It's going to be a long day for me." Andrés sighed. "I wish my mom could be here."

"It's going to be a long day for sure, Andrés, but I hope it won't be a sorrowful day."

"Well, only if you promise to sing the '*Mañanitas*' for me," he said.

"Oh, I will. You can be sure of that. Tomorrow you'll listen to the best '*Mañanitas*' of your life." I smiled, thinking about the big surprise that was being planned for him.

"I can hardly wait," Andrés said. "It will be interesting to listen to you as a soloist singing *a cappella*." Joking with that theme, we started back home.

As planned, the kids showed up long before the sun was out. I had set my alarm to ring before 5:30 a.m., so I was up and ready by the time they entered the house. Some minutes later, José Luis knocked softly on my door and said, "*Socorrito*, come outside to sing the '*Mañanitas*' to *profesor* Andrés." I waited for a few minutes then I came out.

Andrés usually slept like a rock, so, José Luis and two or three boys had to bang on his door to wake him up. Once he answered in a sleepy voice, we sang, all in chorus, the "*Mañanitas*," accompanied by Horacio and his guitar. During the couplets, Andrés opened the door, his hair disheveled, smiling happily and still fixing his clothes.

At the end of the song there was cheering and many congratulations. Although Andrés still seemed a bit confused, it was obvious that he was enjoying the moment. *Doña* Susana called him and explained to him about the chocolate custom. Teresa and another of the maids had everything ready, then Andrés invited everybody into the dining room. The smell of fresh-baked *pan dulce* filled the dining room. The rich aroma of the steamy chocolate woke up everybody's appetite. I sat down with Andrés and José Luis at our usual table. All the boisterous young men found a place to settle, and soon there was no chocolate or bread left.

Doña Susana took over, "Teresa, make some extra chocolate for *profesor* Merla and *profesor* Lauro. They might be here any minute, and the chocolate is finished."

"And you, *muchacha*," she told Claudia, "run to the bakery and bring some *conchas*, *volcanes*, *y polvorones*. Tell the *panadero* to send me the bill."

"Can I have a piece of sweet bread, too, *señora*?" Claudia asked. She cocked her head and clenched her hands.

"Of course, you can have it," I told her before *doña* Susana could say no. After all, the little girl hadn't tasted anything.

"Thanks!" Claudia smiled and rushed out of the restaurant. A few minutes later, she came back biting on a piece of bread, perhaps afraid somebody would take it away from her.

"It was a very nice surprise this morning, and now this treat," Andrés said, savoring the *mole doña* Susana had prepared for him.

"And you listened to the best '*Mañanitas*' of your life, as I promised you."

"Just because you sang them to me, too," Andrés said, winking at me. Then he asked Teresa for another serving of *mole*.

But his celebration did not end there. With *profesor* Merla's permission, the students had a small assembly in his honor that afternoon. They sang and recited a couple of poems. The *director* said some words to congratulate him, and several of the students gave him presents. Andrés looked very happy all the time.

"One thing you can say about the people of small towns is that they are very grateful. This has really been my best birthday ever," Andrés said at the end of the day.

CHAPTER TWENTY-EIGHT

CHAIN OF LIES

One morning, *profesor* Merla and an unknown woman came to the door of the first-level classroom where I was teaching Civic Education. That was quite unusual. Puzzled and curious, I closed my book and went to meet them.

"*Señorita Socorrito*, excuse me for interrupting the class. This is *señora García*, Zoila García's mother. It seems there is a problem related to her daughter. Please handle this situation." *Profesor* Merla had a serious expression, but his tone of voice didn't register any emotion.

"*Muy bien, profesor.* Thanks."

The *director* turned around and went back to his office.

"*Buenos días, señora* García. Nice to meet you." I smiled and extended my hand to her. She gave me a cold stare and a weak handshake. Then she crossed her arms.

The woman's behavior was offensive. An incident had occurred with her daughter the day before. I assumed that would be the reason for her presence. I was not worried. One of *profesor* Merla's qualities as our school principal was that he always backed up his teachers.

"Please, give me a moment to assign some work to my students." I asked one of the most responsible students to keep an eye on the class, then came back to the woman.

"How can I help you, *señora* García? *Profesor* Merla said there is a problem." That time I didn't smile anymore.

"Well," she began with an icy voice, "I felt obligated to come here because my daughter Zoila says you don't like her and you humiliated her yesterday in front of the entire class. She cried and said you scolded her for no reason."

So, I had been right. Zoila had told her mom a story to make her seem a victim. I looked at the woman silently for several seconds. Then I said, "I see. And Zoila explained to you what she did in front of the entire class?"

"What do you mean?" The woman's piercing eyes were narrowed to slits, and her head was tilted to one side defiantly. "I know my daughter, and I know she's well-behaved."

"Well, I asked Zoila to respond to questions of an assigned lesson. She said she had not studied. Since that was the third time she had not been prepared for class, I had to grade her with a zero. This was not a scolding, as you can see. Now, let me show you the real reason I had to reprimand her."

I looked inside the classroom and saw Zoila wiggling in her seat and tapping her desk. She seemed to be watching her mother and me. Her face was noticeably flushed.

"Zoila, please come here and bring your Civic Education book," I said.

She stood up slowly and came to the door dragging her feet on the floor. She pulled her bangs over her eyes, as if she wanted to hide behind a curtain.

"I forgot it at home," Zoila said in a low voice while staring at the floor. I knew she was lying because she avoided my gaze and her lower lip trembled.

Suddenly, the boy sitting behind Zoila's desk came to us with a book in his hand. "Here is Zoila's book," he said. "She threw it under her desk."

Zoila glared at the boy. She tried to take the book away from him, but I grabbed it first.

"So ... you lied to me ... in front of your mom?" I asked her.

She didn't answer. Instead, she bit her lower lip and looked back at her classmates. She then turned to her mom, hoping for support. She ignored her, and Zoila started biting her nails.

"Can you explain to your mom what you did after I graded you with a zero?"

Zoila said nothing, only wrung her hands nervously. Her face was ashen. She looked at me, then stared at the floor again.

"We are waiting to hear your version of yesterday's incident, Zoila," I insisted.

Instead of answering, Zoila rubbed the floor with one shoe, as if she were trying to erase something. I was getting to the limit of my patience, and I still had a class waiting.

"You don't want to tell your mom? Then I'll show her what you did."

I placed the open book in *señora* Garcia's hands. The woman stared at the edges of the ripped pages that stood up from the spine.

Afterward, I walked to my desk and came back with several wrinkled pages that one of the students had rescued from a trash can. I handed them to *señora* Garcia who took them in silence.

"Now, Zoila, please tell your mom what kind of scolding I gave you in front of the entire class. Word for word."

Zoila looked at her mother and didn't say anything. She tapped the floor with one foot and kept pulling on her bangs. Thinking I wouldn't see her, she turned to her classmates and wrinkled her nose at them. They giggled, and I heard the student in charge asking for silence.

"Zoila? We are waiting. Should I ask the group? I don't have all day."

After a long pause, she finally confessed.

"You said you were sure my parents worked very hard to buy me what I need and send me to school, and they didn't deserve my behavior damaging my book."

"What else did I say, Zoila?"

She cleared her throat. "You said you had given me several chances before, but this time you had to give me a zero because I wasn't prepared for class."

The girl started to cry and put her arms around her mom, but she rejected her. The woman was obviously embarrassed and didn't know what to say.

"I hope you are satisfied with the explanation, *señora* García. Now you have to excuse me, but the group is waiting for me. Have a good afternoon."

The woman said something that sounded like an apology and left in a hurry. I went back into the classroom, and Zoila followed me with her chin on her chest. She sat on her chair, shaking and staring down. By the whispers around, she realized everyone was upset at her.

"Let's continue, and no comments please," I said. "I'm sure Zoila learned her lesson."

When the class finished, I went to see *profesor* Merla and told him what had transpired with Zoila's mom.

"Well done, *señorita* Socorro. Thank you for letting me know."

"Of course. You are the school principal, so I expect you to correct me when I'm wrong."

"You always do what you are supposed to do. I don't believe you would ever need to be corrected," he said amiably.

"Gracias, profesor".

I went to my next class feeling happy. I looked at the beautiful blue sky and thought it was a great day after all. I had dealt with a mother who came as a lioness but departed like a lamb.

CHAPTER TWENTY-NINE

TRUTH OR SUPERSTITION?

That same afternoon, Horacio stopped at the door of my room. He asked if he could talk to me for a few minutes. He had a serious expression.

I closed my notebook of the lesson plans I was working on and paid attention to him. "Yes, of course. What's going on?"

Horacio told me that one of his friends told him about the problem I had with Zoila's mother. Since I was relatively new to town and still didn't know the people well, he thought that he should warn me about the mother of a girl in another class. He named her.

"The girl is a good person, but when for some reason the teachers call her attention, she gets angry. Sometimes she threatens to take the complaint to her mother, and that is not good."

"What do you mean, Horacio?"

He looked over his shoulder like making sure no one was listening. "Well, many people say that her mother practices witchcraft."

"Come on, Horacio. You don't believe in witchcraft, do you?" I couldn't help but smile.

"Well yes, *profesora*, it exists, and if you don't believe me, just ask Teresa."

Teresa was sweeping the patio and watering the plants. The smell of wet dirt floated in the air mixed with the fragrance of the colorful flowers in the clay pots. She stopped when she overheard her name.

"Teresa, *la maestra* doesn't believe in witches and black magic. Tell her about it," Horacio invited her.

"Well, let me tell you what happened to Rosa several years back." Before continuing, she put the broom by the door and cleaned her hands on her apron.

I knew Rosa well. She had been *doña* Susana's maid and came by the house often.

Teresa cleared her throat and said, "Rosa was like a sister to me. She got married with *doña* Susana's permission, and she and her husband continued living here with us. One day, she started behaving weirdly. She began to sing something we had never heard before and in the most beautiful voice. At the beginning we were pleasantly surprised, but then, she got on top of the bed's headboard and sang, but like a rooster! She flapped her arms at the same time." Teresa almost whispered the last words.

"Are you serious? Wasn't she kidding?" I smiled skeptically.

"No, it wasn't a joke. What was odd was Rosa didn't remember a thing afterward."

"She always thought we were making up that story," Horacio said, smiling and strumming the strings of an invisible guitar.

"We noticed Rosa did this at the same time every day," Teresa continued.

"That's when somebody mentioned that she *estaba embrujada*," Horacio said.

"Exactly. When *doña* Susana heard this comment about Rosa's probable spell, she decided to take her to a *curandero*."

According to Teresa, he told them that a jealous woman had put a curse on Rosa. Her husband had been a lover of that person. The spiteful woman somehow managed to send her a meal with something bad inside, and that was the reason for Rosa's disorders.

"The *curandero* treated Rosa with brews and special chants," Teresa continued. "He cleansed her by passing some branches over her entire body. *Doña* Susana said the leaves of the branch crackled as if they were on the fire. After several sessions Rosa finally got better. Then the *curandero* gave her an amulet to keep her safe."

"I didn't believe in black magic either until I saw it with my own eyes," Teresa said when she finished her story. "You can ask Rosa when you see her, but she doesn't remember that horrible experience, only what happened before and after it. She knows the rest because we have told her about it."

"Wow, that's an incredible story, Teresa. I'm sure it is true because you witnessed it. Thanks for sharing it."

Teresa managed a smile and returned to finish her work.

"I think you should carry an amulet just in case," Horacio suggested to me.

"Do you carry one?" I asked him.

Horacio laughed and told me again to be careful. Then he walked out the front door of the house, blowing a tune with the mouthpiece of his cornet, while being followed by Duque, his faithful dog.

That night, when we got together in José Luis's room, I shared with them Teresa's narration and Horacio's warning about his classmate.

"You are going to hear a lot of stories like that," José Luis advised me.

"I have heard several, too, nothing new." Lauro didn't seem surprised at all.

"Do you believe them?" I asked.

"Who knows?" Lauro said.

Andrés scratched his head and José Luis just shrugged.

As the days passed, I forgot about the previous conversations, but soon, something would make me remember them vividly.

Some weeks later, when I walked into one of the classrooms, the student that Horacio had mentioned stood up. She had a plate covered with a white embroidered napkin. "*¡Maestra, ésto es para usted! ¡Se lo manda mi mamá!*". Her mom had sent me something to eat as a present.

I pulled up the napkin. The aroma promised a delicious meal. I looked at the students' faces. Most of them looked concerned. All of them must have heard the stories about that lady.

Horacio and two girls said no to me with their finger. The student had her back to them so she couldn't see them. With a kind smile she invited me to try the food.

I remembered that two days before I had warned her in class that if she kept talking with another girl, I would have to separate them. She stopped talking immediately and didn't seem to have been upset by what I said. At least that's what I thought. Could I have been wrong?

"Tell your mom that I appreciate this delight. I'll eat it later because I had breakfast not long ago. Now let's go ahead with the class." I placed the present on the desk.

When we finished, I took the covered plate with me and went to the office. I overheard Horacio asking permission from *profesor* Merla to go to the bathroom. He came running to my side and whispered, "Don't eat it, *maestra*." Then he hurried back to the classroom without waiting for my answer. I stepped into the office. Andrés, who was sitting there reading, raised his head and closed his book.

"What do you have there, Socorrito? Something to share with me?" he asked.

I told him who gave it to me and what Horacio had said before. "You should have seen the faces of the students. All of them must know something about it because some of them indicated to me not to touch it. Horacio just came to tell me not to eat it."

"So, what are you going to do with that food?" Andrés asked, scratching his head.

"Share it with you, of course." I couldn't help laughing.

"Not this time, thanks."

I told him I would get rid of it when we got home and bring the plate back the next day. I didn't want to do this at school because I didn't want to hurt the student's feelings.

On the way home, two of the girls kept me company. One of them reminded me once more to get rid of the food. I told them I didn't understand why everybody was so worried. I explained to the girls I didn't believe in *brujerias* at all.

By that time, Horacio was walking with us, too.

Afraid that I would not take them seriously, one of the girls invited Horacio to tell me what happened to a friend of theirs the previous summer. Then Horacio began the strange story about a boy who suddenly went crazy.

This kid had broken up with his girlfriend. One afternoon, she was waiting for him at the front door of her house. He didn't want to stop for fear of having a discussion, but she talked to him in a friendly way, so he relaxed. It was a sweltering day, so he gladly accepted the cold drink she offered him. They talked for a little while. Suddenly, he went crazy and started running around and yelling.

This behavior lasted for several weeks. The frustrated parents didn't know what to do. Finally, they took him to a *curandero* or *brujo*. The man told them their son became ill because the girl had put something bad in the drink she had given him. The *curandero* healed him with special concoctions. "Since then, the boy has avoided the girl," Horacio said. "So, you see, *maestra*, people can put things in food or drinks capable of driving one crazy. Now let me have that plate, and I'll put the food in the trash."

"Okay, Horacio, you win. I'll throw it away, even if I'm not superstitious."

I said goodbye to the girls and after entering the house I walked to the trash can *doña* Susana kept outside of the kitchen. Then, I remembered something my *abuelita* had advised me to do in circumstances like this.

I removed the napkin and made the sign of the cross three times over the food, while reciting, *"Lo que haya de allá para acá, que haya de aquí para allá"*.

I felt better after saying "What there is from there to here, let it be from here to there." This was supposed to return the bad luck to whoever sent it.

I'm not superstitious, no sir, but … just in case.

CHAPTER THIRTY

HOLY WEEK IN MONTERREY

Around the middle of February 1959, *profesor* Merla and *don* Bernardo López, who was PTA president, invited parents, local authorities, businesspeople, agricultural and union representatives, and anyone interested in the improvement of young people to a meeting. There, the *director* talked about the urgent need for a school building. This would benefit not only the youngsters from Doctor Arroyo, but also those from three other municipalities and small communities around who couldn't afford to go elsewhere to continue their middle school studies.

The *director* gave a great presentation to help ensure the parents' dream of a better future for their children. Everybody enthusiastically supported his ideas. A *patronato*, or committee, was formed with *profesor* Maximino Melchor as president, *profesor* José Luis Pérez as secretary, and Cuquita Rueda as treasurer. Everybody agreed that a formal petition for a new school should be made to the state government of Nuevo León.

In the following weeks, the middle school personnel—including me—met with the students' parents and the town's municipal president. We collected signatures, and many citizens offered contributions of money or construction materials. The theater owners promised fifty percent of the proceeds from a benefit movie function. Father Rangel offered a monetary contribution from the church.

Finally, we received an official letter from the state government of Nuevo León authorizing *profesor* Merla to look for suitable land to construct the school. With a beaming expression and his hands shaking, he showed us the document.

"Congratulations, *profesor* Merla; your dream will become a reality!" José Luis said, placing an arm on the *director's* shoulder.

"We are so happy, especially for you. This is the reward for all your efforts," I added and gave him a heartfelt hug.

Andrés and Lauro expressed their congratulations to him, too.

With a broken voice and wiping his watery eyes, *profesor* Merla said, "Thanks; I really appreciate your words and your support."

At the next meeting, there were several suggestions concerning the school project. The most acceptable was to construct the building on a large lot located on the south edge of the town. *Don* Dustano Muñiz, the town's municipal president and father of two of our students, agreed it was a good choice.

We noticed some parents talking to each other in whispers. Several frowned, and others nodded their heads in agreement. We soon found out the reason for their distress.

"There is a problem!" complained one of the attendees. "We all agree that we cannot let our daughters walk that far alone."

"We would like a closer location," several parents indicated.

It's funny that anybody can consider far some place on the edge of this small town. I looked at the other teachers and they were grinning, too.

"What if *profesora* Camero would be responsible for all of the young ladies?" *profesor* Merla asked. He repeatedly twisted a piece of paper he had in his hands while waiting for my answer.

The proposal caught me by surprise. José Luis, Lauro, and Andrés stared at me in silence. I held my chin, thinking about it. That was a big responsibility, but I would have to accept it if I wanted the project to succeed. Until then, that had been the only obstacle.

The parents talked between themselves again. "In that case, we won't oppose," said the man who was speaking for the rest. "We know *profesora* Camero will take good care of our daughters."

"*Profesora* Socorrito, do you agree to take responsibility for the young ladies?" *profesor* Merla asked me.

I felt the general attention on me. Everyone awaited my answer, especially the *director*.

"Of course, I agree to take care of them," I said. *After all, what can happen in this small town?*

There was a murmur of approval. I appreciated the trust the parents had in me, but I thought *profesor* Merla should have asked if I would be willing to accept such responsibility beforehand.

"Then, the girls will meet in plaza Juárez, across from *don* Amancio Berrones' store," the *director* explained to the parents. "From there, they'll walk to school with *profesora* Camero. And don't worry, the boys will not be allowed to accompany the young ladies!"

The parents smiled with satisfaction. The meeting was adjourned, and everybody went home.

The teachers and I could hardly wait to move into our own building. The school was to be built during the summer vacation. I sighed, wondering if I would be part of that transition or if I would find a teaching position in Monterrey or in some town closer to my family. This would prevent me from returning to Doctor Arroyo and somebody else would have to take care of the girls. That possibility made me sad.

In the last week of March, we went to Monterrey for *Semana Santa*, the Holy Week vacation. That was the second time Andrés and I returned home. Both of us had been eagerly counting the days. Once again, before our departure, our students gave us a lot of goodies.

"My mom sends this to your mom." Gentle messages accompanied the delivery of beautiful items embroidered or crocheted by their mothers.

"Enjoy this with your family." Good wishes were given along with cheeses, chorizos, some jars with mole and preserves, and a box of *tunas*—the Spanish word for prickly pears.

Likewise, I received personal presents from several students. People of small towns are undoubtedly generous.

"Please tell your mom I'm sure my mother will love her presents," I told each student. "Thanks again for mine, too!"

I repacked everything and finished by having a heavy suitcase, a cosmetic case, and a couple of large boxes. I didn't worry about transferring them because I knew somebody would give me a hand when we moved to another bus in Matehuala, and my family would be waiting for me at the bus station in Monterrey.

Everything went as planned, and soon we were on our way to Monterrey. I could hardly wait to see my family and friends.

That afternoon, as the bus arrived in the terminal in Monterrey, we saw the place full of happy travelers. They were leaving the city on vacation to various destinations. Many people from Monterrey, or *Regiomontanos*, as they are called, usually travel during Holy Week to Mexican beaches like Cancún, Acapulco, Tampico, Puerto Vallarta, and Mazatlán. For this reason, at this time of year, the city looked empty.

I spotted my family looking for me before the bus stopped. As soon as I stepped down, I found myself surrounded by the love of all of them. My mom kissed me first, followed by everybody else. My little sisters Norma and Julie took me by the hand as we left the station, while my brothers carried my luggage. We took a cab and joked and chatted animatedly all the way home.

The day after my arrival was Palm Sunday, the beginning of Holy Week. I went to the Shrine of Guadalupe, near our house, with my mother and my little sisters. My brother Cayito had been one of the nine acolytes of that parish for a year and a half. That day, he was helping at Mass, together with another altar boy. At the end, they followed the priest, who approached the faithful to bless our palm branches. The look my brother gave us showed the pride he felt in his work.

The city was very quiet for the next three days. However, the usual seclusion in my hometown, San Luis Potosí, was not felt in Monterrey. In San Luis Potosi, many women dressed in black during this season, as a sign of mourning. Most of the cinemas showed films with religious themes—in Monterrey too, but only in a few places.

Beginning on Holy Thursday, people became notably involved in the spirit of Holy Week. During the day, some radio stations broadcasted re-enactments of Gospel passages, especially the Passion of Christ. In between these programs, they played instrumental or choral classical music.

In those years we kept some traditions that nowadays make us laugh. One of them consisted of covering all the mirrors of the houses with purple or black canvases—I suppose because looking in mirrors had the connotation of vanity. In the absence of the canvases, large towels or sheets were perfect. Tasks such as washing and ironing were also suspended. Another strange custom was not to bathe! Bathing on Holy Thursday or Good Friday was considered disrespectful to the suffering of Jesus.

I followed, as close as possible, the Catholic rites of those days.

Cathedral of Monterrey

On Thursday we visited the seven temples. In my native San Luis, the faithful go to the parish in their neighborhood and then travel by vehicle to the center of the city. Once there, the tour of the six remaining temples is easily done on foot, since there are many of them and they are all very close. In Monterrey, some churches are six or seven blocks away, but others, more than a kilometer away. For that reason, I previously planned my route to visit the churches in a certain order. Despite the crowds, I enjoyed seeing the variety of altar arrangements and prayed briefly. In each temple they gave us a piece of blessed bread, a tiny bottle of holy water, or a small cross made of palm leaves. The streets were a pilgrimage, so the walk was not tiring. As in previous years, I was happy to meet friends I had not seen in a long time.

On Good Friday, I went to the Cathedral to listen to the Sermon of the Seven Words. All the images were covered with purple cloaks as a sign of mourning. On one side, inside a large transparent case was a life-size image showing the martyred body of Jesus. I remembered when, as a child accompanying my mother to the temple, I saw a similar image and my heart clenched, and I struggled to hold back tears.

During the period of Lent, the food on Fridays is special. The main dish is fish, prepared in different ways; in addition, pipián, a mild red paste-like mole; *tortitas de camarón*, shrimp made in small flat portions; and *orejones*, which are dried zucchini cut into thin slices, among other foods. These two last meals are served fried. That Holy Friday, my mother prepared us a delicious fish soup, and of course, the essential dessert at Easter: *capirotada*, bread pudding.

When Holy Saturday arrived, I missed the burning of Judas, a tradition in all the neighborhoods of San Luis and other towns in central and southern México. Gunpowder rockets were added to that figure of the devil, made of papier-mâché, which, when ignited, made the body of the devil spin in the air. People cheered and applauded with enthusiasm when the Judas was burned and destroyed by the rockets and fireworks that were placed on it. In Monterrey, this tradition was followed only in one neighborhood, far from our home.

An icon in San Luis Potosí, the city where I was born.

Holy Week culminated with Easter Sunday. I went with my family to the Cathedral, which was full of people. The first benches were occupied by the nuns of different religious orders and by the seminarians. The pontifical Mass was officiated by the Archbishop and several priests. The singing of the Monterrey Seminary choir gave that ceremony the solemnity that the closing of the so-called *Semana Mayor* deserved. At the end of this day, people used to say that "The doors of Glory had been opened."

My friends Licha and Mari Paz were vacationing outside of Monterrey. This gave me more time to be with my family. They came back in time to get together with me for lunch and to exchange the latest news.

"What's going on with Martín?" Mari Paz asked, raising an eyebrow.

"Well, right now he is in Okinawa. In his last letter he told me that, even when he enjoys the place, sometimes he feels very lonely. After all, it is a different culture, and he is also very far from his family and friends. He promised to come at the first opportunity, so I hope that after he returns to the United States, he will visit me."

My friends exchanged glances but didn't make any more comments. I knew, however, what was in their minds.

Three years had passed since I had last seen Martín. Very soon, I had to make a decision about this long-distance relationship. I couldn't wait forever for him to return. I was only twenty-one years old, but at that time, girls married young.

I spent the rest of my vacation house hunting with my sister Norma. Now that I was earning a little more money, my wish was to move my family to a better neighborhood. We scanned the newspaper, but many times, when we arrived at the chosen house, it had already been rented. Quite often, my sister and I took a bus to visit the neighborhoods we liked, but vacant houses were difficult to come by in Monterrey. Later, I found out that most of the time, people who moved would let their friends know. In this way—even before the current residents vacated—the house had already been promised to someone else.

My two weeks' vacation ended, and I felt frustrated for having failed in that search. On the last day, knowing my little sister was feeling sad, we went to eat at our favorite hamburger restaurant.

"Listen, Norma!" I said squeezing her hand, "in the summer we'll keep looking for where to move, okay? I will have more time for that. Besides, I might get a position in some school in Monterrey."

She looked at me with an expression of hope. I looked away to hide my disappointment and my sadness. *If Dirección General doesn't call me, again I'll be packing my suitcases and heading back to a small town with no road, no water, and no electricity, where everybody can see what you do because you live in a crystal box.*

CHAPTER THIRTY-ONE

UNCOMFORTABLE REQUEST

After my Holy Week vacation, I felt refreshed and ready to work. It was April, and we already needed to make plans for a second fundraising dance, plus the graduation ceremony. Being the only female staff member, I would be teaching the dances for that end-of-year program. Fortunately, I had taken some regional dance lessons and participated in many cultural programs as a student, so I was confident I could take care of this task without a problem.

Our second dance was very successful. We earned enough money to cover all of the graduation expenses and some extra. The students asked me to talk to the *director* about allowing them to have a graduation Mass. I promised to do it. I only had to wait for the perfect moment. I worried about *profesor* Merla's reaction to my request. I knew that a Mass wasn't included in his plans, but it was important for the youngsters. I would tell him that if he would allow us to go forward with this event, it would be done as their initiative, and not an activity sponsored by the school.

The perfect moment for me did not come because one morning, Ernesto came looking for me during recess.

"Maestra," he said, "we want to let you know that a commission of us will request the *director's* permission to have a graduation Mass."

"Are you sure you want to do that? If you are patient, I'll talk to him, as I promised you."

"No, we decided that we'll do it. We don't want you to get in trouble with him, but we would like for you to be present."

"Okay, Ernesto. Choose three other students. We can go to see *profesor* Merla right now because he is free."

Together with the small third grade commission, I went to the *director's* office. At the last minute, they were hesitant to go inside, pushing each other to the front. I signaled them to be quiet, and we entered. The *director* was sitting at his desk typing. He raised his head and stopped writing when he saw us. He gave us a questioning look.

"Excuse me, *profesor* Merla. The students would like to talk to you."

"What's up? Something urgent?" he asked. He sat straight in his chair and crossed his arms.

Jorge Martínez, always serious and polite, took the floor. He was the perfect person to do it. He was not only a good student, but he also came from a very devoted family. He cleared his throat before starting.

"Good morning, *profesor* Merla," he said. "We come here on behalf of all our classmates to request your permission to let us have a graduation Mass. Lots of schools do it, and for us, it would mean a lot." Jorge was a good-looking boy with eyes framed with thick eyelashes.

Profesor Merla pushed back his chair and put his hands behind his head. He looked at the five of us without saying a word. The silence was uncomfortable. I wondered if the boys, just like me, felt like running out of there.

"If you have a Mass, don't expect to see me there," he said, tapping on his desk, "but I'm sure *señorita* Socorro will be attending."

"Does that mean we have your permission?" Ernesto asked eagerly. He was more interested in getting permission than in having the *director* at the Mass. Ernesto was thin and as tall as Jorge. People noticed when something affected him because he blushed easily. At that moment, his ears were red. He switched his weight from one leg to the other and smiled nervously, waiting for the answer.

"You may have your Mass, but I don't want anything to do with it. Now go back to class. Recess time is over." He dismissed them with a movement of his hand. Then, he started tapping on his desk.

On their way out, the boys smiled and winked at me. I didn't want to hear any sarcastic comments or recriminations from *profesor* Merla, so I took my books and went to the third-level classroom immediately for my Nuevo León history class. When I entered the classroom, Jorge and Ernesto were informing their classmates of the result of the brief interview. The students had a thousand questions.

"I need your attention. Please take your seats." I placed my books on the desk. When there was silence, I continued. "As soon as we have an exact date for the graduation ceremony, I will arrange the details of your Mass with Father Rangel, your favorite priest, and mine too."

"Are we supposed to wear our white graduation dresses or something different to the Mass?" Alicia, the municipal president's daughter, asked.

"Can we invite some friends or only our family?" said a boy who stood up waiting for an answer.

"Listen, it's too soon to talk about that. Before you get too excited, remember that the final exams are near. If you want to graduate this year and attend that Mass, you better spend more time studying!" I said.

"I'll graduate this year, without doubt," Pepe said, raising his hand. He was Ernesto's brother, very intelligent and always participating in class. "The problem is for the ones who waste time playing and dating," he said. He intentionally looked at some of his classmates, including his brother. Ernesto felt the allusion and couldn't help blushing. Pepe laughed aloud when he saw that some of his friends didn't find his words amusing.

I observed all those youthful faces and knew in my heart that I would be sad to see them go, but I recognized, too, that one day I would be very proud to hear about their accomplishments.

CHAPTER THIRTY-TWO

THE QUINCEAÑERA

One of my most memorable students was a girl who I will call Juanita. She was small and cute with expressive eyes and long hair. She was quiet and a little shy. One afternoon, she waited for me after school. I was surprised because it was the first time she didn't accompany her friends. As we went home, Juanita started a conversation.

"*Maestra* Socorrito, you know I'll be fifteen years old in a couple of weeks? My family will throw me a little party."

"Juanita, that's fantastic. Tell me about it."

She told me her parents didn't have the money to make a great bash but even so, they still wanted to have a celebration for her at their home. She enthusiastically described the pink silk dress her grandmother was sewing for her. She copied it from a magazine and Juanita loved it. Then she talked about the fourteen girls and fourteen boys who would be in her court. I knew some of them, but others were from Matehuala. They had been practicing the waltz they would dance together. The girl's eyes shone when she mentioned that she would dance the first waltz with her dad.

Suddenly, Juanita became quiet and looked sideways at me. I could tell she had something on her mind.

"Of course, you would never ... no, you wouldn't ..." She babbled incoherently and shook her head at the same time. I didn't know if Juanita was afraid or embarrassed to finish the phrase.

"What are you saying, Juanita? What is it that I won't do?" I asked her.

"Attend my party." She looked at me with teary eyes.

I laughed and gave her a hug. "Of course, I will—if you invite me, Juanita."

"Really? You really would come to my house?" she asked, her eyes wide with surprise.

I couldn't understand her reaction. I asked her why she was so surprised that I had accepted. Juanita explained to me that some other teachers would never have attended for sure.

"We are all different, Juanita, but you can be sure I will love to go to your home to celebrate with you and your family."

Juanita gave a little cry of joy, and then she asked me if I thought the other teachers would like to go, too.

"I trust so, but I'll ask them and let you know tomorrow. By the way, can we invite the lawyer who lives with us? We usually attend all of the parties together."

"Of course, I was going to ask you to invite him anyway," Juanita said. "I'll tell my parents that you are coming for sure and possibly the other teachers and the lawyer, too." With her face beaming, she said goodbye.

That afternoon, I communicated Juanita's invitation to the teachers and Manuel.

"It won't be a fancy party, but the girl is excited to have us over, and I wouldn't want to disappoint her," I said.

They all, including *profesor* Merla, accepted the invitation. For the occasion, the men wore suits and ties. I had a pretty yellow silk dress and white high-heeled shoes.

Juanita had earlier attended a special Mass with her family and friends. Afterward, they accompanied her home for the meal and party in her honor. We arrived when everyone was already there.

The *quinceañera* and her family were thrilled to have us over. We introduced ourselves to some of the guests, and afterward we followed the girl's parents to the large patio where relatives and friends sat around several long tables.

"This is your table. Please sit down. We will bring your food right away," the hostess said.

The family had set a special table for us, decorated with an embroidered tablecloth and a vase with fresh flowers in the center. The aroma of the food intensified my appetite.

We enjoyed a modest but delicious dinner of *asado de puerco*, pork meat cooked slowly with a red-hot chili sauce, a very special dish in Doctor Arroyo. We also had the traditional red *mole*, accompanied by Mexican rice and refried beans. The corn *tortillas* were hot and fluffy.

When everyone finished eating, the tables were folded and removed, leaving room for a special ceremony before the dance.

Someone placed a chair in the center of the patio and Juanita sat in it. She looked beautiful in her pink silk dress with small roses in her black hair that was up in curls for the special occasion. Her only makeup was pink lip gloss. Then Juanita placed her feet on a foot rest in front of her chair. Immediately, her mother walked toward her. The lady carried a pair of white high-heeled shoes in her hands. She knelt on a pillow in front of the *quinceañera* to remove the flat ballerina shoes that she was wearing. Then she replaced them with the high-heeled shoes. Juanita stood up with her mom's help. The new shoes made her look taller and thinner. Her mother blessed her with the sign of the cross and kissed her on the cheeks. The special ceremony representing the change from childhood to youth was over. There were tears and lots of applause.

Juanita's father walked to the center of the patio and offered his arm to his daughter. Father and daughter danced the traditional Mexican waltz *"Sobre las Olas."* The *quinceañera* looked radiant with happiness. Her father looked at her with love and pride and guided her with ease from one side of the patio to the other to the beat of the music. They received an ovation when they finished.

Afterward Juanita danced a waltz with one of her brothers, surrounded by her court of fourteen girls dressed in pink, too, and fourteen boys wearing black suits. They had rehearsed the dance for two months so it was perfect.

Next came the time to cut the pink three-layer cake with a small doll on top. "Make a wish; make a wish!" several guests exclaimed when Juanita bent over to blow out the fifteen candles on it. She succeeded after a couple of tries and everybody cheered. Then, we all sang *"Las Mañanitas"* while she cut her nicely decorated cake.

After we enjoyed a slice of that delicacy, the dance began. Many of Juanita's classmates attended the party. All the boys wanted to dance with her, but they had to take turns. The music and the sound system were very good. All of the attendees were having a good time. We danced for a while, too, and then decided to leave, because we had to prepare our lessons for the following week.

When we went to say goodbye, Juanita said with a radiant smile, "Thank you for coming to my party."

"Thank you for inviting us," *profesor* Merla replied. "We really enjoyed it. Thank your parents for their hospitality."

"You are a beautiful *quinceañera*, and we are so glad we came to your party. Thank you for sharing this special day with us," I said. "And Juanita, I hope the wish you made when you blew out your candles will come true."

"I hope so," she answered. She was still smiling as she closed the front door of her house.

Juanita's invitation opened the door to many others, and soon we had several parties to attend.

CHAPTER THIRTY-THREE

AMAZON APPRENTICE

Life in Doctor Arroyo started to become more interesting. My social activities increased, and I looked for other sources of entertainment. I realized all of this was necessary to survive being away from my family and friends.

One of these fun activities started when two boys on the second level, Lupe Nava and Vicente Castilleja, asked me if I knew how to ride a horse.

Outskirts of Doctor Arroyo. Photo provided by Saskia Juárez.

"Only the ones on the merry-go-round," I said, laughing.

"If you like, Vicente and I will teach you how to ride a real horse, *maestra*," Lupe suggested. "Just say when."

"Really? That would be great, boys. I'll let you know soon." I felt a rush of excitement just thinking about it.

Before I knew it, the weeks went by, and the end of the school year wasn't far away. The next time the boys asked me the same question, it only took me a few seconds to answer.

"Of course. I'm ready, boys. When can we start?"

"How about Saturday morning?" Lupe proposed. "We can go by your house around nine o'clock if that's okay with you."

"That's perfect, Lupe, even though ..." I took a deep breath. "I hope your horse is tame."

"Don't worry, *maestra*; he is quite gentle."

"Great. I don't want to get started with a difficult horse."

"By the way," Vicente said, "some of them don't like skirts, so just in case, I suggest you wear slacks."

"Thanks for the advice, Vicente. I'll see you Saturday, then."

Vicente and Lupe left whistling and playfully shoving each other.

On Saturday morning, I wore pants and a white peasant blouse. In those years, Mexican women wore pants only when they went on picnics or riding, so I knew anyone who would see me would wonder what I was up to.

"Hmm. Going to some picnic, *señorita*?" *doña* Susana asked. She had just stepped out of the kitchen carrying a container of leftovers for Duque. The dog stood up immediately, wagging his tail.

"*La maestra* is going to ride with two of her students," Teresa said for me. She was the only one I had told about it when I had asked her to iron my pants. In a way, I was afraid of *doña* Susana's comments.

"Are you going with those girls who visit you often?" the lady asked, raising an eyebrow.

"No, *doña* Susana, I'm going with Vicente Castilleja and Lupe Nava." I tried not to get irritated by so many questions.

"Hmm. They are good boys. Lupe's father is a teacher. Well, have fun." She went back to the kitchen.

Well, well. I'm glad she approves. Hope everybody else does, too.

A few minutes before nine o'clock, Claudia came running, her eyes wide open, and talking loudly. "*Señorita, señorita*, your students are outside with a horse!"

I couldn't help smiling. "Thanks, Claudia. Now go back to help Teresa."

Claudia just ignored me and followed me to the street, cheerfully skipping. She wanted to watch all of the details of my departure.

In front of the house, Lupe and Vicente waited on top of a nice white horse. Lupe was sitting at the front of the saddle with Vicente behind him. The boys jumped down with ease and removed their palm hats to greet me.

I was surprised to see they had only one horse with them. Were the boys going to walk by the side of the animal all the time? Maybe we would go to get two more.

"*¡Buenos dias, maestra!* Come and let me introduce you to Palomo." Lupe waved his hand for me to come closer. He held the reins in his hand.

I walked to the front of the noble beast who looked at me with his big, black, intelligent eyes. I saw my reflection in them. Palomo gave a soft whinny of pleasure when I passed my hand over his silky mane.

"Oh, I see Palomo likes you, *maestra.*" Lupe patted him, and the horse turned its head slightly to see him better. The animal moved his legs up and down, impatient to start moving.

"Let's go before it gets hot. Right now, the weather is perfect," I said. My real concern was that *profesor* Merla would come by the house and discourage me from doing this. He might say that I could get hurt.

Lupe gave me some verbal instructions, and Vicente showed me the way I should climb on the horse.

After caressing the animal once more, I climbed up as Vicente had instructed me. *Doña* Susana, Teresa, Claudia, and one of the maids observed by the restaurant door. I smiled nervously to them and waved goodbye. They waved back and went inside.

We advanced in the middle of the cobblestone street. Even though the boys assured me Palomo was tame, I firmly held the horn of the horse's saddle with one hand and the reins with the other.

I sat straight, trying not to show fear, but I'm sure the boys noticed I was frightened because after exchanging a glance, they walked on each side of the animal. They patted him from time to time. Palomo walked slowly, with his neck stretched, a proud, gentle beast. His ears moved, capturing the sounds of the noises around him and mostly his master's voice.

We stopped at the main plaza. Lupe told us to wait and walked toward a couple of men sitting on one of the benches across from the church. Their horses were tied to the back of their bench.

I saw the men nodding and Lupe smiling and touching the tip of his hat. He untied the two animals and brought them with him to where Vicente and I were waiting for him. When I saw their size I felt better, knowing my horse was smaller than theirs.

Lupe gave the reins of one of the animals to Vicente who jumped on it right away. The two boys settled onto their mounts, and we got ready to ride.

"How kind are your friends to lend you their horses, Lupe," I said.

"Oh. Those *hombres* are not my friends, *maestra*. In fact, I don't even know them. They must be from some small ranch nearby because they are visiting town. Here, it's customary for them to let the locals borrow their horses, even if they don't know each other," Lupe explained.

"They know we'll return them," Vicente added. "People are not distrustful."

"I'm glad to know that. I wonder if in other places people are as kind as the ones in Doctor Arroyo," I said.

"*¡Somos únicos, maestra!*". Lupe smiled and winked at me.

"Yes, I agree. Doctor Arroyo's people are unique. Everyone has been kind to me."

Palomo picked up the pace to keep up with the other two horses. The boys, riding on each side of me, continued to give me instructions. I tried to assimilate everything they said. One piece of advice from Vicente caught my attention. I didn't know at the time how important it would be later to remember that information.

"Sometimes, the horse starts running wildly. He makes the muscles of the neck so hard and tense that he won't obey the bridle in its mouth. The best thing is to stop fighting it because you can't do anything."

"Vicente, don't frighten *la maestra*, or she'll refuse to come with us again."

Vicente smiled at Lupe's remark and made his horse dance gracefully in a circle.

"You don't have to worry about Palomo, *maestra*. He'll never go wild with you or anybody else," Lupe said to calm me down.

I patted the horse's neck, and he moved his head up and down as if saying, "Yes," to my caress. I relaxed, noticing how the animal responded to any command.

"Where do you want us to ride, *maestra*?" Lupe asked.

I pointed to the opposite side of an area people called *El Paso del Norte*. On one occasion someone told me that there was a very particular house there. Over its roof was a small tower with ten stained glass windows on different levels: four of them at the bottom, then three, two, and one at the highest. The windows were illuminated at night with small petroleum lamps. If the four on the bottom were lit, customers knew the place would be selling only drinks. If only three were lit, then there would be women. Two windows lit meant there would be *menudo*, a spicy red soup very popular in México. When only the one on top was lit, people went to gamble.

"Are the windows ever lit all at once?" I asked that person.

"Oh, yeah. When the ten windows are lit, people know it will be everything I explained to you before. Well, that's what I heard. I've never been there." The person giggled.

Besides the overall description of the place and its activities, I had heard the owner had all of his teeth covered with gold. Regardless of my curiosity about this story, I never dared to go to see if such windows really existed, nor did I have the courage to ask any of my coworkers about it. I never saw the man with the golden teeth, by the way. In time, the story came to my ears more than once; however, someone told me that the place didn't exist anymore. Today, I ask myself if it ever did or if it was only another town legend.

In any case, I suggested that we follow another direction. We rode to the outskirts of town. The weather was warm, and there was a light breeze, with not a single cloud in the blue sky. Tall cacti served as a fence outside of some adobe houses. We went onto an open field where the horses started trotting faster. After a while, I felt my bottom had enough punishment, and I told the boys we would have to continue another day.

An adobe house with a cactus fence. Photo provided by Saskia Juárez.

We returned home and the two boys helped me dismount from the horse.

"Está bien, maestra?", Vicente and Lupe asked almost at the same time when they saw I had trouble walking.

"¡Sí, gracias, muchachos! I'll rest a little bit and then take a bath."

"Do you want to practice again next week, *maestra*?" Lupe asked, leaning over his borrowed horse.

"I'll let you know. Again, thanks for today. I had a great time. I'll see you Monday at school." I patted Palomo's neck and waved goodbye.

The boys answered my greeting and rode away riding the two borrowed animals to return them to their owners. Lupe was pulling Palomo's rein. They told me they would ride him on the way back to their homes.

"*Profesor* Merla was looking for you, *maestra*," said Horacio, who was leaving the house at that moment.

"Oh, does he know I was riding a horse with Lupe and Vicente?"

"Well, he was talking to my grandma, so I'm sure she told him about it."

I sighed, wondering what reaction he would have when he saw me at dinnertime.

I entered my bedroom and collapsed on my bed. I was worried about the way I walked from the street to my room. I shivered at the thought that from then on, my legs may be bowed.

I fell asleep right away and didn't wake up until dinnertime. The aroma of the food was inviting. I washed in a hurry and joined the teachers in the dining room. I studied their faces to see if there were any signs of trouble, but it was the opposite. They smiled and asked me about my day.

Of course, I shared with them my experience. Andrés listened attentively, holding his chin with his right hand.

"It's nice to know how to ride a horse. I'm glad Lupe and Vicente are teaching you," *profesor* Merla said.

I smiled. The *director's* words of approval meant a lot to me. That made me relax.

"So, when are you going next?" José Luis asked. He drank from his cup of coffee while waiting for my answer.

"The way I feel right now I don't know for sure if there will be a next time."

"There will be, believe me. There's nothing like feeling the wind on your face," José Luis said.

In the following weeks, I only went riding a couple of times. Lupe and Vicente had to get ready for final exams, and I still had to deal with everything related to the end of classes and the graduation ceremony.

I told the boys that if I returned the following year, we would continue with the riding lessons. *Only God knows if the Director General will keep me in Doctor Arroyo longer than expected, but if that's the case, I might even turn into an expert rider.*

CHAPTER THIRTY-FOUR

MAY FESTIVITIES

With the arrival of May came the pressure of everything we had to do before the end of the school year. The most urgent task was developing the questionnaires for exams. Then it would be grading them and filling out the final report cards. Besides, we had all the rehearsals for the graduation ceremony program, and to top it all off, we had to participate in some May celebrations.

Teachers in particular love this month because they can take short vacations from work. This practice is called *hacer puente*, which literally means "to make a bridge." With this practice of bridging, you have an additional day off before or after an official holiday, making one less day of work.

On Friday, May 1, 1959, *Día del Trabajo*—Labor Day—banks, factories, schools, and government offices in México were officially closed. Because May 5, the commemoration of *La Batalla de Puebla*, fell on Tuesday, many teachers made *puente* from Friday through Tuesday. That was a nice five days' rest!

On May 10, Mother's Day, there was no bridge, since it fell on Sunday, but on Friday May 15, Teacher's Day, we had a three-day break.

Profesor Merla disagreed with this practice. He talked about the teachers' waste of time to the detriment of the students, so we never took days off from work because of bridges. We didn't work on May 1 but, instead, practiced with the students for the upcoming *5 de Mayo* festivity. This commemorated General Ignacio Zaragoza's victorious battle over the French army in Puebla.

Many people from small towns around Doctor Arroyo came to enjoy the celebration. The Town Council organized several events in the morning, but we did not participate in them.

That Tuesday night, there was an official program in the theater involving several of our students. Our friend Santiago—who had been in town since Labor Day—attended the event with all the teachers except Manuel.

We occupied our usual box on the right side of the theater. Across from us was *don* Dustano Muñiz, the town's mayor, with his family. Two of his children, Dustano Junior and Alicia, studied in our school. They were well-centered teenagers, so their father's position didn't go to their heads.

Don Peregrino de la Garza, the friendly pharmacist, sat in another box surrounded by his wife and happy children. From the balcony, his son Paco and Ernesto Rodríguez spent their time flirting with some pretty girls sitting in the lower part of the theater. The place was completely full, and people carried on loud conversations. Finally, there was silence when the lights dimmed and the program started.

One of our students recited a poem to the *5 de Mayo*. Another read a short biography of General Zaragoza. *Profesor* Merla gave a speech in honor of this hero and his brave troops. He was an excellent speaker, and when he finished, the audience applauded loudly. We left the theater satisfied with our school's participation in the program.

Dimas García was in town for the celebration. As usual, he arrived with the group of men who always accompanied him. The pounding of their horses' hooves on the cobblestone streets could be heard frequently. Sometimes, the rhythmic sound of their boot spurs on the town's sidewalks enticed people to peek discreetly out their half-closed doors or from behind their windows' curtains. Most preferred to see Dimas from a distance and not face to face. I didn't know if all the stories about him were true or exaggerations. Regardless, his presence always awakened the people's fascination in his persona—a mix of fear and curiosity.

Dimas and his group left after the *5 de Mayo* celebration. Everybody was able to breathe freely again, happy that they had not disturbed the town's festivities. Right away, everyone shared notes about what Dimas had done or said. After all, he too had lived in a *crystal box* for several days, so people had observed him closely all of the time.

We didn't celebrate Mother's Day, one of México's most important festivities, in our school. We didn't have enough room to accommodate all our students' families who would want to be there to honor the mothers. The place we rented, an old house with a very large courtyard, was barely enough for our student body.

For me, Mother's Day was a depressing day. I had to hide my tears and my broken heart from everyone around me. It was the first time in my life that I had not been able to celebrate such an important occasion with my mother. I realized that day would be very sad for her because she would be missing me too. Without a phone, the only thing I could do was to send her a telegram letting her know how much I loved her and missed her.

We did have classes on Friday, which was good because we had so much to do in the following weeks before leaving for summer vacation in the middle of June.

On Saturday afternoon, Andrés stopped by my room. He had a pencil behind his ear and looked tired. "Are you done with your exam questions, Socorrito?" he asked.

"I'm almost done." I pointed to the notebook on my table and an open book. "What about you?"

"I'm squeezing my brain thinking how to ask about a specific concept."

"Well, just be sure not to use true or false questions. You know by experience that if the students don't know the answer, they will decide it with the flip of a coin," I said with a smile.

"You are right. I'll have to hurry up because the end of classes is near." He turned around and walked toward his room.

"Oh, and don't forget that we still have Teachers' Day celebration on May 15," I said. "We won't advance much that day."

Andrés stopped to look at me, raised his arms, and shook his head. Surely, he was already feeling the pressure of time.

I wondered if the students would celebrate my Saint's Day, on May 13, as they had mentioned before. *Wouldn't it be funny if I order a couple of baskets with bread, and nobody comes? Knowing Minerva, however, I can bet that she will make sure no one forgets it.*

I smiled, thinking that Andrés would have a fit if he knew that May 13 might be another wasted day.

CHAPTER THIRTY-FIVE

MY SAINT'S DAY CELEBRATION

On May 13, 1959, the students celebrated my Saint's Day, as they had promised. Around 5:30 a.m. I heard them coming inside the house, trying not to make any noise. They whispered outside my bedroom, then they sang the traditional *"Mañanitas,"* accompanied by a guitar that I supposed was played by Horacio. I let them sing for a little bit, before opening my bedroom door. When I did, more than twenty smiling faces were in front of me. Horacio, as I guessed, was the one who played the guitar. The morning air was slightly cool and the plants in the patio smelled recently watered.

"Thank you so much for this wonderful surprise," I told the students when they finished singing. I smiled broadly at them with a warm feeling inside me.

"Congratulations, *maestra!*" was the unanimous exclamation. The girls accompanied their words with a hug.

"*Felicidades*, Socorrito", José Luis and Andrés said almost at the same time. They had joined the serenade before I had opened my bedroom door.

"*Gracias. Muy sinceras gracias".* I was deeply moved.

"Hmm, smells like hot chocolate," José Luis said, sniffing the rich chocolate aroma coming from the kitchen's open door.

"I'll check to see if it's ready." Andrés headed in a hurry to the kitchen.

I smiled knowing that everything would already be prepared. At some point during the week, I had asked *doña* Susana to have *pan dulce* and chocolate *caliente* ready just in case the students would come. She told me that Horacio had already suggested that to her. I paid her for her expenses and asked her not to tell Horacio.

As I thought, a few minutes later we heard *doña* Susana's voice. "Horacio, run to get the *pan dulce*; it should be ready!"

Horacio and Homero quickly went to the neighboring bakery. A few minutes later, they were back. As soon as they removed the cover from two large baskets, the aroma of recently baked bread filled the dining room. Everyone was waiting, seated around the tables, where bread was served on large trays. There were *conchas, semitas, campechanas, polvorones, chilindrinas, y cuernitos.* Teresa and another maid filled up the cups with frothy, steamy chocolate. Soon the bottoms of the trays were visible, and the cups were empty.

Profesor Merla, who always got up early, arrived at the house, and enjoyed the improvised *desayuno* with us. I thought that was the end of my celebration, but the kids had other plans. They had asked the *director* for permission to have an afternoon assembly dedicated to me, and even though we had a lot of work, he had agreed.

That afternoon we all got together in the school courtyard. The students placed some chairs for the five of us teachers, facing them. Minerva, Irma, Josefina, Lilia, Jorge, Horacio, Sergio, and several of their classmates put a program together. To start, everyone sang *"Las Mañanitas"* to me.

Very appropriate, I thought, after listening to the emphasis with which the students sang the first part of the song. I hadn't thought about it before, but the original theme celebrates the Saint's day corresponding to the name, not the birthday.

Éstas son Las Mañanitas	These are the Mañanitas
que cantaba el Rey David	that King David used to sing
hoy por ser día de tu santo	because today is your Saint's Day
te las cantamos aquí.	we sing them to you here.

Minerva, who was just in first grade, was already noted for her gift for poetry and her romantic heart. She came forward and recited an emotional poem. In my mind, I can still see her. She was of average height with a well-proportioned figure and very light complexion. Her short, light brown hair was moving slightly with the wind. Minerva had a deep voice, and every single word was accompanied by a different expression on her pretty face and the soft movement of her hands. She conveyed all of her emotion to us, and we rewarded her with a long applause.

Afterward, Horacio, Homero, and some other boys played guitars while they sang "Jacaranda," a popular song at the time. The girls asked *profesor* Lauro to participate in the program. He willingly accepted and chose to sing the tango *"Cuesta Abajo,"* which he knew I liked a lot. On several occasions, Lauro had played the guitar when we had been gathered in José Luis's room, and I had asked him for this particular tango. The song reminded me of my mother, who sang it with a lot of feeling with her beautiful voice.

The last presentation was by Sergio, *el Guapo*, the Handsome One. He was around the same age as Ernesto and Jorge. Sergio stood for few moments in front of me. He was dressed neatly, as always. He ran his hand through his black hair, straightened his body and said, *"¡Profesora, esta canción es para usted, con todo respeto y desde el fondo de mi corazón!"*.

I smiled at the formality of his words, "Teacher, this song is for you, with all my respect and from the bottom of my heart."

"What are you going to sing?" Irma, taking her emcee role very seriously, asked.

"I'll sing *'Usted,'*" Sergio answered, with the assurance of an accomplished artist.

Oh, no! My heart pounded. The lyrics of the song came to my mind like an urgent telegram. I just knew what would come next, but it was too late to ask him to sing something else. His nice voice was already filling every corner of the patio.

The minute Sergio began to sing, everyone started giggling, even the teachers. José Luis, who was sitting next to me, elbowed me softly. I looked at him, and he was grinning. I felt my cheeks blush. Sergio sang undeterred and inspired, moving his hands appropriately, touching his heart or pointing to me. The song went on relentlessly:

Usted es la culpable de todas mis angustias y todos mis quebrantos.

> You are the culprit of all my anguish and all my brokenness.

Usted llenó mi vida de dulces inquietudes y amargos desencantos.

> You filled my life with sweet concerns and bitter disappointments.

Su amor es como un grito que llevo aquí en mi alma y aquí en mi corazón,

> Your love is like a cry that I carry here in my soul and here in my heart,

y soy, aunque no quiera, esclavo de sus ojos, juguete de su amor.

> and I am, even if I don't want to, a slave of your eyes, a toy of your love.

"Well, well. It seems to me you have a secret admirer, Socorrito," Andrés whispered. He giggled, covering his mouth with his hand.

"Oh, be quiet, Andrés," I said between closed lips. "This is going to go down in history!"

I could feel the youngster's eyes fixed on my face, so I tried to keep a good-humored expression.

El Guapo finally finished, and after I thanked him, he went back to sit with his friends, who patted him on the back. He smiled, pleased with his audacity.

I thanked everybody and remarked it was my first Saint's Day celebration, so I would never forget it. As I collected the presents that several of the students gave me, I looked at profesor Merla. He was still grinning. I was glad he found it amusing. He enjoyed practical jokes from time to time.

I remembered one particular joke. One day, at the beginning of 1959, *profesor* Merla and I had been talking close to the entrance of his office. As a couple of girls walked by us, he suddenly changed the conversation. Raising his voice, he said, "So, *Señorita* Socorrito, did you say today is *profesor* Andrés's birthday? Maybe you should tell the kids, so they can sing *'Las Mañanitas'* for him." There was a twinkle in his eyes, and his lips curled up in a smile.

I raised an eyebrow and half-opened my mouth. I didn't know what he was talking about. The topic of our conversation didn't relate to Andrés at all. The girls whispered something, and before I reacted, they left for their classroom in a rush. I saw Andrés putting his jacket on, taking his books, and walking to his first class. Moments later, *profesor* Merla headed in the same direction. He invited me to follow him with a movement of head. There was a mischievous expression on his face.

We were in the middle of the patio when we heard a loud uproar coming from the classroom where Andrés had entered. The students were singing *"Las Mañanitas"* to him! We walked into the classroom, and we saw the entire class standing up. Andrés was facing them and seemed to be telling them something.

"¡Éstas son 'Las Mañanitas,' que cantaba el Rey David!", the students enthusiastically chanted. *"¡Hoy, por ser día de tu santo te las cantamos aquí!"*.

"Aren't you listening?" Andrés said, raising his voice. "It's not my birthday. How in the world did you get such an idea?"

The students continued singing, oblivious to Andrés's pleas and to our presence. They even sang louder when they saw *profesor* Merla's big smile.

Andrés was so frustrated that he walked out of the classroom. The *director* and I couldn't help laughing. He followed Andrés to calm him down and explain to him what had happened.

I was left alone with the students who looked confused by Andrés's reaction. Pretending ignorance, I asked them, "Why were you singing *'Las Mañanitas'* to *profesor* Andrés if today isn't his birthday or his saint's day? He certainly didn't appreciate that."

"But *profesora*, I overheard the *director* saying that today was *profesor* Andrés's birthday," said one of the girls we had seen in the hall.

When I recognized the student, I understood *profesor* Merla's idea. That girl had a bad habit of carrying and spreading everything she heard. Just the day before, she had made a classmate cry by commenting on an alleged criticism of another girl. The *director* scolded her for it. So now, when he saw her in the hallway, he set her the trap to teach her a lesson. He was sure she would spread the news, and he was right.

"Well, I guess that's why it's important not to repeat anything until we have all the facts. You should know it," I said. "If you had asked me, I would have told you *profesor* Merla was joking. I just hope *profesor* Andrés won't be angry now."

The girl didn't say anything. I saw her blushing and nervously biting her fingernails.

Andrés returned smiling. He took the joke gracefully and continued with his class after clarifying the date of his birthday was February 4. At that time, he didn't know the students would really surprise him some weeks later on his birthday with a serenade.

While I was reviewing that anecdote, I had been saying goodbye and thanking all the students again for the assembly they had held for me. It was time to go home with my collection of gifts. It was clear to me that this would be one of the days that I would remember forever.

CHAPTER THIRTY-SIX

UNFAIR ACCUSATION

So far everything was going smoothly, but it wouldn't be for long.

One afternoon, I was walking home with a group of girls, among them Minerva, the declaimer. Suddenly, she said, "*Maestra*, my mom would like to invite all of you to have dinner with us this coming Saturday. Could you please ask the other teachers and let me know tomorrow if you can come?"

"Are you celebrating something?" I thought it might be a birthday celebration.

"Oh, no. My mom just wants to enjoy the pleasure of your company."

Minerva and her family are always so polite. "Okay. I'll extend the invitation to the other teachers and let you know tomorrow if all of us can attend."

"Don't forget to ask *profesor* Merla," she said, touching my arm.

"Of course. You know we all attend events together."

"See you tomorrow, then." Minerva waved goodbye, smiled with satisfaction, and walked away with the other girls.

At dinnertime, I told the teachers about *doña* María's invitation.

"I don't know," *profesor* Merla said, scratching his temple. He looked at us in silence for few seconds. "Okay, if all of you want to attend, I'll go, too," he said. He wiped the corner of his mouth with his napkin.

José Luis, Andrés, and I decided to accept the invitation. We were sure Lauro would go too.

"Being so, *señorita* Socorrito, please let Minerva know and just ask her at what time is the appointment," *profesor* Merla said.

Once this was settled, we continued enjoying the delicious pork stew *doña* Susana and the maids had prepared for that day.

On Saturday, the *director* arrived at our house, punctual as ever. Lauro was already there. He had come earlier to have time to visit with us. The teachers wore jackets and ties. I made a point of wearing a dress made with one of the colorful pieces of material Minerva and her family had given me for my birthday. I always wore high-heeled shoes, and this day was no exception.

We left for the Rodríguez' home, which was around the corner from where we lived. The day was sunny, but the weather stayed pleasant.

Minerva opened the door at the first knock. *"Bienvenidos a su casa"*, she said in greeting. It was another way of saying "my home is your home." She looked at us with bright eyes and a big smile.

We followed her around a large patio full of pots with different kind of flowers. Her parents, *doña* María and *don* Max, waited by the door to the living room, as did her brothers, Ernesto, Pepe, and Roberto. Maybe because we came from a bright day outside, the room appeared dark.

Profesor Merla, who was in front of us, suddenly hesitated. As I looked behind the family, I understood the reason for his surprise: the town's three priests, including Father Rangel, were sitting there!

The *director* turned around and stared inquisitively at me. I raised my eyebrows and shrugged.

Doña María proceeded to introduce the priests. Andrés and I had met Father Rangel on our first trip to Doctor Arroyo, and I had talked with him several times. I had seen the other priests only during Sunday Mass but had never spoken to them. They, however, did recognize me and knew who I was. There were the customary handshakes, and I noticed that they greeted me in a friendlier way. I felt a knot in my stomach, seeing *profesor* Merla's half-closed eyes and clenched jaw.

"Well, I invited all of you so you can talk and get to know each other better," *doña* María said.

I realized her intentions were good, but this was only going to aggravate a situation that I had tried so hard to soften. I can't remember the rest of the visit, except for a tense and cold conversation, mostly between *profesor* Merla and the priests. By the time we left the Rodríguez' house, the *director* was fuming. He walked in front of us, stiff lipped, and his arms swinging. His hat was twisted toward one side, an unmistakable sign of his anger.

As soon as we arrived home, he asked me abruptly, "Did you know your friends were going to be there?"

Andrés, José Luis, and Lauro watched silently.

My cheeks were burning from *profesor* Merla's outburst. I understood his unfriendliness toward me because I had been the spokesperson for Minerva's invitation. I was innocent, however, of planning what I thought would be a well-intentioned meeting.

"*Profesor*, first of all, it was a surprise for me, too. Knowing how you feel toward the Church and the priests, do you think I was going to take the chance of making you angry? Of course not."

He didn't say anything. He stared at me with his hands in his pockets and his head tilted to the side, digesting my words. I saw, in the slight smile of José Luis, Lauro, and Andrés, and in their furtive gesture of "don't pay any attention to him," the confidence they had that I was telling the truth. That put me at ease.

"Second of all, why do you refer to the priests as my friends? The only one that I have spoken to is Father Rangel, and he is everybody's friend in this town."

"Well, not everyone's; he isn't my friend!" *profesor* Merla stated. "In fact, none of them are."

The vehemence of his comment made us all laugh.

From now on, I'm sure they'll never be. I just hope this incident doesn't interfere with the students' graduation Mass. I'll talk to Minerva tomorrow, so this won't happen again. She owes me an explanation as to why she put me in such a bind.

"Oh, and by the way, regarding the graduation Mass ... " *Profesor* Merla paused. He was standing by the door, ready to leave.

Oh, no! Here comes the prohibition and sooner than I expected! How am I going to explain this at school?

"Well, you know that after today, more than ever, I won't be attending any Mass." He placed his hat firmly on his head. I noticed that his hat was now straight.

"It's possible that some students expected you to change your mind about attending their Mass, but I'm sure they'll understand," I said.

"It won't matter really if I'm not there, after all ..." *profesor* Merla said in a softer voice.

"... *Señorita* Socorrito will be there," I said, finishing his sentence.

"How did you know I was going to say that?" He raised an eyebrow.

"Past experience," Andrés said, as he twisted his moustache and winked at me.

I smiled, remembering a phrase from my mother for similar situations: "I know my people."

The *director* scratched his temple and waved goodbye to us.

"What a day!" I told my teacher friends. "From now on, I'll be sure to ask who else is invited to any get-together."

"It was an uncomfortable situation," José Luis said.

"Yes, it was, but it's over. Now let's have some fun." Lauro placed a hand on José Luis's shoulder.

"Will you join us in playing cards?" José Luis asked me as I was ready to enter my room.

"Well, I don't know; it all depends. Who else did you invite?" I asked in a dramatic tone.

They looked at me with surprise, then they understood the reference and we all laughed.

CHAPTER THIRTY-SEVEN

A TERRIBLE DROUGHT AND *DON* FERNANDO'S WATER

1959 was a year of extreme drought in Doctor Arroyo. For several months we hadn't had a drop of rain. The grayish dry ground showed thousands of twisted cracks like thin arms stretching to the sky begging for water to satisfy its thirst. Plows remained abandoned in the fields, and farm animals didn't have enough to eat. Some animals scouted the ground looking for the smallest source of food. Others just lay down in the scarce shadow of a tree, too weak to move. Worse yet, there was a general fear that a time of famine was coming soon.

Cistern in Doctor Arroyo. Photo provided by Profa. Lilia Nava.

One afternoon, I was walking home with the teachers when we came across two *rancheros*. They rested their hunched backs against an adobe wall while carrying on a conversation.

"We won't have a harvest this year if it doesn't rain soon," the younger said. "I don't remember in all my life a year as dry as this." The older, white-haired man looked at the clear blue sky and sighed deeply.

The two men stepped off the sidewalk to let us pass. They tipped their hats as a sign of respect to us.

"*¡Buenas tardes, señores!*", we said almost in chorus.

"*¡Buenas tardes, maestros!*".

"*¿Cómo va todo, mi amigo?*", *profesor* Merla asked the mature man with genuine concern. The *profesor* knew almost everybody in town, and, of course, everybody in the region knew him, too.

Removing his battered hat, the old *ranchero* answered, "*Nada bien, profesor* Merla. This year is looking bad. The corn isn't growing, and we're probably going to lose the crop because of lack of rain." There was a tinge of sadness in his voice.

"I'm sorry to hear that," the *director* said, looking at the two men with sympathy.

José Luis, Lauro, Andrés, and I waited a few feet away and listened to the conversation silently.

"I guess you, too, are having a hard time, aren't you?" *profesor* Merla asked the younger *ranchero*.

"That's how it is! We are buying everything on credit," he said. He had his hands in his old jeans pockets and rested his thin body on his right leg. "Most of us have reached our limit. We fear that soon we will not be allowed to charge more to our account and ... what are we going to do then?"

"We have family to feed. Their old rags can endure but not their hungry stomachs," the old man lamented, looking down at his own ragged and faded clothes. He had a gentle face. His white hair contrasted with his wrinkled bronzed skin.

"True," the younger man said. "It breaks my heart when my children ask for an extra serving of food and there is none." He sighed and avoided looking at us.

"Well, don't despair, *amigos*. We might have some rain soon." *Profesor* Merla placed a hand on the old man's shoulder.

"¡Que Dios le oiga, profesor!", he answered, while his eyes were clouded with tears. We felt the man's despair in his words when he said, "May God listen to you, *profesor*!"

We said goodbye and walked without talking for a few minutes. Then, *profesor* Merla broke the silence.

"These are hardworking men, like most of the men in Doctor Arroyo," he said. "Not being able to work the land is what forces so many to go to the United States to earn some money to feed their families. If they could, they would rather not be away from their homes, believe me."

"With good rains, they can grow corn or collect *mesquite*," José Luis noted.

I was surprised to hear the last part. "I never knew about the *mesquite*," I said. "What do they do with it?"

"They sell it as food for the animals. It can give them good earnings," he answered.

"What *profesor* Merla said before is true," Lauro said. "These are family men. They hate to be separated from their families and their friends."

When we arrived home, we parted but probably with the same thought: *As long as there isn't any rain, there'll be sadness, frustration, and anguish for many people.*

During the next weeks, we saw many men sitting down on the sidewalks or in the plazas with nothing to do. They seemed lost or bored. Some entertained themselves blowing smoke rings from their cigarettes into the air, and others sat on the hard benches, observing people go by. Here and there a group played, knocking down empty cans by throwing pebbles at them. I wondered about their families back home. Would they have something to eat? Would the children be attending classes? How many of these men were drinking out of boredom and frustration? I prayed for rain, too.

Some days later, I heard the water in one of the three *aljibes* was almost gone. There was only one full for the townspeople, and another for the domestic animals. Manuel suggested we should buy one of those big bottles of water from Matehuala and divide the cost. Andrés, José Luis, and I thought it was a good idea, thus we soon had it delivered.

People started talking about the danger if the second *aljibe* became dry.

"We could get water from the well, but unfortunately there is only one faucet," *doña* Susana informed us. "Getting water for everybody will be very difficult."

"I can't understand it," Andrés commented. "How in the world did the first colonists choose this place to settle down in without a river or lake nearby?"

"I wondered the same thing," I said. "There are no natural resources in this place—no rivers, lush vegetation, or close mountains. Why did they stay here?"

"Maybe they felt safe," José Luis explained. "Dangerous people would not imagine that someone could live here."

"You could be right," I said. "Such reasoning never occurred to me."

More weeks went by without a drop of rain, not even a distant cloud. One day, as I walked back from school with my girls, I noticed several groups of people talking on the sidewalks.

"Something is going on, *maestra*," Minerva said. "Do you see those two women on the corner?"

I looked at them. They were covering their mouths and noses with their hands. The women turned toward us as if they wanted to share some information. I didn't want to hear anything that would upset my students, and I looked away.

"Do you want me to ask them what's happening?" suggested Josefina.

"No, Josefina, thank you. Better hurry and find it out at home." As we arrived at plaza Juárez, I dismissed the girls, and they headed to their houses.

I rushed to get home and entered through the restaurant. Nena was there with a cup of coffee in her hand, talking to *doña* Susana.

"*Maestra*, did you hear the horrible news?" Nena asked. Her face was pale and serious.

"No, what kind of horrible news? I saw several groups of people whispering on the street, but I didn't want to hear any bad news in front of my girls."

Nena didn't answer right away. She sat next to one of the tables and pulled out a chair for me to sit down next to her. Without delay, Teresa placed a cup of coffee in front of me.

"Thanks, Teresa." Then, turning toward Nena, I asked her apprehensively, "What's happening?"

"Well, you'll see. It's about this man named *don* Fernando. Everybody knows about his heavy drinking. Sometimes he sleeps in places away from his home. Three days ago, he didn't show up, so his family started looking for him." Nena paused to drink some of her coffee. "They looked everywhere and couldn't find him. They asked everybody, but nobody had seen him." She paused again.

Doña Susana, who sat in the closest chair, couldn't wait for the end of the story. She cleared her throat and intervened. "The point is that this morning one of the *aguadores* went to the *aljibes*, the cisterns. As he filled up his cans, he noticed something black in the water. He thought it was a bird and started throwing stones at it."

Nena took up the story. "On one of those occasions, the stone fell closer to the black thing, and you won't believe it." She wrinkled her nose. "The *aguador* saw a man's face! The black thing was the person's hair. When the body was pulled from the water, they realized it was *don* Fernando. The man who had been missing for three days."

By this time, the maids had suspended their work and were listening attentively to what was said.

"The horrible thing is that people had been drinking from there for three days," Teresa said.

"Oh, my God! What did you use for this coffee, Teresa?" I placed my cup of coffee on the table as if it were burning my hand.

I looked at Claudia and almost laughed to see her expression. She had one hand on her throat and the other on her stomach. She started making faces like she was ready to vomit.

"Don't worry. Fortunately, we stocked up the day before the contamination of the cistern, but we'll need more soon," Teresa said.

Claudia let go of her neck and stopped making faces. "I prefer to be thirsty," she announced.

"The worst thing is that now we can't drink of the deposit where *don* Fernando drowned. It'll be for the animals, and that will leave us with only one cistern available," *doña* Susana said.

I knew the *aljibes* were very large cisterns at floor level where rainwater was collected.

"What are we going to do if we finish that water, too?" Nena asked, raising an eyebrow.

We all looked at each other in silence, and we just shrugged.

The worst was yet to come. A lot of people complained they felt sick with what everyone called *"el agua de don Fernando."* There was a general paranoia. Several of our students were absent because they felt sick to their stomachs. Then some people decided to get water from the well to drink. The flow was so low that it took forever to fill up a small bucket. People grew impatient.

Finally, someone went to check on the well. With horror, they discovered several dead rats and other animals floating there. At that point, we feared people would really get sick and even die. *Salubridad y Asistencia* was called urgently. They came from Matehuala to vaccinate the people and board up the well.

We were lucky to have our own five-gallon refillable bottle, but most of the people had to wait for the tanker truck sent by the government.

For a long time, people talked about *el agua de don Fernando*. It had a tremendous impact on the town. Meanwhile, we continued to pray for some rain.

The day it finally rained, I stood in the middle of the patio with my arms open, thanking God and getting wet. As the drops ran on my face, I wasn't sure if it was the rain or tears of happiness that were pouring from my eyes. I walked to the hotel's main entrance door and saw several persons on the street hugging each other under the rain. *Doña* Susana and the maids came out, too, and got their arms wet while Claudia, like some other little kids, splashed in the stream that ran along the sidewalk, giving small cries of happiness.

I had never in my life received the rain with the gratitude to God and nature that I did that day in Doctor Arroyo.

The drought had been a sadly unforgettable experience.

CHAPTER THIRTY-EIGHT

PROJECTING THE GREAT EVENT

The graduation ceremony for the third-level students was about six weeks away. *Profesor* Merla summoned an after-class meeting to plan for the event. The first item on the agenda was to choose the definite date, followed by nominating a *Padrino de la Generación*—as the sponsor of the graduating class is called in Spanish.

A date was approved on the calendar, and after several suggestions we decided to offer this honorary title to *don* Dustano Muñiz, the town's mayor. We were confident that he would accept. After all, his oldest daughter, Alicia, would be one of the graduates. The *director* would personally invite him.

Having determined a date and a sponsor of the generation, we proceeded to develop the program for the graduation ceremony. Lauro would be the master of ceremonies. José Luis would open the event with a greeting to the graduates and the audience. Andrés would be in charge of teaching a poem and a song to the students, and I would choreograph two dances. The students who would participate would be exclusively first and second level. Their classmates from third level, the graduates, would be spectators in the preferred rows. *Profesor* Merla, being the school *director*, would give the final farewell speech. Finally, *don* Dustano, the graduation class' sponsor, and *Profesor* Merla, would hand the diplomas to the young graduates.

There were some other urgent tasks pending, like drafting the invitations. First, though, we needed the names of the song, poem, and dances, plus the names of the students participating in the program. Andrés and I had to make our selections fast, which would give us, at the most, five weeks to practice. We would also have to add the name of the sponsor of the generation, but we still did not know if *don* Dustano would accept our invitation.

The most important thing was missing: the names of the students who would graduate. We wouldn't know who they were until we had graded their final exams and averaged the results. Until now, our only certainty was the graduation date. We started to feel the pressure of time to do all of these tasks. Invitations and diplomas would be printed in Matehuala because there wasn't a printing shop in Doctor Arroyo. *Profesor* Merla was confident they would be delivered on time.

Once the graduation's date was defined, I arranged all of the details for the Mass. Father Rangel was quite happy and promised he'd conduct the service with a special sermon for the young graduates. He informed me about the charges, which included the white flowers for the altar. We would cover this expense with part of the money raised from the dances.

The following morning, the *director* went to the third-level classroom. He informed the students about our plans for their graduation. They responded very excitedly.

"What kind of clothes will we wear?" Alicia Muñiz asked. She was beaming after learning her father would be the sponsor of that generation. *Profesor* Merla had visited him right after our last meeting, and *don* Dustano had gladly accepted.

"The boys will wear dark suits, white shirts, black bow ties, and black shoes. The girls will dress up in white dresses and white shoes," the *director* said, "and you can have sponsors—males for the boys, and females for the girls."

There were several shouts of joy. Having sponsors or *padrinos* and *madrinas* meant they would get a nice present from them, like gold medals, jewelry, clothes, or money. That was the custom.

Some young people began to express the name of their candidate. Then, discussions also arose fighting for the same sponsor.

The noise stopped when the *profesor* intervened again. "Listen to this warning: make sure your parents don't plan any kind of spending until they know for sure whether you will graduate or not."

A complete silence followed his remark. Nobody smiled anymore.

"I'm sure everyone will work really hard from now until the last day of school," I told him, but looking at the kids, "and I have no doubt that they will all go on stage for their diplomas."

"Well ... I hope they won't disappoint you."

"They won't. You'll see."

Some students recovered their smile, and some others gave me a look of gratitude. The *director* continued to explain that they would need a picture for their diploma. They would have to go to Matehuala because there wasn't a professional photographer in town. Some youngsters said their parents couldn't take them.

"*Señorita* Socorro, would it be possible for you to take the girls to Matehuala for their pictures?" the *director* asked me.

"*Por supuesto*, but of course, I'll be glad to do it."

"Great. I'll ask *profesor* Andrés to take the boys on a different day."

Juanita, *la quinceañera*, raised her hand and asked, "When would we go, *profesora*?"

"When we know if you'll graduate or not," the *director* answered before me.

His response silenced the group again. The students looked at each other. Several of them shifted nervously in their seats. *Profesor* Merla was the only one smiling. He looked around the room, said goodbye, and left.

The next day, Saturday, I sat in my room reviewing my notes in reference to the graduation ceremony. I had the music and the list of possible participants and had designed the costumes the students would need for each dance. The experience had taught me that parents always cooperated willingly by making or buying their children's costumes. To be chosen to participate in any function was a special distinction. I sighed, satisfied with what I had accomplished.

I heard a soft knock on my open bedroom door. When I turned around, I saw Andrés standing by the door. Even though we lived in the same house, we treated each other with respect, and we never entered someone else's room without asking permission first. Andrés looked tired, his hair was disheveled, and there was a shadow of a beard on his face.

"Come on in, Andrés. What's going on?"

"I hope I'm not bothering you, Socorrito, but I'm having trouble finding a poem and a song to teach the students," he said. "I was wondering if you have any suggestions." Andrés ran his fingers through his wavy hair.

"This is your lucky day, Andrés. I have two new books of poems. Maybe we can find something you like, and we'll think about the song later."

"You have two books of poems? That's great!"

"Yes, and I bought some records in Monterrey, thinking that I would be the one who had to teach the dances to the students, although they are only instrumental music."

"You planned ahead," Andrés said, chuckling. "I should have done the same."

"Well, I learned something from my mom and my *abuelita*. One of their favorite sayings was 'a forewarned woman has the value of two.' I always try to remember their advice." I sighed, thinking about how these two wise and wonderful women had influenced my life.

Andrés and I looked through the books' pages and we found two classic poems that were very popular: *"El Brindis del Bohemio"* and *"El Seminarista de los Ojos Negros."* "The Toast of the Bohemian" and "The Seminarian with Black Eyes." The only problem was length: they were too long.

"I know the perfect person to recite either of these poems," I said. "Minerva Rodríguez."

"I was thinking the same. She will be great. Minerva has a fantastic memory, so she'll learn it fast. I'll talk to her tomorrow;

she'll surely accept, so, that part is done. Now we have to look for a song."

"Well, *'Las Golondrinas'* is traditional in farewells, and the lyrics and melody are very appropriate and beautiful," was my opinion.

"Quite so! However, they might play it when the students are getting their diplomas. I'll ask *profesor* Merla, but just in case, we should look for another option."

"You are right. Let's think about it, and we'll decide later."

"Okay. So, tell me, what dances do you have in mind, Socorrito?"

"I'll be teaching *'Moliendo Café'*, 'Grinding Coffee' and *'Cantando bajo la Lluvia,'* 'Singing in the Rain.'"

"Um. Do you think the kids will learn the dance routine in the time left?"

"Oh, I'm not worried about it. We'll be practicing daily until the eve of the ceremony. Right now, I'm more concerned that the graduates learn the graduation waltz. I might need the help of all of you."

"You know you can count on me, and I'm sure Lauro and José Luis will be willing to help, too."

"Thanks, Andrés, but listen, we have a beautiful day, and I think that it's a sin to waste it indoors! How about taking a walk before dinner?"

"That's a great idea. I was getting bored and sleepy."

"Bored with so many things pending? Are you kidding?"

Andrés just smiled instead of answering.

At that moment José Luis came from the street. "Hi. What are you doing? Something new?" He was in good spirits, and we invited him to walk with us, but he found an excuse to stay home and went to his room.

"Tsk, tsk. Do you think he's worried he might be scolded?" Andrés joked, holding his chin, as was his habit.

I understood what Andrés meant. "Well, certainly it won't be for walking in public with you," I said, laughing. "But please, don't embarrass him with questions on that topic. Since he never mentions his girlfriend, we can't tease him about it. You know how private José Luis is about his personal affairs. He must have his reasons. I appreciate him a lot, and the last thing I want is to cause him any kind of problem."

"Well, with the way that rumors spread here, the less other people know about your private affairs, the better," Andrés said.

"True."

"Um. Is there anything people ignore about others' private lives?" Andrés frowned and crossed his arms.

"Not in a small town like this, Andrés. You should know that by now. Don't ever forget that we live in a *crystal box*." Then, I added, "And just wait until you find a girlfriend here. All eyes will be on you, and tongues will wag."

"Well, that's something I should consider." He was thoughtful.

"The truth is that if you find the right girl here, you won't even care about *'el que dirán'!*" I said, patting his shoulder. No, he wouldn't care about 'what would people say,' for sure.

"Do you really think I can find my dream woman here, Socorrito?"

"Maybe. *'Dale tiempo al tiempo y no comas ansias'*".

"You are right with what you said, 'Give time to time and don't get over-anxious.'" He sighed and half closed his eyes, like he was trying to look into the future.

"Hey, you won't find anybody staying home. Let's go for our walk. I'll keep my eyes wide open to recognize a good candidate for you," I said as I stood.

"I'll remind you of that promise, Socorrito."

"I won't forget it, Andrés, and now let's hurry up before it gets dark. There is a whole world outside just waiting for us."

And who knows? Maybe one day I really can help him find the girl of his dreams.

CHAPTER THIRTY-NINE

PICTURES, REHEARSALS, AND A PROMISE

By the end of May, we knew that all third-level students would graduate. The news was received by them with different expressions of joy: tears from some, smiles from others, and hugs from all. Once they had their emotions under control, we told them everything they would have to do for their important graduation day.

As *profesor* Merla suggested, I would take a small group of girls to Matehuala to have their photos taken.

The day of our trip arrived; before the sun rose, we were already boarding the bus. The girls wore their best dresses, and some even sported pretty hairstyles. They were excited to go with me.

"It's like going on a special trip," said Marta Meléndez, one of the oldest girls.

"Besides, we won't see you for a long time if we go to study in the city." Raquel Gutiérrez's voice had a sad tone.

"You might see me if they transfer me to Monterrey and you are there."

"We would love to see you in Monterrey, but you are needed here," said María Teresa Niño. "Minerva and some other students commented you promised them to be here until they graduate."

I smiled without answering, and while they chose seatmates for the trip, I thought about some months back when Minerva, her brother Roberto, Josefina, and Irma were gathered in a small group at recess time.

That day, I saw Minerva talking and shaking her index finger in front of other classmates. They listened and made some comments from time to time. Minerva had a stronger personality than her brothers Ernesto, Pepe, and Roberto, who also attended our school. She was intelligent, and definitely born to be a leader, always participating in class discussion, either with interesting questions or with smart answers.

"*Maestra*," Minerva said in her deep voice, "we were just talking about how we would like our graduation to be."

That made me smile. "Your graduation is two years away, Minerva. You might change your minds by then."

"I doubt it. But by the way, could you be a sponsor too?"

"Unfortunately, no." Noticing the disappointment on her face, I said to all of them, "You know that all the teachers will be in charge of the program, so we will keep busy all night. In my case, I don't even know if I'll return next year."

"*Maestra*, you have to!" Minerva said with a frown on her pretty face. "You, my classmates, and I came to this school at the same time, you as a teacher and we as first-level students. We don't want a new teacher. We want you to be with us until we graduate. It's just right."

"Promise, *maestra*, promise!" Minerva said, placing her two hands on my shoulders. "You will be back, won't you?" The rest of the students added their pleas to Minerva's.

I felt deeply touched listening to their words, but I couldn't promise it since I wanted to be close to my family, too. All that I could say was, *¡Ya veremos, ya veremos!* "We'll see, we'll see."

"You'd better, or we'll do something to bring you back," warned smiling Josefina González. She was Minerva's closest friend and one of the oldest first-level girls, a polite and good student. Josefina had a very pleasant, strong personality, too.

That had been the extent of our conversation, and again, I hadn't promised anything, but I guess Minerva and the other students took it for granted.

That had been months ago, but now I was on the bus with a group of third-level girls who chatted and joked all the way to Matehuala. This was the fourth time I had done that tour, but this time it seemed shorter to me, perhaps because the girls' conversation kept me distracted. We had left Doctor Arroyo when it was dawn and arrived in Matehuala at midmorning. The weather was mild, and the sky was very blue and clear.

We rented three rooms in a small hotel in the center of the town, and after we got ready, we looked for a photography studio. After a short walk, we found two. We decided on one of them after seeing some samples of his work on the windows.

"*¡Hola! Puedo ayudarlas?*", a friendly man said when he saw us. "I'm the photographer."

"Well, yes, I hope you can help us, *señor*. My girls here need to have their certificate pictures taken, but we need them *pronto*, right away, because we are from out of town."

"I see. Where are you from?"

Smiling proudly, one of the girls answered, "We are from Doctor Arroyo."

"I know a lot of people from Doctor Arroyo. They are my customers. I'm sure if you ask them, they will tell you I'm a good photographer." He mentioned several names we recognized.

"Yes, we know them. I'm glad we chose the right person then," I said.

"Your pictures will be ready tomorrow morning," he told the girls. "Now let's see, who wants to go first?"

After indecisions, nervousness, corrections, and lots of laughs, the photoshoot finally ended. The photographer promised to choose the best shot in each case. When we said goodbye, he returned to assure me that the photos would be ready the next day.

That afternoon we went to a nice restaurant. Although they offered us the menu to select a dish, we preferred to order *comida corrida*. It was cheaper, and it was already prepared. The stew and the two side dishes were delicious. Leaving there we walked a bit around the city and went to bed early.

The next day we picked up the photos right after lunch, and the girls were pleased with them. I wanted to be sure we would be back in Doctor Arroyo that afternoon, so we arrived at the bus office early. I was glad I had made that decision because two passengers who came after us had to wait an extra day in Matehuala because all the seats had been sold. The parents had entrusted me with their daughters, and I wanted to return them on time, just as I had promised.

When we arrived in Doctor Arroyo, we had so much dust from the road that, as usual at the end of every trip, we looked like ghosts.

The girls' parents and a lot of curious people waited in the plaza for the arrival of the bus. We tried unsuccessfully to look presentable but to no avail. We had dust on our clothes, hair, and even in our nostrils.

All of the parents thanked me for taking the girls to Matehuala, and everybody went home.

Luckily for me, none of the teachers was at home at the moment, and Teresa had already warmed a bucket of water for my bath. She carried it to the small room designated as a bathroom. By the time the teachers returned, I was presentable and ready to sit at the table with them.

The *director* came by, and I told him about our trip. He thanked me for that collaboration. Then he addressed everyone. "Let's review what progress we have in the program for the graduation ceremony."

He let us know the certificates would be signed and ready for that date. José Luis said he was writing the opening speech. Lauro reported he was putting the program in order. Andrés said Minerva had agreed to recite the poem *"El Seminarista de los Ojos Negros,"* "The Seminarian with Black Eyes." Then it came my turn to report.

"What about you, *señorita*? What dances will you teach the students?" *profesor* Merla asked.

"They are going to dance *'Cantando Bajo la Lluvia'* and *'Moliendo Café,'* 'Singin' in the Rain,' and 'Grinding Coffee,'" I answered, very proud of my choices.

Profesor Merla stared at me silently for few seconds. Suddenly he gave a loud laugh.

"What are you doing, *señorita* Socorrito? These people are *rancheros*! They aren't used to those kinds of dances. Teach the kids something regional they know, like a polka, a *jarabe*, or something similar. What do I know!"

"Excuse me, *profesor*, but not all of those in the audience members will be *rancheros*. There'll be more sophisticated people, too. I've already selected the dancers and given them a sketch of their costumes, so they can have them done right away. We'll start practice tomorrow." I finished almost out of breath.

Profesor Merla and my coworkers didn't say a word, only stared at me in silence.

"It's going to be okay, believe me. I already explained the dances to the kids, and they are excited and eager to perform."

"Well, it's your problem. Don't say I didn't warn you." He shrugged, unconvinced of my arguments.

The following days I met with the students after classes to practice. I didn't allow access to anybody but the dancers. In that way, it would be a general surprise. Other than the dancers, no one had an idea of what we were rehearsing, but I felt confident the performances would be a success. The kids learned the dances quickly. Several local seamstresses were already working on their costumes, which would be ready one week before graduation. This was part of the surprise with which I hoped to convince the audience and the *director*.

TEACHERS AND PLACES OF DOCTOR ARROYO

Profa. María del Socorro Camero Haro. Photo provided by Prof. Víctor Manuel Nava.

Prof. Rogelio de León Garza. Photo provided by Prof. Víctor Manuel Nava.

Prof. José Luis Pérez Hernández. Photo provided by Prof. Víctor Manuel Nava.

Profesor Merla. Photo provided by Delia Merla.

Prof. Francisco Merla Moreno. Photo provided by Prof. Víctor Manuel Nava.

Prof. Jesús Lauro Villarreal. Photo provided by Prof. Víctor Manuel Nava.

Prof. Andrés Tejada Zúñiga. Photo provided by Prof. Víctor Manuel Nava.

A stone house. Photo provided by Saskia Juárez.

A house in Doctor Arroyo. Photo provided by Saskia Juárez.

Albarcones ruins, close to Doctor Arroyo. Photo provided by Saskia Juárez.

Store Casa Contreras and the Contreras family home. Photo provided by Rodolfo Contreras.

Street in Doctor Arroyo. Photo provided by Saskia Juárez.

Old building of store Las Alazanas.. Photo provided by Saskia Juárez.

CHAPTER FORTY

PANIC IN THE THEATER

Another of my tasks was to rehearse the graduation waltz. Since there were more boys than girls in the third-level class, I needed to choose some of the older second-level girls to complete the pairs.

Once I had the necessary number of boys and girls, I gathered them in the middle of the courtyard. This would be the first rehearsal. I first explained some of the rules of the dance to them.

"You'll line up by height. Boys at the left, girls at the right. The student next to you will be your dance partner. There won't be any changes. That would be rude, and it would hurt the other person's feelings, understand?"

Some youngsters answered with a *"Si, maestra."* Others just nodded.

My fellow teachers were there ready to help. José Luis and Lauro carefully positioned the students in the correct place. There were some short ones who were far back, only to be close to their friends. They tried standing on their toes when the teachers went by, like a boy who I'll call Victor, only to be moved toward the front while the rest of them laughed.

"What were you doing with the tall boys?" I asked him after Lauro moved him to the front. "You know well you didn't belong there."

Instead of answering me, Victor shyly nodded toward the girls' line. I looked in that direction, and I understood. He wanted to be the dance partner of a particular girl. Victor was always kind and polite, therefore, I decided to help him.

"Don't worry," I whispered, "you'll dance with Rosalía a couple of times at least."

"Really? I don't see how. She is so far away from me." Shyly, he kept his gaze fixed on the girl.

He's a lot shorter than she. I hope she doesn't snub him. As I turned around, I saw Rosalía smiling and waving at him, inviting him to move across from her. *Well, it seems that the two like each other. I'll see what I can do for them.*

As the lines of girls and boys started getting close to each other, I noticed some of them counting to see who their partner was going to be. Some of the boys tried to move smoothly next to the girl they liked, only to be sent back to their original place.

"You were given some instructions before getting started. If you can't follow them, step to the side to be counted out of the dance," José Luis said with a deeper frown than usual.

Nobody moved. Of course, I knew that many of them wanted to have as a partner who they considered the most popular, the most attractive, the most intelligent, the funniest, or the prettiest. I pretended not to notice. I wanted them to learn that at this point they were all equal.

As for Victor, I'd be true to my word. He would have the opportunity to dance with Rosalía, the girl he liked so much.

When I was about to give the next instructions, Andrés came and took me aside. José Luis and Lauro were watching that the students did not get disorderly.

"Socorrito, I know you don't want the boys to change on a whim, but there is a problem with Sergio."

"What about him?" I asked.

"Lizette will be his partner, and you know those two don't get along."

I turned to see the boy, who was motionless with his arms crossed and his eyebrows raised.

"Wow!" I exclaimed. "He even seems to be in shock."

I smiled, remembering the day Sergio had played a joke on Lizette. Everyone knew her family didn't have much money. The girl, however, always pretended otherwise. She frequently spoke about the delicious meals that were served at her home. She was a pretty girl, but nobody took her seriously because of her pretentious ways.

One afternoon, as they walked into their classroom, Sergio asked her, "So, what did you eat today for your birthday, Lizette?"

"I had cake and frothy chocolate for breakfast and turkey for dinner," she answered, raising an eyebrow. That was her usual way of answering. She turned her back to him and placed her books on her desk.

"Well, apparently, you didn't brush your teeth well. You still have a turkey feather between them!" he said, laughing mockingly.

Lizette turned to look at him arrogantly and when she opened her mouth to reply, her classmates saw the soft brown pinto bean shell sticking to her teeth. Everyone laughed. That was what Sergio had called a turkey feather.

Lizette blushed. "I hate you!" she yelled. Then she sat at her desk and covered her face with her hands.

The boy shrugged and cocked his head to the side still smiling. Then he went back to his desk. Since that day, Lizette didn't like Sergio.

"This should be a happy event for both of them, not an ordeal," I said. "I'm going to solve it."

I moved another girl to the front, trying to avoid more conflicts. Sergio was delighted with this last-minute change. Lizzette on the other hand, would have to accept her new partner without arguing. I wondered about how she would react.

It was a pleasant surprise to see Lizette talking and smiling at the boy who would be her partner. That was a successful change after all.

I divided the couples into two large circles. I made sure that Rosalía and Víctor stayed in the same one. When everyone was in place, Victor turned to see me.

Rosalía was now in his group, but far from him. I pretended not to notice. Instead, I started showing them the first basic move.

After a few waltz steps with their partners, they began to form a chain. To do this, the boys moved in one direction and the girls in another, always in a circle. They walked by holding the hand of a person of the opposite sex all the time: boy, girl, boy, girl. There were mistakes and laughter. After a few repetitions, they did it without error.

When Victor and Rosalía met, I made everyone stop. Then she and the other girls twirled around their own partners twice. Victor looked at me smiling from ear to ear. In another movement, Rosalía returned to dance with Victor. He winked at me in appreciation. The students learned all the choreography at the end of the day. The rest of the rehearsals were effortless, and I was delighted to see all the students enjoying the company of their dance partners.

My other two dances—"Singin' in the Rain," with the participation of ten girls, and "Grinding Coffee," performed by six boys and six girls—were ready, too. Finally, we could rehearse on the theater stage.

When we went to check it out, I noticed the curtains on the background were black, old, and dirty. It seemed like no one had washed them in quite some time. Their appearance greatly displeased me. Then, I had an idea.

I approached Father Rangel, and after I explained this situation to him, he lent us some of the church's long dark blue curtains. They were clean and neatly folded. That made me happy. I thanked him and recruited some boys to hang them after our rehearsal. I couldn't wait to see the change. It was very close to graduation, and I wanted everything to look as nice as possible.

"*Maestra*, we are ready to hang the curtains," Jorge Martínez advised me when we finished practicing.

Ernesto Morín, Armando Castilleja, Nicolás Oliva, Francisco Molina, Miguel Huerta, and others of my faithful students were there to help. We had brooms to clean the stage after they finished.

"Okay, guys, pull the curtains down!"

As soon as they did it, a cloud of dust filled the stage. We all started coughing. Suddenly we heard a strange flapping, and within seconds, a flock of bats was unleashed, flying from one side to the other over our heads. While the girls screamed in terror, the boys grabbed the brooms and ran behind the bats, hitting them and making a big fuss.

Jorge reacted fast. He pulled one of the clean curtains from my hand and threw it on top of the girls and me. "Stay covered and don't remove it until I tell you!" I heard his steps going in another direction.

"Open the doors and let them go!" I yelled, but I don't think anybody heard me.

It was chaos. The sound of the boys' shoes on stage mixed with their screams, and a thud was heard every time they hit a bat. Under the curtain, some girls hugged; others held hands and listened to all the commotion in silence. Lupita Torres, one of the smallest girls, grabbed my arm with her shaking hand. She was a very sweet girl, and I knew this was nerve-wracking for her. I put an arm around her shoulders to calm her down.

Finally, Jorge removed the curtain that covered us. "Don't look now, but there are a lot of dead bats on the floor. I think we caught them all."

"Was anybody bitten?" I asked. I knew that bats can transmit rabies.

"No, don't be alarmed, *maestra*." Jorge grinned with amusement. "We are all safe."

Even if we didn't want to, we had to see all of the dead bats scattered around on the stage's floor. I was worried that some girls might feel nauseous when seeing them. As we walked carefully around them, one bat that was still alive jumped and moved his wings. This caused jumping and screaming again. Horacio finished off the animal with his broom.

The boys carefully removed the dead bats by putting them in some paper bags, then, they placed them in a trash can. Afterward they hung the borrowed curtains. We women folded the old damp-smelling curtains. I would hand them over to the theater owner, hoping for him to wash them, and then hang them up. At the end of the event, I had to return those that had been loaned to us in the church. The girls helped me clean the dirty floor. When we finished, we were tired but happy that the stage already looked presentable.

"That's all. Let's go," I said. "Tomorrow, we'll have a last rehearsal. It's going to be a long day!"

We all went home. We had two days until graduation, and once this was over, we would need two extra days to close the school and pack to leave. That afternoon, the teachers and I crossed one more date off the calendar. For the last two weeks of the semester, we had been counting the days left before we would go home. Despite everything, it had been a good year at work for me, and my heart was already attached to the people and the town of Doctor Arroyo.

I went to bed feeling full of emotions. Before falling asleep, I could hear in my head Minerva's deep voice saying, "Promise, *maestra*, promise you'll be back!"

"I think I will," I whispered while turning to the other side and pulling my blanket up.

"You better, or we'll do something to bring you back," said another deep voice.

That was strange because it sounded like *profesor* Merla's voice. I opened my eyes with a start and realized it had been a dream.

That dream—would it mean anything?

CHAPTER FORTY-ONE

THE GREAT GRADUATION DAY

The night before graduation I went to bed thinking about everything that could go wrong. Would the record player work well? A defective needle had scratched a record before, so I had bought a new one recently and replaced it. Still, the slightest jolt could make the needle jump and ruin the dance. There were still decades to go before the digital players were invented that would free us from this latent danger.

Would all the dancers be present? The previous day, two girls had complained about headaches. If one of them did not show up, her partner would not participate in the dance. That would be terrible. It wasn't only that the pattern of the dance would be incomplete but also the disappointment of the person who wouldn't participate, plus the useless expense the parents made in their costume.

And then the dances. Would the audience like them? *Profesor* Merla had warned me to teach the students something the townspeople knew, of regional style, but I insisted it was time they should see something different. Regardless of the consequences, I was proud of the result. After lots of thinking, I finally fell asleep.

I got up earlier than usual in order to be on time for the graduation Mass. I put on a blue organza dress with tiny roses made with one of the fabrics Minerva and her brothers had given me on my Saint's Day. Once in front of the mirror, I was quite pleased to see how pretty my dress was.

Nena and Eva came looking for me. Since they were sponsors, they had been invited to the Mass also. Both of them looked very pretty in their new dresses.

"Buenos días, amigas", I said. "I love your new outfits!"

"We love yours, too," Eva answered.

Nena smiled and nodded.

"Gracias. The material was a present from the Rodríguez family. Now, we'd better go, so we can sit close to the front."

When we arrived, we saw that the church was almost full. Radiant youngsters in their graduation outfits and family and guests wearing their best clothes occupied the front seats. We sat behind them. I was pleased to see that everything looked special. On the altar, shiny candelabras held lit candles, and fragrant white flowers filled large crystal vases.

I can't remember if any of the professors were present, but I'm sure *profesor* Merla wasn't there. He had previously warned us he would not be attending. We respected his decision and didn't expect him to change his mind.

Father Rangel delivered a special sermon for the students, and they listened to his words with attention. Most of them went to Communion. Father Rangel gave them a special benediction and another to the rest of the people. We stood up and waited respectfully for the priest to leave the altar before we left the church.

The celebration had begun with a good start.

By eleven in the morning, we left to rest and get ready for the ceremony that would start at five o'clock. All of the participants had to be at the theater one hour early. Everyone, including sponsors, already knew what to do because we'd had a general rehearsal the day before.

I felt sad that José Luis wasn't going to be there. He had taken the student's certificates to have them signed in Monterrey. Unfortunately, he got sick and had to send the documents back with another person.

Andrés and I had an early dinner. We took a break for a couple of hours, and by the time *profesor* Merla came by the house, we were ready.

We headed to the theater, where the most important event of the year for our school awaited us. Lauro, who would be the master of ceremonies, was already there. I looked at my fellow teachers. The men all looked sharp in their suits, crisp shirts, neckties, and shiny shoes. Their faces look freshly shaved, and all three gave off the scent of a soft cologne.

I was now wearing a black lace dress lined with pale pink silk to highlight the design of the lace, and high-heeled black shoes. I styled my hair into a French twist.

Seated in a special place was Lauro's girlfriend, *maestra* Esperanza, who had come from Monterrey to attend the event as a guest of honor. We had been introduced by *profesor* Merla before the ceremony, when we had only exchanged some polite words. I still had a lot to supervise with the students for the development of their program, for which I apologized and went to take over those tasks.

When the dancers arrived, I gathered them behind the stage and exhaled in relief. Everyone was there.

"Wow, you all look so pretty!" I exclaimed, seeing the girls who looked so lovely with their makeup and colorful outfits.

"And you, too, *señorita* Socorrito," said several of them, giving me a big hug.

"*¿Y qué de nosotros, profesora?*", Horacio claimed, crossing his arms and raising an eyebrow. I smiled at Horacio's question "What about us, teacher?"

"You boys look quite handsome, too." Everyone laughed.

I asked them to speak quietly. Then I went to the back of the theater looking for the person in charge of the sound system and the record player. I gave him my records. "Antonio, please be careful with this. It's the only music I have. If they get lost or scratched, it will be a disaster."

"Don't worry, *profesora* Socorrito. Nothing will happen to them. I'll keep them safe with my own life," he joked. "I'll be paying a lot of attention to the program. You just give me a signal the minute you want me to start."

I thanked him and told him the order of the music. I went back to the group of anxious dancers, who continually checked for the arrival of their family and friends.

The theater filled up fast. *Profesor* Merla and *profesor* Andrés were in the open courtyard located next to the place, lining up the graduating students and their sponsors. Inside the enclosure, the students in charge of order ensured that nobody sat in the rows of reserved seats. Lauro, who would be the emcee, tested the microphone volume.

Behind the stage, I gave the final instructions to the group of dancers, trying to sound perfectly relaxed. In reality, I had a knot in my stomach. I prayed the kids wouldn't forget their choreography and that nothing would go wrong with the sound system.

Profesor Merla looked at his watch, made sure we were all ready, and gave the order to start. Lauro adjusted his tie, buttoned his jacket, and approached the microphone. "Good evening, ladies and gentlemen," he said in his well-modulated voice. A couple of minutes went by before the packed theater was silent. Here and there one could hear the sound of a chair scraping the floor or a nervous cough. "Let's welcome our students and their sponsors." Loud applause sounded throughout the theater.

The sound of the "Triumphal March" from the opera *Aida* filled the entire theater. The girls entered first, followed by the boys. Each student paraded down the center aisle of the theater alongside his or her sponsor. The spectators craned their necks to see their relatives or friends. The girls reminded me of queens on parades, waving a hand discreetly when they heard someone calling their name. The boys were also smiling, showing great pride.

The *director* was already at the front of the stage, making sure the students sat on the left side of the hall and their sponsors on the right. He was meticulous even to the smallest detail. The previous day he had made sure that the youngsters had practiced everything, from sitting in the right place, to the way to receive their diploma.

Lauro knew well how to use the microphone and keep the noise of the people in the theater under control. He made sure that the attendees remained attentive and entertained. He was doing a great job as master of ceremonies.

He opened the program, instead of José Luis who had been scheduled to do so, by giving an inspired and moving speech. He was often interrupted by applause as he played with the words and alternated the nuances of his voice. We all congratulated him and joined in the well-deserved ovation once he finished.

"It's my turn, *maestra*. Wish me luck," said Minerva after she heard Lauro announcing her name. She smoothed down her new dress, which enhanced her natural beauty.

"Oh, you'll be okay. You know the poem by heart." I gave her a little push. She smiled and straightened her shoulders, then she took her place in the middle of the stage.

Minerva recited *"El Seminarista de los Ojos Negros,"* "The Seminarian with Black Eyes."

The story of the silent and impossible love between a seminarian with very black eyes and a beautiful young girl with blond hair and eyes the color of the sky poured from Minerva's lips in a cascade of love. When she described how they loved each other at a distance, and later the girl's grief seeing a funeral go by her house and realizing it was her seminarian who had died, many people had tears in their eyes. The public rewarded Minerva with a resounding ovation.

Her poem was followed by one of the dances. The first group of six couples performed *Moliendo Café,* "Grinding Coffee." The girls wore mid-length, colorful, full skirts with a big ruffle at the bottom.

They had on sleeveless white blouses with wide embroidered ruffles at the neckline. Sandals and a large, colorful flower worn above the ear completed their costume. They held a small basket that they later placed on the floor.

The boys wore white pants rolled up to mid-leg on only one side. The shirt was also white, knotted in the front, with long sleeves and two small colored ruffles at the top.

They danced a samba, gracefully moving their bodies rhythmically, very well synchronized. They made no mistakes and were delighted when the audience applauded long and hard. I prayed that the second dance would be just as successful.

After Andrés's group of students sang, my ten girls danced *Cantando Bajo la Lluvia*, "Singing in the Rain." They all wore the same style of dress: short sleeves, square neckline, and a full skirt with a stiff crinoline. Each one was a different color with a matching umbrella. The dancers opened or closed their umbrellas throughout the dance, forming different patterns. The performance was perfect, and I was relieved that it went so well. It was gratifying for the girls and for me to hear the long and enthusiastic ovation of the audience. *Profesor* Merla had been wrong. People enjoyed watching something different, so that made me happy.

"Ladies and gentlemen," Lauro said, "let's receive with applause the mayor of our municipality, *don* Dustano Muñiz, sponsor of this generation of students. He will present the diplomas together with our school principal, *profesor* Francisco Merla Moreno."

Don Dustano stood from his seat of honor at the front and went up on stage. He walked slowly, stretching his neck and buttoning his navy-blue jacket. This was a special honor, and he seemed to enjoy the moment. He grinned and waved, acknowledging the enthusiastic applause of the people.

Among the graduating students was his daughter Alicia, who looked at him full of pride.

When the theater fell silent, Lauro called the students, naming them one by one. *Profesor* Merla gave the diplomas to *don* Dustano, and he, in turn, handed them to each youngster.

"Congratulations!" he said to each one. People clapped and the family and friends of each graduate screamed with excitement. Lauro, Andrés, and I lined up next to the *director* to shake hands with the graduates and congratulate them. Most of the girls hugged me instead.

The youngsters returned to their seats, and it was the *director's* turn to deliver the last speech. Several of the girls cried when he told them than more than likely they would leave their homes and their town, as well, since most of them would follow their dream to continue their studies in a big city. They must have comprehended at that moment that they would be leaving the school for good. Several of the boys cleared their throats, trying not to show weakness with their tears. At the end, all of the graduates and the audience stood to applaud the *director's* speech. My fellow teachers and I gave him a hug.

"Ladies and gentlemen, this concludes our graduation ceremony. Thank you so much for your attendance," Lauro said. "We invite you now to the graduation dance in the courtyard next door."

Everyone rushed out of the theater to get a good seat. The recent graduates remained inside, waiting for the signal to make their grand entrance into the courtyard. I made sure that the girls who had accepted the invitation to dance the waltz with the boys without a partner were there. I calmed down knowing all of them were present.

Most of the people already occupied seats around the courtyard, leaving space in the center clear for the dance. The orchestra from Matehuala was in place, waiting for *profesor* Merla's signal to start.

The *director* walked to the theater doors. The eyes of those attending were fixed on him. After a brief pause, he opened the two doors slowly. The first couples of the graduates were in sight. *Profesor* Merla nodded. This was the cue for the orchestra conductor to start. He raised his hand, and the musicians started playing the "Triumphal March" once more, which was performed live this time. To their chords, each couple made their way around the courtyard and took their place for the waltz. The girls looked to me like a flock of white butterflies with their tulle and lace dresses. The boys looked handsome in their dark suits and bow ties; I was sure that for most of them this was their first suit.

I went to where the graduates formed two perfect circles waiting to start dancing. I gave a signal to the orchestra, and a few seconds later, the notes of the "Blue Danube" waltz filled the space. People stopped talking and paid attention to the dance. I looked at Victor while the girls twirled around the boys. Rosalía whispered something to him, and he answered with a smile. I was moved to see his dream of dancing with her become a reality. When the waltz finished, all the youngsters hugged each other, and the audience stood to applaud them. I felt happy that my contribution to the celebration had been a success.

After walking in high heels all afternoon, I felt exhausted. I joined Eva and Nena who were standing up and looking around for a seat. All the places were already taken. Just then I saw José almost lying across three chairs, waving an arm to call my attention.

"I think somebody reserved some seats for us," I commented, amused, and walked toward him.

"I saved these chairs for you and your friends." José smiled with satisfaction. He ignored the chilly stares of some women who, he said, had asked him to let them sit there before our arrival.

"Thank you, José. I can always count on you." I sat down with a sigh of relief.

"By the way," Nena said, looking in the direction of Lauro and Esperanza who were talking to *profesor* Merla, "have you met *maestra* Esperanza yet?"

I told them what had happened before the graduation ceremony.

Just then, I saw Ernesto Rodríguez and his brother Antonio coming toward us. Antonio had recently arrived in Doctor Arroyo, so his family had given him a welcome party. We, the teachers, and Manuel, the lawyer, had been invited to the reunion.

As soon as Antonio arrived, rumors started about all the girls who had an eye on him, but he continued being the serious person that people knew.

When they came to where we were sitting, they stopped to say hello. At that moment, the orchestra started playing, and Ernesto extended his hand to me. "Would you do me the honor?"

I looked at Ernesto in surprise. He waited with his hand extended and a big smile on his face. I was speechless and looked at Eva and Nena. They shrugged and smiled. The people sitting next to us stopped talking to watch us.

"After all, I'm not your student anymore," he said.

"He's right, *Socorrito*. They are not our students anymore. Go ahead and dance with him," Andrés said. He had come with Santiago, who arrived in town two days before.

I looked at Andrés and almost laughed because he sounded like a big brother giving me permission to accept Ernesto's invitation.

"We'll wait for our turn," Santiago advised, giving Andrés a light nudge.

"Do I have an opinion on this?" I stood up.

"I don't think so," Ernesto intervened mischievously. He took my hand and gallantly directed me to the center of the dance floor.

After two melodies, I asked him to take me back to my seat. He thanked me for the dance and went to look for his brother Antonio. As soon as I was back, Santiago took his turn.

"Somebody got ahead of me," he said. He shook his head and smiled while we started dancing.

"Santiago, there were several girls sitting. Why didn't you invite any of them?"

"I was afraid that if I did, they wouldn't let me go," he laughed aloud.

"They will hate me! You should invite all the single girls in town."

Santiago didn't answer. He was enjoying the music from the orchestra. After two or three dances, I also asked him to return me to my seat.

He looked at me in a way that made me laugh. He didn't look too happy.

"Yeah, I know," he said. "You don't want people thinking something is going on between you and me just because we danced more than one melody. Look, I'm going to invite one of your friends, so people won't talk."

As he promised, he danced with Eva for a couple of songs and then with Nena.

I saw Lauro and Esperanza dancing. They made a nice couple. Lauro was tall, slim, and handsome, and she was medium height, pretty, with straight black hair, and well-dressed. I didn't doubt that they would get married eventually. One fact was certain, Lauro wasn't coming back the following year. I had the feeling José Luis—who was in Monterrey—wouldn't return either. Lauro and he had already been in Doctor Arroyo for three long years.

I was sad, thinking that both of them would be leaving our lives, maybe forever.

What if Andrés didn't come back either? I felt an emptiness in my stomach. I preferred to ignore those sad thoughts and just enjoy dancing to the sound of the orchestra.

I remembered Doris Day—"*¡Qué será, será!*" "What will be, will be!"

CHAPTER FORTY-TWO

SUMMER AT HOME

The long year away from my family finally ended. I said my goodbyes to the people and to the town of Doctor Arroyo with a rush of mixed feelings. I was happy to go home but at the same time sad, knowing that Lauro wasn't coming back and more than likely neither was José Luis. Plus I was leaving behind my new friends, my pupils, and a stimulating and rewarding job.

The day before our departure from Doctor Arroyo, there was a continuous parade of parents, students, and friends by the house. They brought many treats and presents. When saying goodbye, they always asked, "Are you coming back, *maestra*?" or "Are you and the other teachers coming back?"

"For sure Lauro isn't coming back, the rest of us I don't know," I answered automatically. "We'll have to go wherever the *Dirección General* decides to send us."

"Can you request to be assigned to this place again?" several of them asked.

"I really don't know. Let's wait and see." That was the truth. My future was uncertain.

Soon I finished packing and was ready to leave, but we had to wait for the next bus. The *director*, Santiago, and Manuel the lawyer would be traveling with us, too, although the latter would be taking only a short vacation.

Profesor Merla came to see us. "Listen, how would you like to try other route? The bus takes more or less the same amount of time, but it won't go to Matehuala. Besides, it would be a nice change of routine. It's a short cut to the main highway; there we can take a bus to Monterrey."

We liked the idea. A short cut meant we would arrive earlier in Monterrey. At least, we thought so.

The day of our departure finally came. After we said goodbye to everybody, the deteriorated bus took us on a route none of us knew. I noticed the driver had placed an old rifle to the left of his seat, within reach of his hand. That made me feel uncomfortable. Why did he have a weapon with him? Was there any kind of danger along the way? I looked at *profesor* Merla. He seemed very relaxed, and so were the rest of the passengers.

Soon I learned the reason for the rifle. Any time the driver saw a distracted rabbit, he stopped, took his rifle, and got off the bus. All of the people stood up and craned their necks to see through the front window. The driver would quietly aim and shoot at the rabbit, but the little animal was always faster than his bullets, so the man would come back grumbling. Everyone laughed at his frustration while they went back to their seats.

"Don't despair, *hombre*. You'll get it next time," said *profesor* Merla.

"You bet I will," he agreed, placing the rifle next to his seat.

This happened several times, to everybody's amusement. Stop, fail, and go. Stop, fail, and go. Soon it could be seen on people's faces that it wasn't funny anymore. Now we were hoping he wouldn't see any more rabbits on the road.

Finally, the next time the driver stopped, an old *ranchero* stood up and told him, "You stay here, *hombre*. Let me show you how to kill a rabbit."

The *ranchero* quietly got out the bus, grabbed a large stone, took aim, and threw it at the little animal that seemed unaware of the danger. Everybody applauded when the man came back holding the dead gray rabbit by the ears. People started teasing the driver about his poor marksmanship.

"Forget about the rifle," one passenger said. "I think you need a cannon to hit it."

"Either that or some eyeglasses," another joked.

The driver just laughed and started telling us about all the rabbits he had killed before. "This time was just bad luck, believe me," he said, shaking his head.

I looked at my watch. "This route has taking us more time than going through Matehuala." I said to *profesor* Merla who was sitting next to me. "If I return, I'll never take it again."

"Oh, you'll return." His tone of voice was enigmatic. There wasn't any doubt in his words, and it wasn't the first time. *Does he know something I don't know? Well, I won't worry about that now. I'll enjoy my well-deserved rest. By the end of my summer vacation, much will be different.*

I was finally home. Before returning, I wondered if after living away all this time, I would again adjust to the family routine and all the noise around. I didn't need to be concerned. After a couple of days, it felt normal to hear my siblings' constant laughter and teasing. As usual I enjoyed my mother's delightful conversation and her beautiful singing. Even the loud baseball games my dad listened to on his radio and my dog's excited barking any time somebody passed in front of our house were pleasant sounds to me.

After the silence and loneliness in Doctor Arroyo, I even welcomed the noise from the traffic on the bridge near my house. Nothing bothered me, not even the early sounds of the street vendors offering their merchandise over a loudspeaker. I felt happy to be home with my family.

One of the rewards of being a teacher is the two months of summer vacation. When I lived at home, I spent part of my free time in San Luis Potosí. For me it was almost a necessity to visit my aunt Timita and my cousin Guillermina, whom I consider my sister. We had grown up together and with the exception of one year, we had never been apart. She was my playmate, and we always went to the same schools. In 1953, for lack of a well-paid job, my dad was forced to move our family to Monterrey. We had parted painfully, and for that reason I took every opportunity to visit them. But now it was different; I was hungry for my family. So, when my brother Javier asked me if I was going to San Luis as usual, I replied that summer I planned to stay home. Sharing time with them, my immediate family, was the most important thing at that time.

"Hope to see you a little more, Javier. You are always stuck in the library. You must have read all the books there by now," I joked.

"One never finishes learning, Coco. The more I read, the more I realize all that I still lack in knowledge. Learning is for life."

He had always been like this. He read insatiably since he was little. When we were in elementary school, every time my books disappeared, I already knew who had them: Javier. And I was four grades ahead of him. He had a prodigious memory. So, while the rest of my siblings were more studious, Javier was able to read a book only once and memorize whatever it was.

My boyfriend, Martín, was still fulfilling his US military duty overseas. I enjoyed his letters with detailed stories of military life and seeing through his eyes the exotic places where he was stationed. I wondered if one day I would share with him the experience of living in one of those foreign lands. We hadn't seen each other for three years, and I felt it was necessary to find out soon if his plans for the near future included me too.

I wanted to take advantage of my two months' vacation to acquire new knowledge. I enrolled in arts and crafts classes to learn how to make papier-mâché items, wax flowers, and jewelry made of bread dough mixed with glue. I also took classes at a beauty academy I had attended before leaving for Doctor Arroyo. It was located half a block south of the Cathedral, in front of plaza Zaragoza, Monterrey's main plaza. Between taking classes and visiting family and friends, my vacation days were going by swiftly.

I saw my friend Mari Paz on weekends when we went to the movies and Licha occasionally, when I visited her at home or when the three of us attended some dance. Licha's father was very strict, so she didn't have the freedom to socialize that Mari Paz and I did.

I met Licha when I entered "Colegio Excélsior" to study to become a teacher. Later we transferred to the "Escuela Normal del Estado," where we attended the second and third year of our teaching careers. We were classmates and worked as student teachers in the same schools in the two years prior to graduation. In the evening, after school, Licha, her aunt Isabel, and I would go home on the same bus. For three years Isabel had to accompany Licha to the school where we studied, and she had to wait inside the building for the entire class period until dismissal time. That was Licha's father's stipulation to allow her to study at night.

"Do you know I was also offered the same position as you in Doctor Arroyo?" Licha asked me when I saw her.

I raised an eyebrow listening to this revelation. She had never mentioned it before. "So, how come you didn't take it? We could have been together."

"Coco, you know my father. I knew he would never let me go. I had to reject the assignment right away." She sighed and shrugged.

"I'm so sorry, Licha. How fantastic if you had been there with me!" I said.

She told me she was happy with her job in the Colegio Israelita. She was teaching young children, had a small group, and enjoyed the atmosphere of the place. All of a sudden, she was silent and avoided looking me in the eyes. *She is a sweet caged bird. Would her father ever let her fly to reach her dreams?*

Mari Paz, on the other hand, had just graduated. She would have to wait until August for a school assignment. Maybe she could ask for a position in Doctor Arroyo. At least, I would have one of my two dear friends with me. With this thought in mind, I planned to go to see her the following day. I could hardly wait to share my idea with her.

"Mari," I said when I saw her, "wouldn't it be fantastic if I stayed in Doctor Arroyo and you received an assignment there?" I placed my hand on her arm and squeezed it gently while I waited for her answer.

My question took her by surprise. She blinked a couple of times before answering.

"No, Socorro," she answered, "I could never work in a small town. That's not for me, I'm sorry. Hopefully, they'll assign me a job in the city."

I looked at her sideways. "Your sister Lala said you cried for a long time because I was away. So, don't you miss me any longer?"

"Of course, but I don't want to be away from my family. You understand, don't you?"

Mari Paz held my hands and waited for my answer with her head tilted. She smiled shyly, showing her perfect teeth.

"You'll be back soon, you'll see," she said in her well-modulated voice. "We'll have fun together as before."

She was trying to cheer me up, but I felt really disappointed.

Then, in her easygoing way, she elbowed me and said, "Cheer up. Let's go for a hamburger."

"It's too hot to go anywhere." I dried the sweat from my face with a small handkerchief.

"Get a fan and no more excuses. Let's go!" She grabbed her purse and stood up.

"Okay, okay. Sometimes I'm glad I don't see you that often."

"Big liar, you miss me, too," Mari Paz said, laughing and placing my purse and a fan in my hand.

When August arrived, I went to the *Dirección General* to see if there was any news for me about some possible transfer.

"The assignments are just coming in," one of the secretaries informed me. "However, preference will be given to the people who don't have a job."

"I see. And how long will it take for changes to be authorized?"

"Who knows?" the secretary said, shrugging with indifference. "Be grateful you have a job. There are a lot of teachers waiting for any kind of assignment. In any case, you'll be notified at your address if there is any change for you."

She returned to her desk with a voluminous pile of folders. I wondered if mine was among them. I left the place discouraged, even more so when I saw the large number of recently graduated teachers waiting to know if they would get a place. They looked just as I had the year before.

I realized how anxious my mother was, but there wasn't anything I could do except wait patiently. Still, it hurt me to see the sadness on her face when I told her the latest news.

I was heartbroken to see the disappointment in my sister Norma's eyes when she overheard me talking to my mom. In our free time, we had been looking for a house to rent without any success. "Maybe something will come out one of these days; do not be discouraged," I said to comfort her.

My vacation ended, and no message about a transfer had arrived, nor did we find a rental house. I packed my suitcases to return to Doctor Arroyo. My family was sad that I would leave again.

On the day of my departure, there were some teary eyes when I hugged and kissed everyone before boarding the bus. I just prayed, hoping it wouldn't be as hard for them as it had been for me the first time. We waved to each other until the bus turned the corner and I couldn't see them anymore. I felt lonely and lost again. I knew that José Luis would be working in another school in Monterrey. It would be difficult for me not to have him and Lauro around. We had worked together for a year, and I lived under the same roof with José Luis. We were like family. I just hoped Andrés did return because I knew I could always count on him.

I wondered what kind of people our new coworkers would be. Would we have at least one female teacher this time? What if Andrés didn't come back? Would it be three new male teachers instead of two? It was better to put worries aside. In a few hours, I would have answers to all of my questions.

That day I covered my head with a long scarf to protect my hair from the dust of the road. I hoped the new teachers wouldn't see me looking ghostly upon my arrival and prayed that if they were staying at *doña* Susana's none of them had taken my room.

That would be a bad beginning, really bad. I closed my eyes, trying in vain to fall asleep. Finally, I decided to admire the beautiful landscape of the Sierra Madre.

CHAPTER FORTY-THREE

NEW SCHOOL AND TWO
NEW TEACHERS

As soon as I arrived at Matehuala, I hurried to the Doctor Arroyo bus terminal. My heart skipped a beat. Andrés wasn't there. I boarded the bus and sat alone at the front, behind Chepa, the driver. As people got on the vehicle, they greeted him and me, too. I didn't know most of the passengers, but they knew me for sure because they addressed me by my name and title.

"Did you have an enjoyable vacation, *maestra*?" Chepa asked, looking at me in the small mirror up in front of him.

"Very pleasing, Chepa, thanks! By the way, can you tell me if *profesor* Andrés is back yet?" I held my breath waiting for his answer.

"He came back yesterday. And two new teachers arrived two days before."

I sighed in relief that Andrés returned to town. On the other hand, I wanted to know about the new teachers. "Is one of them a female teacher?"

"Nahhh, both of them are males. But they are very different from *profesores* Lauro and José Luis."

"Very different? What do you mean?" I bent closer to hear his answer better.

"I meant just that. They are ... different. You'll see." Then he added, "So, you will have new coworkers and a new school. What do you think?"

"Aww! Is the school finished already? How fantastic!"

Chepa straightened his wide shoulders and started whistling to the song from the radio. He alternated his gaze from the unpaved road to the small mirror. He adjusted it from time to time to check on the noisy passengers in the back of the old bus. *"He knows the road so well that he can drive with his eyes closed," say the people. Well, I'll make sure he won't do it this time.*

As we got close to town, I tried to brush off the white dust of the road. At least my hair was clean thanks to my large silk scarf. I didn't wear any mascara on my eyelashes either. The previous time, they had become white and stiff, so they made me feel like a clown.

I looked at myself in the mirror. Not too bad. Still, I needed some time to look presentable before meeting the new teachers. *¡La primera impresión es la que vale!* Yes, the first impression is the one that counts.

When we rode by the main plaza, I saw several of my students walking toward the bus stop. It lifted my spirits to know that they were waiting for me.

"Welcome, *profesora* Socorrito!" The cheerful greeting came from Horacio. As soon as he saw me by the door, he extended his hand to help me down.

"Thank you, Horacio. I see you brought a lot of company."

"Welcome back, *señorita* Socorrito," Josefina González said, giving me a big hug, followed by Lilia Nava, Matilde Briones, José, Eleuterio Obregón, and some other students.

"Hi, everybody. Thanks for coming." Their reception warmed up my heart and put a smile on my face.

"I'll carry your suitcase." José, always helpful, stepped in front of Horacio. He had waited quietly behind everybody else, greeting me from a distance.

"Go ahead, José," Horacio encouraged him, amused. He already had one of my two suitcases.

We all headed toward the house.

"*Maestra*, your new coworkers came three days ago. They are staying at our place," Horacio said.

Some students said they had already met the new teachers. I was surprised when all of them agreed they were very different from Lauro and José Luis. They also started telling me excitedly about the new school. Before they could elaborate anymore, we arrived at the hotel.

Andrés stood by the large open door.

"I beat you in the return this time, Socorrito," he said, smiling and giving me a friendly hug. "*Profesor* Merla and I planned to go to the plaza to wait for you, but I see the bus arrived early today."

"It's okay. I had a good welcoming committee." I pointed with my head to the youngsters around us who smiled at the compliment. "I was worried you wouldn't come back because I didn't see you at the bus terminal in Matehuala."

"I decided to come a day before, not only to get situated and have a good rest, but also to make sure I got a good room in case the new coworkers decided to live with us." He winked at me mischievously.

As we walked inside the hall, *doña* Susana came out of the kitchen, wiping her hands on her apron. She pushed the small wet curls away from her forehead. Her wrinkled face looked happy.

"*¡Bienvenida, señorita!*", *doña* Susana said. "You have your same room." She removed the lock from the bedroom door and pointed to Horacio to bring in my suitcases.

All of the students had left, with the exception of José, who waited with my suitcase. He stubbornly refused to give it to Horacio. He swung it around every time the other boy tried to take it from his hands, which made us laugh. José didn't look amused at all. That was his personality, so we were already used to it. Once he heard that I would stay in my previous room, he triumphantly took my suitcase there, and in a comical act of rudeness, stomped his foot in front of Horacio and said good night.

"Good night, José, and thank you so much." I laughed.

He waved and left in a hurry. Then I turned to the owner. There was something I had wanted to ask her for a long time.

"*Doña* Susana, thanks for not giving my room to anybody else. By the way, since I don't have any family here, would you allow me to call you *Abue*?"

She looked at me with surprise. "You want to call me Granny?"

"I really would like to call you that."

"Then you can do it, of course you can do it." *Doña* Susana beamed with satisfaction. She went back to the kitchen, followed by Claudia, who I had already seen at the bus stop. Duque changed places and lay close to my room.

"What was that, Socorrito? Are you adopting *doña* Susana as your grandma?" Andrés asked.

"Well, she doesn't receive many expressions of affection, so I thought I would show her mine by calling her *Abue*. Anyway, I do need a granny. The only grandmother I had died recently and left a big emptiness in my heart."

"Okay, if you say so." Andrés shrugged. "Now, just leave the purse in your bedroom, and let me introduce you to our new coworkers."

I removed my new scarf and looked at my clothes. They didn't look too bad after all, but I could feel the dust on my face and on my arms.

"I had thought of taking a bath first, but there is no way the teachers won't see me if they have their bedrooms doors open. Just let me wash my face and comb my hair. I'll come by your room as soon as I'm ready."

Ten minutes later, I knocked on Andrés's open door. "Let's go now. Afterward I need to eat something because I'm really hungry."

Andrés and I walked to the other side of the patio where there were lots of clay pots full of blooming flowers. They added a nice splash of color against the white walls of the house. A big jasmine spread its perfume through that part of the patio. I would ask Teresa to move that pot closer to my bedroom. I recognized the singing of some of the birds. This was something I didn't have back home. *I wonder if birds recognize people, and if they do, do they remember me?*

We stopped in front of a bedroom and Andrés knocked softly on the door that was ajar. From inside, somebody with a deep voice invited us to enter. As we did, I saw a man lying on the bed and propped up on one elbow. An open book rested close to him. He stood up as soon as he saw us. He immediately tucked his shirt inside his khaki pants.

Andrés made the proper introductions. His name was Rogelio de León. He was slightly older than Andrés and me, and for this reason I started using the deferential Spanish term *usted* when I talked to him.

Rogelio was of medium height and slightly heavy. He had a small double chin under his round face. He wore the waist of his pants low, revealing a small belly under his blue shirt. I thought he was extremely serious, but there was kind glint in his eyes. He wasn't a bad looking man.

"This is from happiness," he said, rubbing his tummy, "and my cute, upturned nose is my best feature." He pushed his small nose up with the index finger.

He made me laugh. "Okay, *profesor* Rogelio. I'm glad you have a good sense of humor. You made me feel a little bit intimidated, and I was ready to run and hide in my room."

"But, why? I'm adorable, like a plush teddy bear!" he continued to joke.

Andrés and I laughed aloud. "Well, now I feel completely at ease with you," I said.

"*Señorita* Socorrito, welcome back," Teresa said, standing by the door. "*Profesor* Merla is looking for you. He's in the dining room with *profesor* Gerónimo."

"Thank you, Teresa. I'll be there right away."

The three of us went to the dining room. On the way, Andrés told me that the *director* would be eating with us daily, since his wife was now in Monterrey accompanying their two daughters who were studying there.

Profesor Merla was seated at our usual table, and next to him was a young man. He was slim, with dark skin. He had straight black hair. After the *director* greeted me with a hug and a big smile, he introduced him to me. "This is *profesor* Gerónimo Llanes," he said. The young teacher remained seated.

"Nice to meet you." He extended his hand across the table and gave me a weak handshake.

I introduced myself, but Gerónimo just stared at me with a raised eyebrow and a blank look. Afterward, he turned his head away and continued his conversation with *profesor* Merla.

Teresa brought a plate with warm food that *doña* Susana had kept for me. It smelled delicious, so I started to eat right away. She served the others sweet bread and coffee.

When we finished eating, the *director* said, "Well, all of you must have heard that our school building is completed and we will start classes there on Monday."

"Yes, we heard about it. I still can't believe the school was built so fast," I commented.

He also explained that they worked hard during the holidays and that now the school was ready to receive our fortunate students more comfortably. He also informed us that all the girls would wait for me in the plaza Juárez, in front of *don* Amancio Berrones's store, to walk with me to the new building.

"Don't forget that you are responsible for all those young girls," he reminded me before retiring.

"Don't worry. They'll be well guarded. I promised I would watch over them, and that's exactly what I'll do." *Of course, nothing bad can happen to them if they walk with me. Or can it?*

A girl in plaza Juárez. Photo provided by Prof. Victor Manuel Nava.

I also said goodnight to the teachers. I was tired and wanted to take a bath before going to bed. Teresa had the hot water ready. An hour later, I felt really clean and rested. While my hair dried, I unpacked and put each thing in its place. Soon, everything looked the way it had before summer vacation.

The following day, I decided to wait until Monday to see the new building. Besides being fatigued from the trip, I had to attend Sunday Mass and get everything ready for work. I couldn't wait to see my former students again and to meet the new ones. Undoubtedly, I would miss the ones who had graduated two months before.

Monday morning, I had an early breakfast. As I got up from the table, Rogelio and Andrés came into the dining room.

"Are you done, Socorrito?" Andrés asked, raising an eyebrow. "How come you didn't wait for us?"

"I'm supposed to meet the girls in the plaza, remember? I have to be in school before all of you, so I'm leaving right now. See you later, guys."

"Good luck with all the girls, Socorrito!" said Rogelio, taking a warm *tortilla* from a small basket.

I went to my bedroom to collect my purse and my textbooks. I said a small prayer for a good school year and walked to plaza Juárez to meet the girls.

Several of them were already waiting. As soon as they saw me, they ran to hug me.

"*¡Profesora Socorrito!*" Minerva exclaimed, patting my back with her accustomed friendliness. "You were true to your promise and came back!"

"*¡Bienvenida, profesora!* We are so happy to have you back," Matilde Briones said. She was one of the most outgoing girls in school, cheerful, with an effervescent personality. She expressed her emotions through her big dark eyes.

Lupita Torres, one of my sweetest students, just hugged me quietly and gave me a big smile. Small in stature, she wore long braids adorned with large bows.

"We missed you, *profesora*!" Socorrito de la Garza said, looking at me shyly behind her eyeglasses. She was a blonde girl, with big green eyes. Her personality, gentle and quiet, was the opposite of her brother, Paco, an outgoing boy who always had a loud and contagious laugh. I would miss him a lot now that he had graduated and left to study in San Luis Potosí. I heard that soon, two of his sisters, Cuquita and Malena, would be our students, too.

"Thank you, girls. I missed you, too. I am happy to return and very eager to use a new building and start classes. Now, please introduce me your new classmates."

Matilde told me their names. Some of them seemed very shy, but I knew they would be comfortable with me and everybody else in a little bit of time. After all of them arrived, we headed to school. I was curious to see the new building.

Middle School in Doctor Arroyo. Photo provided by Profa. Lilia Nava.

The girls walked in small groups, chatting like little birds. They wore nice dresses, and some had been to the beauty parlor. I smiled, thinking they wanted to make a good first impression.

After crossing the Plaza 5 de Mayo and walking a few streets, we arrived at the new school. The adobe building was designed in an L shape, very simple and painted white inside and out. It had an entrance hall that led out to a large courtyard with a volleyball court. On the right side of the building there were three spacious classrooms with large windows that opened onto a quiet street. The furniture was the same old desks that we had previously. A large blackboard was placed in the front of each room.

Besides the three classrooms, there were three smaller rooms. One was the *director's* office. The second was the teachers' room, located on the corner of the building. There were no windows, but it had double doors that we kept open all the time, so we could see the almost-empty street. That office had a large table, some chairs, and a file cabinet where we kept our belongings. The third room was small and held materials such as books, maps, and other things.

The bathrooms were located on the south side and away from the building, one for the boys and another for the girls.

In coming weeks, we would find out other important details.

Our school didn't have a carpet, but that made it easier to clean the cement floors. We didn't have air conditioning, not even electric fans, only the breeze entering through the open windows. On windy days, however, we kept the windows closed so the classrooms would not fill with dust from the unpaved streets around the school.

We also realized that when winter came, we would have to place the desks a bit further away from the windows to keep warm, as we didn't have heaters. However, we had lots of natural light and could see the street. This was not distracting, because we were on the town's edge. Occasionally, some vehicles crossed the almost-always-empty street, or someone went by on a horse, a donkey, or a bicycle.

With the exception of a clock and the large blackboard, the white walls of the classrooms were empty. If we needed a map, we brought one from the office and placed it on the blackboard. When we finished, we returned it to its place perfectly rolled. There was a globe of the world that we all shared. *Profesor* Merla provided us with the textbooks for the subjects we taught. Besides, each one of us had a few books of our own. Everything was limited, but regardless of this, we felt happy with what we had. Of course, we would have loved to have a projector and mimeograph to print tests, notices, and questionnaires, but we didn't complain.

As there was no drinking water, the students brought it from home or waited until they returned. There was water for cleaning the septic bathrooms and mopping the floors. That came directly from the *aljibes*. We couldn't drink it without boiling it, as we knew it was full of tadpoles.

Despite our shortcomings, having our own building meant the world to the students and to us, the teachers.

CHAPTER FORTY-FOUR

IN THE COMPANY OF *DOÑA* ROMANA

The school custodian was *doña* Romana, a middle-aged woman. She was a good, hardworking, uncomplicated person. She was present in school twice a day—all morning and afternoon. She ran school errands during the day and cleaned after we all had left. In wintertime, she went home when the sun was setting.

Doña Romana was the only adult female company that I had within the school, and on occasions we shared adventures.

"So, what happened yesterday, *doña* Romana?" I asked our custodian as we walked between the cactus and magueys on the large plot next to our school. The day was bright and warm.

She had a long stick in one hand and a kitchen knife wrapped inside a towel in the other. *Doña* Romana narrated to me her ordeal with a nervous cackle at the end.

Someone had closed the lock on the bathroom while she was cleaning it, and the poor woman had been there without being able to leave. She screamed and screamed, but there was no one to hear her. Finally, it was getting very dark, when a man riding a donkey near the school heard her. *Doña* Romana threw the key out the window and the man opened the door for her.

Crying, she immediately informed *profesor* Merla, telling him that she believed she had seen Horacio. He promised that he would investigate and if true, he would punish the boy severely.

"Can you imagine if I had to spend the night there? Not even the potter next door was around."

"Were you afraid of *La Llorona?*" I asked her naughtily.

"Who knows? A lot of people have seen her or have heard her weep. I would have died of fear if she had appeared to me." She shuddered and crossed herself.

"Well, one of these days we might find out who the joker was, and he is going to be in real trouble," I said.

"One thing I learned with this is never to leave the padlock on the door. Now I carry it with me in one of my pockets."

"That's good, *doña* Romana. Now tell me, why are you carrying such a long stick?"

"Oh, it's in case we find a snake. There are many around; keep your eyes wide open so you don't run into them. And don't get pricked by the thorns of the cactus."

I looked at her to find out if she was joking, but her expression was completely serious. I wasn't afraid of the spines from the cactus, but snakes were something different.

That time, *doña* Romana was the one who laughed when she saw me looking apprehensively at the ground around me. There were places where the magueys grew very close to each other, so anything hiding under them couldn't be seen.

"We'd better hurry up, *doña* Romana. My next class starts in thirty minutes."

She stopped in front of a big *nopal* full of red prickly pear fruit—or *tunas*, as we called them. She looked for the ones that were ready to eat and cut several of them. She grabbed them with a paper towel to avoid the spines and skillfully cut the skin across and on both sides. She exposed the inside of the *tuna* and handed it to me.

"*Doña* Romana, this *tuna cardona* is delicious." I enjoyed the sweet flavor and texture of the fruit. I closed my eyes and thought about the taste of the different types of *tunas* I ate during my childhood. She gave me two more, and she ate some, too.

"Do you know I'm a *Tunera*, *doña* Romana?"

"Oh! are you from San Luis Potosí, *señorita*? Because that's how they call people from there."

"Yes, I'm *Potosina* but moved to Monterrey when I was fourteen years old, so now I'm a *Regiomontana*."

"Um! no wonder you knew the name of these *tunas*!"

I checked the time on my watch. Twenty minutes had already gone by.

"Let's go back to school, *doña* Romana. It's almost time for my next class."

She cleaned her knife and placed it back into the towel. "Tomorrow I'll bring a box and I'll cut some more *tunas* for you and the teachers. I'm sure they will also like them. Will you come back with me?"

"Sure, we'll come on my free time," I said. "Do you think you can get some *aguamiel*, too?" I was referring to the sap of the Mexican maguey. This sap, called honey water, has a sweet flavor, and it's found in abundance among the agave plants.

"Yes, *señorita*! Tomorrow I'll bring a large jug. I'll make a cut in the *maguey*, and I'll leave the jug overnight to collect the juice. You can take it home in the afternoon."

"Great, *doña* Romana. I can hardly wait. It has been a long time since last time I tasted it."

Then, as an afterthought, *doña* Romana said, "Just don't forget to bring it to a boil before drinking it, or you could get blisters in your mouth."

"I promise I won't forget. I'll ask *doña* Susana to boil it for me."

That afternoon at dinner time, *profesor* Merla informed us that, according to several students, Horacio had been with them the day before, and they confirmed that he did not participate in the prank on *doña* Romana.

Time passed. We never found out who had locked up our concierge.

A pottery business faced the patio on the east side. The doors to the small place were always open. From the school, we could see an old man creating his clay pots by patiently turning a wheel with pedals. Afterward, he would place his clay pots to dry outside in the sun. We told the students not to kick any ball in that direction or they would have to pay the man for any damage they caused.

One day, during a class period that I had free, I asked *doña* Romana to walk with me to the pottery. I was curious to see how the pots were made.

We had advised *profesor* Merla that we would be gone for half an hour and I would be back on time for my next class. He said it was fine, and we left.

"*Buenos días, señor*", I said, standing by the door. "I'm one of the schoolteachers. Would you allow me to see you make one of your pots?"

"*Buenos, señito*", the potter answered, using the popular abbreviation of the word '*señorita.*' "*¡Por supuesto, con mucho gusto!*". He invited us to come in with a movement of his head. There was kindness on his dark face full of deep wrinkles. He cleaned his mud-covered hands on his old apron.

The potter sat straight on his high bench with a serious expression. He looked like a surgeon ready to conduct an important operation. As he worked, he explained to us all the necessary procedure to create his craft.

The potter placed a ball of hard gray clay in the center of a round wood surface. He added some water and kneaded it to let the air bubbles out. The wet clay smelled the way the ground smells after a rain. He rhythmically moved his right leg on a pedal, making the upper part spin. There was a peculiar sound, and I wondered if it came from the table or from his old legs. Placing one of his wrinkled hands on the center of the clay, he transformed the ball into a cylinder as it spun. Using both hands, he ran them up and down the cylinder, skillfully shaping it into the form of a pot. He took another small amount of mud, rolled it on top of the table, then flattened it and shaped it into the form of an ear. That was the handle. He placed it on the side of the pot. The old man looked satisfied at his work of art. Using a piece of wire, he separated it from the table. He stood up and carefully carried it outside. He placed it next to other pots of different sizes and shapes that were already drying.

"There is good sun, and they will dry soon. Maybe in a couple of days, I will be able to paint some designs. After that, I'll bake them," he explained.

"What do you do when they are completely finished? Do you take them to Matehuala?"

"No, *señito*. It's very expensive to try to sell them in the city. They need special packing, or they would break easily, plus the cost of transportation,"

"So, what do you do with them?"

"I sell them here in town. I have many customers that come and buy them directly from me. They know it's cheaper than buying them in the store."

I had always lived in the city, and I had no idea of the time and effort it took to make the clay pots that were sold in the markets. I had just learned it from the old potter, from preparing the soil to baking the pots. These crafts sold very cheaply, consequently the potter didn't make much money with his trade. I realized how hard it was for some people to put food on their table and wondered how many members were in the potter's family. I checked my watch. It was time to go back, so I didn't ask him.

"You are doing a beautiful job, and I really enjoyed watching you. Thank you so much!"

"You are welcome, *señito*, and if you ever need a pot, I'll make one specially for you," he said in a gentle tone of voice.

"I'll keep that in mind, but now I have to go. It's almost time for my next class."

The old man smiled and went back to his shop. I turned around to greet him one last time and saw him placing another gray ball of clay on top of the table.

Doña Romana and I walked back to school. In the distance, I heard the sound of the spinning pottery wheel, like the painful sound of old creaking bones.

CHAPTER FORTY-FIVE

LEARNING THE HARD WAY

Despite being away from home for two years, I still missed my family a lot. We had always been together and now, out of necessity, we lived many miles apart.

My family resided in a big city where there was much to see and do. Instead, I lived in a small town with many shortcomings and limited entertainment. On occasion, this made me feel sad and homesick, but knowing I was helping my home was enough to encourage me.

Although I would have preferred a job close to them, I felt glad to be back in Doctor Arroyo. I loved my students and my job, and although *profesor* Merla and I did not always agree, I recognized that I had learned a lot from him.

The school year would involve a big change in our working environment. Rogelio and Gerónimo were different from Lauro and José Luis in ages and personalities. However, I promised myself never to make comparisons. It would be best for all of us to get along and work in harmony.

The students were already familiar with Andrés and me, but they still had to get used to the new teachers. At the beginning, the kids felt intimidated by Rogelio because he seemed so serious. Once they knew him, they realized that with mutual respect, his kind character emerged. Rogelio was a good teacher, with great knowledge, and he knew how to discipline the students. Gerónimo, on the other hand, had problems establishing discipline in the classroom, maybe because of his youth. He even had confrontations with some students.

"Horacio, why is *profesor* Gerónimo having so many problems in the classroom?" I asked him.

"Well, he jokes a lot with the students; and when he wants to assume his role as a teacher, they don't obey him. Then he gets angry."

"I see. I might try to help him," I said.

So, the next time he started complaining about the poor behavior and lack of interest of the students in the subject he was teaching, I tried to share some useful suggestions with him, just as Lauro and José Luis did with Andrés and me.

"*Profesor* Gerónimo, maybe it would be good idea if —" I started.

"*Maestra* Camero," he interrupted coldly, "I don't require your advice. Thank you. If I need it, I'll ask *profesor* Merla for it." He stood up from the table where both of us were having dinner with Rogelio and Andrés.

"Well, that's fine with me. I was trying to help you because you are new here. I thought a suggestion might benefit you, but I see you don't need any help."

"Not yours anyway." He turned and went to his room.

There were some minutes of uncomfortable silence as we looked at each other.

"I don't know what's wrong with Gerónimo," Rogelio commented, shaking his head and frowning. "It seems it's hard for him to take any suggestions from a woman."

"Maybe I shouldn't have said anything, but I tried to help him. After all, he doesn't seem to have a lot of teaching experience."

"Let him learn the hard way, Socorrito," Andrés opined, squinting his eyes. "You and I never had that kind of attitude."

"Hmm, I'll have a talk with him," Rogelio said. "We all should get along, but if he's disrespectful to you, *profesora* Socorrito, you better let *profesor* Merla know."

"Not a problem on my part," I said, "but I can tell you that, from the beginning, I felt that Gerónimo was going to be a little bit antagonistic toward me. I don't know why."

"And what did you think about me when you met me?" Rogelio asked with his usual humor. "Oh, I know—my little upturned nose revealed my nice character from the beginning."

Andrés and I laughed about this physical reference, now familiar to us. After that, we talked about different subjects and forgot about Gerónimo. We explained some of the town customs to Rogelio. We told him about the friends who visited us from time to time, like Santiago, Alberto the chemist, and the engineers. We also talked about the projects we had during the year in order to raise funds for the students' graduation.

Rogelio expressed his eagerness to get involved in any activities and to meet the friends we had mentioned. "The more things we have to do, the better," he said. "This way time will go faster."

Rogelio must have talked to Gerónimo because in the following weeks he was friendlier toward me. However, I decided not to offer him any advice in the future. I felt it would be better to let *profesor* Merla guide him in any problems he had. I was sure they would present eventually, and I was right.

One morning, *profesor* Merla and I walked outside of the classrooms where Andrés, Rogelio, and Gerónimo were teaching. The *director* showed me something he wanted to have fixed on the building. Each classroom had windows to the street, but only a door facing the courtyard, therefore, we did not distract students as we passed.

Occasionally, the *profesor* visited the classrooms to see how everything was going, so on our way back, he went into the classroom where Gerónimo was teaching. I waited by the door. Suddenly, something about Gerónimo infuriated him. Without hesitation, he scolded him in front of all the students. I found it very humiliating. The whole group was stunned, and Gerónimo went from blushing to becoming pale and vice versa. I walked away from the door because I didn't want to embarrass him more.

The *director* had never acted like that with any of us, and I wanted to be sure it would never happen to me. Even though the scolding might be deserved, I didn't approve of the way it was done. I felt sorry for Gerónimo.

As soon as the *director* stormed out of the classroom, I followed him into his office. He dropped into his chair as I stood in front of his desk, still shaken from the incident.

"Excuse me, *profesor*, I would like to talk to you."

"*¡Dígame!*", he said, his lips trembling slightly.

"With all the respect you deserve as my *director*, I would like to ask you that, if for any reason you think I should be reprimanded, I would appreciate if you do it privately and not in front of the students. That's all."

The *director* squinted his eyes and pushed his chair back, away from the desk. I felt a knot in my stomach, and I thought he would order me out of his office. Conversely, his countenance became friendly.

"Well, I don't think you'll ever behave like *profesor* Gerónimo." With that, he got ready for his next class, and I did, too.

"You don't know what happened in the other classroom, *maestra*?" one of the girls asked the moment I entered the class.

"Kids, I'm sure you wouldn't like other people making comments when your parents scold you," I said, "so, please don't say anything else. And don't repeat anything outside of school."

Of course, that was easier to say than to do.

That afternoon, as soon as I sat to have dinner with Nena, she told me, "I heard *profesor* Merla scolded *profesor* Gerónimo in front of the students in an ugly way. What happened?"

"How do you know that?" I asked, raising an eyebrow.

"One of my customers mentioned it. She said her daughter had told her that *profesor* Merla was furious with *profesor* Gerónimo."

I can't believe this has already been released. Well, it was to be expected, there were many witnesses. Some of them shared the incident, despite my recommendation not to.

"Nena, I was so busy with my classes that, even though I heard something about it, I didn't have time to ask Gerónimo what happened. Moving on to another matter, have you received the new merchandise you ordered recently?" I asked, trying to change the conversation.

"Yes, it arrived this morning. There are some things I'm sure you are going to like."

"I'll go by this afternoon, but I can't afford to buy anything right now," I said. "I have to start saving money to buy Christmas gifts for my family."

Later, *profesor* Merla explained to me the reason for that scolding. I agreed with him that it was well-deserved, but also that we didn't have to divulge it later. Now Geronimo would no longer need to go to him for advice. The *director* would have him under his radar, and Gerónimo would learn the hard way. That had been his choice.

CHAPTER FORTY-SIX

ON THE BRINK OF A TRAGEDY

After a few weeks, daily life again became a routine. This aroused in me the desire for something different that would bring a little emotion to my existence. At that time, I had no idea that my wishes would soon be fulfilled, but not as I expected.

One afternoon in September, Minerva and Irma stopped by my house. After a short conversation, Minerva told me the reason for their visit. They were there to invite me to ride horses with them on the sixteenth. She commented that many people would come from nearby villages to celebrate México's Independence Day and that they would be glad to lend us their horses for a while.

"We really want you to accompany us," Irma said.

Having practiced only few times with Lupe and Vicente, I wasn't confident of my ability to ride a horse.

The girls stared at me, waiting for an answer.

"Okay. I'll do that *paseo*, but remember I'm a beginner, not an expert like you guys." I felt a little apprehensive.

"Don't worry, *maestra*. We'll take good care of you," Minerva told me.

"We are good riders," Irma said. "We won't let anything bad happen to you."

Minerva added that four other girls would join us and they would come for me at midmorning. After giving me a big hug, they left, chatting animatedly with each other.

September sixteenth was a beautiful day with a clear sky and pleasant weather. I fixed my hair back in a ponytail and wore black pants with a white embroidered Mexican blouse and a colorful sash around my waist.

As soon as I heard the horses' hooves and the girls' laughter, I stepped outside the house. I was a little tense knowing that I was going to ride an unknown horse. Six young, pretty, smiling faces greeted me. Judicita, one of the oldest girls, was riding a beautiful black horse and holding the reins of a chestnut animal. She dismounted easily. Pulling both horses by their reins, she walked toward where I was.

That extra horse must be mine. I'm glad it looks so gentle.

"¿Lista, maestra?", she asked me.

"Yes, I'm ready." I took a deep breath and turned to the chestnut horse.

"Not that one. This is yours." Judicita handed me the reins of the horse that she'd been riding.

My heart skipped a beat. "Judicita, I'll be glad to ride this one." I pointed to the chestnut horse.

"Don't disappoint me, *maestra*. I got this one especially for you."

"Are you sure I can ride it? He's so big!"

"I'm sure you can do it, *maestra*."

Judicita helped me to get on the saddle. I saw that Teresa and a couple of *doña* Susana's maids were outside of the restaurant watching us. *Hmm. I hope they didn't leave anything on the fire, or it's going to be burned by now.*

I waved goodbye to them, and they waved back. *Teresa looks worried. She knows I'm a novice, and I think she's scared to see me riding this huge beast.*

The six girls and I headed toward the main plaza. Before that day I had ridden only Palomo. However, the current horse felt very different. *I guess the size of him freaks me out, but, what do I know about equines?*

As we arrived at the corner, Minerva's horse reared up on his hind legs. I started to worry when mine got restless. With my free hand, I held the horn of the saddle firmly. Three men stood talking at the corner. While two of them watched Minerva, controlling her horse with great expertise, the third man approached me.

"Excuse me, *señorita*," the rancher said, tipping his hat, "but I think you shouldn't ride this animal. It's not good. Believe me."

I thanked him for the advice and told him that it would be a short walk. The man again tipped his hat and went back to his friends.

Minerva had regained control of her horse, so we continued with our *paseo*. None of the girls had heard the conversation between the rancher and me.

I noticed the three men talking and pointing at either me or the horse. *He must be telling his friends what he told me about this animal. Maybe he thinks that because I'm a city girl I will scare easily. However, they look too serious. I don't know ...*

The girls were in a good mood, joking and laughing as we passed by the west side of plaza Juárez, where the military detachment was. This detachment had been sent there by the government precisely to pacify the region, since many homicides had been occurring prior to my arrival in town.

Outside, next to the entrance gate, three men were talking. I recognized one of them. He was a client of *doña* Susana's restaurant. He had the rank of lieutenant. He always ate alone, and outside of the customary greeting, I had never struck up a conversation with him. At that time, he was talking to two soldiers. When he saw us, we nodded to him. He abruptly interrupted their conversation. With a strange expression on his face, he hurried across the street, leaving the two soldiers dumbfounded.

The lieutenant held my horse by the bridle, forcing me to stop. The girls and I gaped at his action. We were really surprised.

He seemed very agitated. "Good afternoon, *señorita*. Please excuse me, and don't consider me rude, but I advise you to get down off this horse right away. This is not a good animal." A chill ran up my spine.

For the second time I had been warned about the horse. I had ignored the stranger, but this time it was different. The lieutenant was an acquaintance, so he would have a good reason to advise me so strongly. *I better pay attention. My instinct tells me that there is something wrong with this animal.*

He continued holding the bridle. The horse moved impatiently, like he was trying to escape his grasp. The girls and the lieutenant waited expectantly for my reaction.

"I'm sorry, girls, but the lieutenant is right. There is something strange about this animal. I think I'd better get off."

"*Maestra, maestra, por favor,* at least let's just go to the edge of the *'campo de aviación,'* to see how many people came. Then we'll come back," Minerva pleaded, clasping her hands as if praying.

"*¡Si, maestra! ¡Vamos, por favor!* Only for few minutes, we promise," several girls said.

I looked at them and wriggled my shaky hands. They were eager to go.

"Lieutenant, thanks for the advice. I'll go with the girls where they want, and then I promise I'll get off," I said with a forced smile.

"You should get off now. I'm telling you—this is a tricky animal." The lieutenant shook his head and let go of the horse's bridle.

"I will, lieutenant. Soon. Don't worry, and thanks again." I wasn't speaking with conviction.

The man stood motionless on the sidewalk with a worried look on his face as we continued our ride. I paid more attention to the horse's strange behavior. Even though we hadn't run, its skin was quite damp, and it shook more often as we approached the flight field. The beast's nervousness made me uneasy.

The name *campo de aviación,* "airfield," to describe that dusty open area was an inappropriate expression. Several people told me they had started calling it that after a plane landed there in an emergency.

We came to the edge of the field, and we spotted a crowd of horsemen. I had never seen so many of them before. Their horses moved impatiently from one side to the other, snorting and neighing and scratching the ground with their hooves, while the men laughed or talked to each other. Many people stood around just watching. The girls told me the horsemen were getting ready to participate in *"La Chiva Enterrada."* This was the contest in which a live goat is half buried in the center of the area. Only it's head and four tied-up legs are visible.

I remembered that two teams of horsemen would take turns trying to pull the goat out of the ground. Once one of them accomplished this, the other one would try to take it away. Lauro had commented that unfortunately sometimes in this contest the poor animal ended up disemboweled. I had refused to witness such a barbaric thing on one occasion, and now I was there because of the girls, but would stay only for few minutes.

By then, although we were on the edge of the field, my horse was extremely restless. It was enough. I decided to leave before anyone noticed my presence. Some girls protested because they wanted to get closer and stay a little longer. My heart beat faster when the animal started pulling against the reins.

"There is something wrong with this horse, girls. We have to go right now!" An uncontrollable nervousness began to creep over me.

"Okay, *maestra*, if that's what you want. C'mon, girls! Let's go back!" Minerva said.

Everyone looked a little disappointed, but even though I felt sorry, I didn't want to watch the contest or ride any longer. *I'll ask Judicita to trade horses. She seemed very comfortable on it.*

Just as I was going to talk to her, my horse pulled up its head and sniffed the air.

What happened next seemed like a nightmare that lasted an eternity.

Before I knew it, the horse started running at full gallop into the middle of the two large groups who were waiting for the start of the contest. I felt horribly embarrassed. *What are people thinking of me? Do they think I've gone crazy?* I felt red to the roots of my hair.

There was a stunned silence, interrupted only by the sound of my horse's hooves and his heavy breathing. Out of the corner of my eye, I saw some people with their mouths agape and their eyes as wide as saucers. After a short distance, I somehow managed to turn the horse around. The crowd was still gaping in disbelief when again I crossed in front of them at full gallop. This time, there was a deafening clamor, as if I was doing an exhibition. But knowing that I wasn't part of the program, I wanted to escape fast from there and hide. I had done an unintentional theatrical entry, but I was certainly not feeling like the heroine of the movie.

I pulled the horse's reins a couple of times. Nothing happened. The horse's neck was rigid. A chill ran up my spine when I remembered Vicente Castilleja's words, "If the horse stiffens his neck hard, you'll never make him obey. That's when we say that the horse is *desbocado*." I realized that was what was happening with this animal. He was completely out of control.

I wanted to scream for help, but no sound came out of my mouth. The crowd had already been left behind, far from me, but to my horror, the horse headed now in the direction of the mesquite trees. My instinct told me the mad animal was going to throw me against them! *This is not happening ... it can't be happening ...* My peripheral vision blanked out, and I focused forward. Beads of cold perspiration formed on my forehead, and my shaky hands felt wet. I held the horn of the horse's saddle as firmly as I could to keep from falling. My stomach squeezed tightly. We were so close to the trees. *They warned me twice. Why did I ignore them?*

I loosened the leather reins, and with one hand, untied a folded blanket on the rump of the horse. I managed to sit sideways and hold my breath. Suddenly, I pulled the reins hard. The surprised horse half stopped for a couple of seconds, and in a fast decision, I jumped off, holding the blanket. I hit the hard ground on my side, falling—I don't know how—on the blanket, and then I rolled for a couple of meters.

I didn't get up right away. As I listened to the beast galloping away, I moved my limbs slightly to make sure there were no injuries. I felt the ground, almost grateful that it didn't move. I was still terribly scared, but relieved to be safe from the horse.

With my head close to the ground, I heard a sound like thunder and felt the ground vibrate. Confused and alarmed, I raised my head. The sound and tremor came from the multitude of horses running toward me. The horsemen who had been waiting to participate in the contest of the *Chiva Enterrada* were rushing to see what had happened to me.

Dazed and coughing, I stood up, trying to shake the dust from my clothes. Looking toward where my horse had run, all I saw was the cloud of dust he had left behind.

Faster than the horses, a truck came ahead of them. To my surprise, Father Rangel and the lieutenant jumped out of the truck. They ran up to where I stood shaking.

"Are you okay?" they asked at the same time.

"Yes, I'm fine, thanks." I looked at the ground, embarrassed.

"I warned you it was a tricky animal," the lieutenant reproached me with a pale and serious face.

"And I believed you, but the girls begged me to come to see this for few minutes." I excused myself, ashamed of the outcome. "I was ready to go back, but the horse got crazy and started running in the middle of the field." I stopped talking, afraid I'd start crying.

"*Señorita*, that wasn't just any horse," the lieutenant said. "It was a mare in heat! That's why it went crazy when it smelled other horses." He shook his head in disapproval. "I was afraid of something like that, and I decided to come, to insist on dissuading you. I'm sorry I didn't reach you in time."

The large contingent of horsemen who had arrived immediately after the priest and the lieutenant remained close, observing the scene and listening to the conversation.

"How in the world did you choose to ride Dimas Garcia's mare?" Father Rangel asked. He raised an eyebrow and crossed his arms waiting for my answer.

The neighing of the horses and the whispering of the riders was so much that I thought I had misunderstood.

"Wha—Wha—What did you say, Father?" I placed a shaky hand on his arm while feeling a knot constricting my throat.

"That you were riding Dimas Garcia's nasty mare," he said in a louder voice. He seemed amused by my reaction. "I'm sure you've heard what is said about his horses, that they don't stop until they reach his ranch."

"Oh, my God! I didn't know, Father. One of my students simply chose that horse for me." A wave of terror welled up from my belly.

By that time, everybody present had been listening in detail the conversation. I went from my cheeks burning with embarrassment to feeling that all my blood had drained from my body. I was afraid to pass out.

My girls had caught up to me. They dismounted and hugged me, distressed.

"I'm fine, girls, really. Please don't worry."

"You were very lucky, *señorita*. That's all I can say." The lieutenant's face was as grim as his tone of voice.

"God was watching out for you," Father Rangel said in a calmer tone. "Now let me take you to your house."

He held my arm, and the lieutenant walked in front of us, making way amidst the curious and noisy crowd. He opened the truck's door and helped me into it. I sat next to Father Rangel who offered to take the lieutenant back to his barracks. He declined the invitation, saying he would stay to watch the contest.

The kind priest drove me back to my house. On the way there, he told me the horse was sold to Dimas because it had thrown the previous owner against a tree. As a result, the man had been paralyzed. By the time I arrived home, my legs felt like rags. I couldn't control the shaking, thinking about the serious consequences that could have resulted from a simple paseo.

"Now go and rest," said Father Rangel, helping me get down from the truck.

"Thanks, Father! I'll do that."

Entering the house, I saw *doña* Susana with her hands on her hips and her right foot tapping the floor. Her squinting eyes staring at me made me shiver.

"Don't bother to tell me anything. I already heard all that happened."

I didn't like her tone of voice.

"And I don't want anybody else coming to ask me if you are badly hurt; you better put a dress on, and then stand where people can see that you are okay."

La señora didn't wait for any answer. She turned around and stomped to the kitchen. Even the brave Duque ran out of her way with his tail between his legs while I stood there, speechless, shaking, and about to collapse.

I found it hard to understand *doña* Susana's anger, but I realized she was right about trying to stop the people's insatiable curiosity. I went into my room to wash and put on some clean clothes. Afterward, I combed my hair and put on some lipstick.

The teachers, the lawyer, and Horacio were not at home. Otherwise, they would be checking that I was okay. I knew that they would appear as soon as the news reached them.

A few minutes later, the girls came to the hotel. Judicita was crying because she was the one who had chosen the horse for me, and she felt guilty for what had happened. Finally, she calmed down after I told her I was fine.

"Would you believe that by the time I arrived, *doña* Susana already knew what had happened? How did the news travel faster than Father Rangel's truck?" I asked them.

"News and secrets are like that in the small towns," said Minerva.

"You're right. We live in a crystal house. Now, please let's go and stand up by the door so the curious can see that I'm okay." *Will people ever forget what happened to me on this fateful day? Unfortunately, I doubt it.*

I had complained about the monotony of the daily routine and longed for a bit of excitement, but since that day, I have always remembered the saying: "Be careful what you wish for because it can be fulfilled."

CHAPTER FORTY-SEVEN

INNOCENCE OR MALICE?

For days after naively riding Dimas García's horse, I had nightmares about what could have happened. I didn't know if what was rumored about him was true or just another town legend, but this was still hunting me.

I kept reliving in my mind that crazy and embarrassing ride in front of the surprised spectators of the *Chiva Enterrada* contest and the moment when I jumped from the unruly horse and hit the ground. A cold sweat invaded me just thinking that the horse could have dragged me or kicked me. I frequently woke up sweating after listening to the sound of the galloping of hundreds of horses in my dreams.

I thought about the different ways people around me had reacted. Father Rangel expressed surprise that I had ridden such a horse. The lieutenant seemed disappointed that I hadn't listened to his advice. My students had been heartbroken. On the other hand, *doña* Susana became very angry with me, and Nena had laughed. My coworkers had shown concern; however, the one who really surprised me was *profesor* Merla.

The day after the incident, he had been understanding and friendly. I had been concerned he would be upset with me for my unwanted celebrity. I assumed that he already knew because by then, the story had probably reached Matehuala, thirty-one and a half miles away. However, he chuckled and said, "I heard you were the star of the show yesterday. Are you okay?"

"I wish yesterday hadn't happened, or that people would forget it did. That has been one of the most embarrassing moments of my life." I blushed as I gave him the details of the story.

"I need to talk to Judicita. Why in the world did she let you ride that mare in heat, knowing the danger that she was exposing you? Didn't she know?" The frown on his forehead told me of his anger.

"I'm sure there wasn't any malice on her part. She just wanted me to have the best horse."

"Hmm ..." he murmured, shaking his head slightly. He didn't say anything else to me.

He did talk to Judicita, however. He called her to his office, and later on, I saw her come out crying. She apologized profusely when she saw me.

"Don't worry about it, Judicita," I reassured her. "I told you before that I understood your reasons." I gave her a hug.

"But everyone is mad at me. The *director* scolded me, and even my friends are very upset about all of this; they blame me for what happened." More tears flowed down her cheeks.

"I'll talk to them at the first opportunity. Everyone will understand. You'll see. Now wipe your tears and go to your music class. *Profesor* Andrés just walked into the classroom."

Judicita shuffled her feet as she left. She didn't look like she wanted to answer any questions about what had transpired in the *director's* office.

I hope we'll have a better day. There has been enough excitement for today. I had just finished thinking this when one of the students came running to ask *profesor* Merla if he would go to Andrés's class. The *director*, on leaving, told me to accompany him.

I wondered what was happening. The student ran ahead before we had any chance to ask him about it.

When we entered the classroom, we saw Andrés with his arms crossed and his body leaning toward one side. He was frowning, and his eyes were squinted.

Horacio stood up in the back of the classroom. His leather jacket was slightly opened, and it looked very bulky. There was a music pattern on the blackboard, and Andrés was holding a ruler.

"Did you send for me?" *profesor* Merla asked in a stern tone. "What's going on?"

"This young man disrupted my music lesson," Andrés said, pointing with his ruler to Horacio. "While I faced the blackboard, with my back to the students, a noise came from the back of the room. Of course, all started laughing."

"A noise?" *profesor* Merla asked. "What kind of noise?" He crossed his arms and raised an eyebrow waiting for an answer.

"Show him," Andrés ordered to Horacio.

Horacio opened his jacket. "Baaaahh!, baaaahh!" The sound came from a small baby goat he had inside the garment.

All of the students giggled. Andrés's frown grew deeper, and he ordered the class to be quiet. "Would you mind sending Horacio home so I can continue my class peacefully?" he asked the *director*.

I noticed *profesor* Merla looked amused, even though he pretended to be displeased.

"Horacio, take your books and follow me to my office," he ordered.

Horacio obeyed the order, but just before he reached the door, he opened his jacket again. The baby goat gave another bleat. Again, everybody laughed. Andrés held his chin with one hand and looked at Horacio with murder in his eyes. I rushed out of the classroom, afraid I might start laughing, and followed the boy into the *director's* office.

"So, what's this, Horacio? Why did you bring a baby goat to school?" *profesor* Merla asked, as he pulled out the chair behind his desk. He settled into it and put his hands behind his head like he did anytime he was going to hear a long explanation.

"I'm innocent, *profesor* Merla," Horacio said. "Look, I was coming to school, walking by myself in the middle of the street, when this poor animal came out of nowhere and started following me. He even followed me inside the classroom. I didn't know what to do, so I put him inside my jacket, hoping he would go to sleep."

"Why didn't you ask *profesor* Andrés's permission to put him outside?" I asked him.

"I was going to, *maestra*, but the baby goat looked at me with such sad eyes that I decided to wait until the end of the class. I couldn't leave him in the street and put him in danger of being run over."

"Let's see, explain to me why the goat began making such a fuss," *profesor* Merla said.

"Well, in reality it was *profesor* Andrés's fault. The little animal was asleep but woke up when *profesor* Andrés started singing." Horacio's sarcasm told us he wasn't telling the truth.

"Horacio, I think you'll have to go home," *profesor* Merla said. "I'm sure you did it on purpose to make the other kids laugh. Now we'll have to talk to your grandma."

With the palms of his hands up and a hurt tone in his voice, Horacio said, "But, profesor, how can you punish me for being nice to a poor animal?"

"Don't argue, kid. Go home before you make me angry, too."

Horacio took his books, closed his jacket with the baby goat inside, and walked past me.

"You better return that baby goat," I said, "or you'll be in trouble with his owner."

"I would if I knew who he belonged to, *maestra*, really." Then, scratching his head, he added, "Hmm. We haven't had a *cabrito* dinner in a long time. My grandma would be happy if I tell her it is a present for her."

"Horacio, don't tempt your luck. Go home—now. You are already in trouble with *profesor* Andrés and *profesor* Merla and maybe me and your grandma too." I tried to rush him.

He shrugged and left. Horacio walked down the middle of the street, blowing the mouthpiece of his bugle. He put the baby goat on the ground and the little animal followed him. Horacio turned around and saw *profesor* Merla and me watching him from the school door. He threw his arms up and disappeared in the distance, followed by the baby goat.

Hmm! Horacio had a good idea after all. Would this cabrito taste as good as the ones in Monterrey? I wonder if we'll have a surprise meal today. And, something else, will I start dreaming now of crying baby goats, too, besides galloping horses?

As the days, months, and years went by, several persons have asked me various questions regarding the incident with Dimas García's horse. Reviewing what happened and listening to the comments of others, I saw that many things could have a logical and easy explanation, and that I wouldn't like it.

However, I have always preferred to see the bright side of the people I deal with, so I decided to keep thinking that it was all a mishap without malice.

As for Horacio, I have no doubt that there was no malice in his deeds but, as usual, his innate desire to amuse others.

CHAPTER FORTY-EIGHT

BITTERSWEET CHRISTMAS

The weeks that followed were quite busy. First, we had the fundraising dance, which was very successful and left us looking forward to the next one. Then came December with the fun of the annual town fair. Right after that, we had the school's midterm examinations. That meant reviewing tests and making report cards. By that time, we were exhausted. We started counting the days until we went home for the holidays. The end of 1959 was just around the corner.

I anticipated the Christmas vacation with conflicting emotions. On one hand, I was thinking about the pleasure of spending time with my family and friends. As I mentioned before, that has always been my favorite season of the year with the traditional *Posadas*, the magic of Christmas, and the excitement of the new year when dreams and hopes were renewed. That year, however, two circumstances had changed the mood of this wonderful period for me.

One of my dreams had been that my boyfriend, Martín, finally would come to see me as he had promised. Unfortunately, he had informed me that this would not be possible. He would go abroad on another Air Force assignment. Once again, I felt sad and disappointed. Instead of his presence, I would have to settle for receiving his letters. Four years without seeing each other!

I realized that this was not enough for me anymore. While my friends enjoyed the company of their boyfriends, I was totally alone, of course, by choice. True to my word, I wanted to wait for Martín's return, but it was the fourth Christmas we had been apart.

"What kind of courtship is this, with both of you on opposite sides of the world?" some of my friends asked.

"You're wasting your time, and the years are going by fast," some others said.

I never doubted my boyfriend's good intentions, yet there was always some reason for him to postpone his visit. One of my New Year's resolutions was that if Martín couldn't come sometime during the year, it would be better for each of us to go our own way. That would break my heart, but it was better sooner than later. Spending four years alone had already been enough.

The other reason that Christmas season would be different for me was because at the end of September my mom had informed me that my brother Cayito had joined the *Seminario de Monterrey*. He had been an altar boy for quite some time, but we had never imagined he wanted to be a priest.

The news had been a shock for me. I tried to feel happy knowing Cayito had chosen something he felt in his heart, but at the same time, I had a sense of loss. When my brother was little, I had taken special care of him and wondered if his decision to join the seminary was because he missed me like I missed him. Now, I was afraid the house would feel empty without his presence. Cayito was very active inventing games, and he entertained us all the time. I thought it must be difficult for the family—especially for my mom—to have two of us not living at home. *At least my mom knows I'll be back soon, but what about Cayito? How does my mom really feel? I know she is a very devout person, but even so, it must be so difficult for her to come to terms with my brother's decision.*

Cayito was only twelve years old, an age when young people are easily impressed. Maybe for this reason it didn't surprise me to learn that his best friends—Baltazar González, Francisco Escamilla, the twins Ramón and Raymundo Rodríguez, and Alfonso Rodríguez— had entered the seminary, too. They were six *monaguillos*, or altar boys, who had served at the Sanctuary of the Virgin of Guadalupe. Father Ochoa, rector of the Shrine, commissioned a tailor to make their cassocks and bought them the black suits that they should wear every time they left the seminary building.

I was eager to go visit my brother. I wanted to see with my own eyes if he was really happy there.

I was finally back in Monterrey. I was ecstatic to be home again to spend a couple of weeks with my family. After sharing with all of them the goodies that several of my students had given me, I asked my mom if we could visit Cayito.

"Oh, I'm sorry, *hijita*, but we can't see him now. The seminary is strict about its rules. The seminarians can only see their family every two weeks—on Sunday afternoon, from four to six. It was Cayito's turn last Sunday."

"You mean I have to wait two weeks to see him?" I said in dismay. "That will be by the end of my vacation!"

"Well, fortunately Cayito will be allowed to come home on Christmas Day."

"Really? That's great!" My mood changed immediately. With better spirit I asked her, "How many days will he spend with us?"

"It won't be days, *hijita*, only a few hours," my mother answered. "We'll pick him up the twenty-fifth in the Cathedral, after the ten o' clock Solemn Mass. We'll bring him home, but he has to be back in the seminary at seven o'clock."

I tried not to show my disappointment. My mom looked at me with watery eyes, trying to smile. She was trying to be brave, so I had to do the same.

My heart was overwhelmed when I noticed how loose her clothes were. Evidently, she had lost weight.

"Okay, *madrecita*." I tried to sound cheerful. "Let's plan the *Posadas*."

The *Posadas* were a happy daily occasion during the season. The praying of the *Rosario*, the procession with lit candles, the singing of *la Letanía*, the candies, and the piñata were almost as I had remembered. I say almost because Cayito wasn't there with his jokes and pranks.

We were sad because for the first time, the family would not be complete to celebrate the traditional *Acostada*. That was the culmination of *Posadas' novena*. I was glad to see that we all got distracted by the din of the party, a least for a few hours.

On Christmas Day, the whole family and I attended Mass at the Cathedral where Cayito would sing with the seminary chorus. I tried to locate my little brother among the huge group of singers, but at a distance it was hard to do since they all wore a black cassock and a white surplice on top. At the same time, I tried to pay attention to the special Christmas Mass officiated by the Archbishop and several priests. The rest of the seminarians filled up the front rows. The choir sang beautifully, and I marveled at the solemnity of the ecclesiastic rituals.

I finally saw my brother and felt happy and proud. He also recognized us and let us know it with a discreet movement of his fingers.

When the Mass finished, Cayito changed out of his chorus uniform into his black suit and came to meet us in the atrium of the church. After everyone hugged him, we went home, a big happy family, together again, even if it was for just a few hours.

At dinner time, we chatted and joked like always. We had a thousand questions for my brother. "So, tell us a little bit about your life in the seminary," I suggested.

Cayito told us about his daily routine and his schedules, the sports that are practiced there, and how he enjoyed rehearsing in the choir. He told us about the modern building that had just been opened. They had recently moved out of the old premises behind the San Luis Gonzaga church. The only thing that remained to be finished in the new building was the chapel, since some frescoes were being painted there. For now, they were listening to Mass and praying at a makeshift altar. He told us how the nearly 200 seminarians had celebrated the *Posadas*, but also how much he had missed ours.

Then, smiling broadly, he told us, "Do you know that the older students chose me to participate with them in a play? I think I've already displaced the one who used to play the role of little boy, because they already asked me to participate in their next presentation."

I could see on everyone's faces that they were as proud of Cayito as I was. He meanwhile explained that the nuns and novices cooked and washed their clothes, but the boys did not see them.

"What do you talk about during meals? Do you make jokes?" Héctor, who was also an incorrigible joker, wanted to know.

I wonder how Cayito's absence is affecting him. After all, the two of them were very close, too.

"No, we are only allowed to talk during the three meals on Thursdays and Sundays. The rest of the week we eat in silence, listening to classical music or readings."

"It must be very difficult to abide by that discipline," my mom said, pensive.

"*Mi madre* could never be a seminarian. She would always forget the rules about not talking to her friends," Héctor joked, causing a general laugh.

"At Easter, they will allow us to visit our homes for a few hours and in summer for two weeks," Cayito continued. "Then we will go to our summer house in Saltillo to finish the vacation period."

I noticed how much this news affected my mom. There was sadness in her eyes, and her lips trembled a bit. *Will we ever get used to this separation? When is it going to stop hurting?*

Soon we realized that it was time to take Cayito back. The seminary was a long way from our house, so we had to plan enough time to avoid his being late. Norma sat next to Cayito on the bus, and they talked all the way. Julie and Ernesto, who were sitting behind them, got up from time to time to listen to the conversation.

Finally, we arrived. With his cassock and his surplice folded inside a paper bag and some presents we had given him, Cayito hugged each one of us at the seminary's front door and said goodbye, wishing us a Merry Christmas.

"Merry Christmas to you, too!" we said to him.

"And a happy New Year," I added when he entered the building.

Other seminarians were also arriving. Cayito turned to greet us one last time. I could see a hint of sadness on his face.

We stayed there, standing close to each other until we saw him disappear down a long hall. I felt a lump in my throat, and my eyes were full of tears. I didn't want to look at my mom because I knew she was feeling the same emotion. Norma and Julie held hands and wiped their eyes. Ernesto did, too. My father and my brothers Javier and Héctor were just quiet. We returned home by bus in heavy silence, each locked in our own thoughts.

That night it was difficult for me to fall asleep. I still couldn't adjust to Cayito's absence. I tried to think of any clues that showed his penchant for the priesthood but couldn't find any. In the morning I asked my mother about it.

"I don't know, *hijita*. I imagine that, being an acolyte in the Sanctuary, he was liking that religious atmosphere."

My sister Norma intervened with an important clue. "Mom, several times when you went shopping, Baltazar came to play Mass with Cayo."

I knew the boy was also an altar boy and that he lived two blocks from our house. He was one of Cayito's best friends.

"And how did they play Masses?" I asked her.

She continued, "They put on their cassock and roquette that they used in the Sanctuary. They made the chalice out of aluminum foil and Baltazar brought two candles from his house and the bell on the door. At some Masses one was the priest and the other the acolyte, and then they changed roles. Julie, Ernesto, and I were the parishioners—and even the three kittens!" She giggled at the last part. Then she told us that the two boys covered Mom's sewing machine with a sheet to serve as an altar.

"Did you hear that? My sewing machine serving like an altar!" said my mother. Then she cupped her chin and narrowed her eyes. "I remember now. Every year, the parish priest of the Sanctuary took all his acolytes to the Cathedral on the day of Saint Peter and Saint Paul. The Archbishop celebrated a solemn Mass for the ordination of the new priests. That must have impressed Cayito a lot."

"It's true! And when Cayo came back, he was always singing in Latin," said Norma.

"Well, all that explains why he has entered the seminary, *madrecita*," I concluded.

"We want him to return. We always invented games with him." Norma's eyes filled with tears and her voice cracked.

"I miss him too, *hijta*," my mother said, taking her by the hands, "but we must pray for his vocation."

Seeing their faces, I only managed to say, "Well, let's remember that phrase: 'There are many called, but few are chosen.' God will decide his destiny."

In addition to the presents I had given to my family for Christmas, I had a surprise planned for all of them. I hoped that it would soothe the pain of the absence of Cayito and mine.

I was impatient to see their reactions.

We didn't have much at home—little furniture, not many clothes, only some toys, and hardly any decorations—but there was so much love and joy that we didn't miss any material things because we had each other. Our only electronic possessions were an Oster blender for the sauces and milk shakes, a steam iron that replaced the old irons that we used to warm on top of the stove, and a small radio that gave us lots of hours of enjoyment. Now that I was working and earning a salary, I was determined to start giving my family some small luxuries to the extent I could afford. I began thinking about what they wanted and considered the ones that were a necessity.

About two years earlier, our next-door neighbor, Conchita Contreras, had bought a large television—black and white, like all of them then. To the delight of my younger siblings, she invited them to watch their favorite shows with her daughter Malena, who was Norma's age.

Conchita also invited my mother to see music variety shows and some series.

Thinking how much my family enjoyed watching TV, I promised myself that I would buy one for them sometime in the future. However, there were priority needs. For that reason, once I bought a Christmas gift for each member of my family, I decided to use the money that was left over to purchase a group gift.

Even though I usually took Norma shopping with me, on that occasion I went alone to a popular furniture store. There, I bought a dining room set. The table had a beige Formica top. The eight chrome chair seats were covered with a beige vinyl material with blue flowers. I would have loved to acquire a wooden dining room set, but I could not afford it at the time. I also bought a three-piece living room set since we didn't have one. As a bonus, the store gave me a coffee table and two side tables. I was thrilled with my purchases.

I wasn't worried about the cost because I had it well planned. I would continue sending half of my salary to my mom to help with household expenses, and with my half, I would be paying my rent, buying small necessities, and making monthly payments for my purchase.

That afternoon, as we sat waiting for dinner, I announced, "Mom, Dad, we have to make room for some new furniture I bought today. It will be delivered tomorrow afternoon."

While my mom was surprised and excited to learn I had bought a dining room and living room set for them, my dad was not happy at all when I told him I had bought them on credit.

"You should have asked me first," he reproached me with a stern voice. "I don't want anyone pointing his finger at me or knocking on the door collecting late payments."

I told him to trust me and that I would make my payments on time. "Don't worry, Dad. I won't disappoint you." I smiled and gave him a hug and a kiss on his cheek.

"Hmm, okay, just be sure you pay on time." The tone of his voice was gentler.

The following day, they brought the furniture when Dad was at work. My siblings were thrilled. My mom had a radiant smile, and her eyes shone with emotion. When we had moved from San Luis Potosí to Monterrey, we had only brought the most essential furniture with us. I was happy with my decision to make this purchase without checking with my dad first. He would have opposed the idea, and I would probably have obeyed him. I felt even happier looking at his reaction when he saw it. He smiled broadly as he sat down on the new sofa.

"The room looks so nice with this furniture, *hijita*, but remember, you have to keep good credit by always paying on time."

"Dad, you and Mom taught me to be responsible. Stop worrying and enjoy it. I promise I'll be as punctual with my payments as you."

"Hurry up, Dad," said Julie pulling him by the hand. "Come and see the new dining room."

We went right away. All of my siblings, with the exception of Cayito, were already sitting around the table. Dad took his place at the head of the table, and my mom and I sat on each side of him. There was a smile on all our faces.

"Well, it looks like this table deserves a set of nicer dishes," my dad said, looking at all the mismatched plates. "See if you can find a set of dishes that isn't too expensive." This time he spoke directly to my mom. "We'll make small monthly payments. We'll receive 1960 with new furniture and new dishes."

My mom smiled widely, and we did the same. I felt so proud I had given them that moment of happiness that I hoped it would last for a long time.

With the arrival of 1960, my vacation was over. I packed my luggage again and had to say goodbye to my friends and family.

Soon I was on my way back to Doctor Arroyo, wondering what the new year would bring me. I promised myself to furnish the house bit by bit. I also planned to buy new clothes for all the family. I was happy to contribute to their well-being, but loneliness weighed on my soul.

Despite this, I vowed to myself that nothing would break the strength of my spirit.

CHAPTER FORTY-NINE

MEN ARE CURIOUS TOO

When I first came to Doctor Arroyo, I asked José Luis how they had fun in the small town. "We always find a way," he had replied on that occasion, without giving further details.

As the days and weeks went by, I realized that was true. Manuel—the lawyer, the teachers, and I had gathered every evening in José Luis's room, to play cards, listen to music from his battery radio, or just talk. The topics of conversation were schoolwork, politics, town news, and, occasionally, some personal matter.

Lauro and José Luis had invited into our small circle the out-of-towners, like the civil engineers and the chemist Alberto, who were in Doctor Arroyo for work reasons. Santiago and Francisco Ramón, another teacher that Lauro and José Luis knew, came to visit us quite frequently, adding variety to our routine. I continued to be the only woman in the group, and I was grateful that they always included me. I considered them as an extension of my family and vice versa.

Some afternoons, Lauro played the acoustic guitar and sang for us. He had a beautiful and well-modulated voice. He used to sing the Argentinean tangos expressing all the emotion of that genre of music. Occasionally we formed a choir and sang some popular songs. Those were joyous moments that distracted us from our loneliness.

We—the five teachers and Manuel, the lawyer—went to the movies twice a week. From time to time we attended some small events like birthday parties and other social gatherings. Another distraction was participating in patriotic festivities like those on *5 de Mayo*, Independence Day, and the Anniversary of the Mexican Revolution. However, the most anticipated celebration for everyone was the week-long town fair, at the beginning of December. This celebration brought many visitors. Their presence was always welcomed; it added excitement about possible new romantic relationships.

When Lauro and José Luis didn't return to Doctor Arroyo, many of the dynamics changed. We didn't get together in the afternoons as often as we had before. Rogelio, who was married, used the afternoons to write home or to read. He also used to take naps after dinner. Gerónimo, the youngest of all of us, liked to go out. Sometimes I heard he was dating someone, but in reality, I don't remember whom. On occasions, he invited Andrés or Rogelio to go with him for a walk. We still went together to the movies with *profesor* Merla and to any parties to which we were invited. We took every chance to distract ourselves.

When Nena was available, we did other activities for fun, like walking around the main plaza after she closed her store or getting together with Eva and her sisters to play *Canasta Uruguaya* or to dance.

Many times, trying to kill boredom, we took advantage of even negative circumstances, like the darkness of the night.

Usually, Nena came by the house late afternoons to have a light dinner, *la cena*. Then we went to the main plaza to burn off the calories of such a dinner. At that time, there wasn't any electricity yet, so it was beautiful to walk under the moonlight—that is when there was a moon, obviously—but most of the time, it was completely dark. Generally, as we went around the plaza, we saw shapes of people coming in our direction, but it was impossible to distinguish their features. Only when we exchanged greetings did we recognize who they were from the sound of their voices.

One pitch dark night, Nena and I went for our regular *paseo* on the plaza. Several silhouettes passed us in the opposite direction.

"Buenas noches", we greeted them.

They answered our greetings by calling us by our names. From the voices we knew they were *doña* María Eguía and her children, Ernesto, Pepe, Roberto, Minerva, and a couple of little ones.

Nena and I continued our *paseo.*

"Can you believe how dark some nights are?" I said to Nena.

"Yeah, and that gives me an idea. Let's play a joke on Andrés and the lawyer." She told me her plan.

"I don't know. I don't think it will work."

"Hey! Do you think that only us women are curious? I'll make you a bet."

"No bets. Let's do it and see what happens."

We put our plan into action. During the following days, we started telling each other things, supposedly in code.

"Maestra, don't forget next week," Nena said, winking at me blatantly as she was leaving. We had just had dinner together as usual.

"Don't worry! How could I forget?" I answered her, as I sat with Andrés and Manuel, at their table.

Nena waved at all of us and left.

The door was still swinging when Manuel asked me, "What is it that you shouldn't forget next week, Socorrito?"

"Oh, it's something personal. Nothing really important."

Andrés stared at me, frowned, and twisted one side of his mustache, but he didn't ask anything. Manuel removed his eyeglasses, cleaned them, and put them back on, while I smiled at them. Then we continued our conversation.

On the following days, Nena and I did the same thing. She would drop a hint like, "Three more days, *maestra*." The last time, she said, "Ready for tomorrow?"

We made sure Andrés and Manuel could hear us, even though we spoke in a low voice.

On the appointed day, both of us dressed as if we were going to attend something special. Nena came by the house to pick me up. We were giggling and acting excited about our "secret."

"Hurry up. It's time to go," Nena said, raising her left arm so I could see the time on her watch.

"See you later," I told Andrés and Manuel as we were leaving.

They were sitting in the dining room having some café and pan dulce. They stared at us with a puzzled expression on their faces. Nena and I rushed outside. We walked to the center of the street where it was darker, so they couldn't see the direction we took.

"Did you see the way they looked at us?" Nena said, giggling.

"Yes, I did. Let's see what they'll do next, but let's hurry."

"They must think we have a date. They just don't know with whom."

Instead of walking on the main street toward the plaza, we went around the corner. The night was pitch black, but we had a flashlight. We directed the light onto the uneven and unpaved ground and moved forward supporting each other. We found it very difficult to walk wearing high heels. We couldn't stop giggling.

"We better hurry up. They will surely want to come and find out who our date is with." Nena was very confident in her deductions.

We made it to the plaza and looked for an empty bench on one of the paths where we supposed they would pass. All that we could do was see the shapes of people and listen to their talk. Not long after that, we recognized their voices.

"Where would they go?" asked Andrés.

"I'm sure they came in this direction," Manuel answered. "Let's go around to see if we can find them."

Nena and I covered our mouths to muffle our laughs. We didn't want them to discover us.

"I told you they would come," Nena whispered. "I would have won the bet."

They went around and around the plaza, and we had a hard time not laughing aloud.

"Do you think they are in the other plaza?" Manuel asked. They had stopped very close to our bench. Nena covered her mouth and almost dug her nails into my arm.

"They are definitely not here. Maybe they're over there. Let's go!" answered Andrés.

"Before that, let's go around once more, and this time let's ask people if they have seen them," Manuel suggested.

"Time to go," I whispered to Nena as soon as they walked away. "Don't answer if someone greets us."

"Now I'm really nervous, thinking they might see us," Nena said in a strained voice.

We rushed, hoping nobody would see us walking on the dark, empty back street. Nena came inside the house to say good night to *doña* Susana and then left before Manuel and Andrés returned. I said good night to the lady and Teresa and closed my bedroom door. A little bit later, I heard Andrés and Manuel come inside the house.

"They came back," I heard Andrés telling Manuel. "Socorrito is already in her room."

"I wonder where they were, and with whom," Manuel said in a low voice.

Nena was right—men are curious, too.

CHAPTER FIFTY

AN EXCURSION TO OBLIVION

Almost at the end of my second school cycle at Doctor Arroyo, I had a dangerous experience that could have had terrible consequences.

Everything started when Vicente and Lupe invited me to ride again. Probably that would be the last time since they would be graduating that year. We set the time they'd pick me up. We would visit a school in a small village close to Doctor Arroyo. The boys explained they only had one extra horse. For that reason, they couldn't invite Andrés. They said next time they would try to get one more so that he could accompany us.

On Saturday morning, I waited with Andrés by the door. The boys came riding Palomo and a chestnut horse. When they stood in front of us, Lupe dismounted the white horse. He guided it by the reins to where we were. The horse marched, raising one leg at the time as if showing off. I smiled with happiness.

"*¡Buenos días, maestros!*", Lupe said.

Vicente greeted us with only a movement of his head and a tip of his hat.

"Ready, *maestra*?" Lupe asked, rubbing the horse's mane.

"*¡Buenos días, muchachos! ¡Hola, Palomo!*", I said, stroking his neck.

Palomo turned his head to the side to see me better and shook his pointed ears as though he recognized me. Lupe held the stirrup to help me get in the saddle.

"What happened to the other horse?" I asked when Lupe jumped on the back of Vicente's horse.

"We'll pick it up on the way," Lupe said.

"Okay, then. Let's go before it gets hot." I turned to see Andrés and waved goodbye.

"Have fun, Socorrito, and don't ride too fast," he said with ironic humor.

"Seriously? Don't worry. I'll have enough to do to keep from falling off the horse when it trots." We started riding toward the main plaza.

Some blocks farther, Lupe jumped down easily from Vicente's horse. He knocked on the front door of a big old house. A middle-aged man opened and looked at me with curiosity. Lupe explained to him they were taking me to visit the school in a neighboring village and that he needed to borrow a horse. The man nodded his head in approval and went inside the courtyard. Soon he came back bringing a pretty black horse with him.

"Here it is," he said, handing its bridle to Lupe. "Take your time. I'm not going anywhere."

We thanked him and headed toward the town's outskirts. Soon we lost sight of Doctor Arroyo. The ground on the road we followed was bumpy and dry. There were large magueys and lots of cacti and mesquite trees. Dust from the unpaved road covered the plants. Only the red prickly pears, or *tunas*, put a splash of color on the landscape. They looked like red lipstick on a gray face. We would enjoy good weather as there were huge white clouds above us.

"Let's take this shortcut here," Lupe said, pointing to a narrow path.

We followed each other with me at the front. We were talking about different topics. On several occasions I had to put my head down so low tree branches wouldn't hit my face.

"*Maestra*, here. Wear my hat to protect your face," Vicente said behind me.

"I appreciate it, but I don't think it's necessary. I'll just take care of —."

I had just turned around to answer Vicente, who had his hat in his hand, when I felt myself flying through the air. I hit the ground headfirst, only a few inches from a big rock.

In a few seconds Vicente and Lupe were next to me, helping me get up. I was still confused, brushing the dust off my pants the best I could, when I heard a scared horse's neighing. Then I saw Palomo standing up on his back legs, trying to avoid the lashes Lupe was giving him.

"Stop! Stop! What are you doing?" I grabbed the arm that held the whip, while rubbing my head with the other hand.

"He has to be punished!" Lupe said, his face pale and his lips tight.

"But it wasn't his fault!" I realized what had happened. "Look, I didn't see that dry stream that we just passed, but the horse did.

When he jumped it, I was holding the reins loosely, so when he got to the other side, I flew over his head."

Then, still with shaky legs, I walked toward Palomo, but Lupe stepped between us.

"Better get on my horse, *maestra*. I don't want you to ride Palomo anymore."

"What are you saying? No! I want to ride Palomo. It was my fault; he'd never hurt me."

"Are you sure you want to ride him?" Lupe asked, raising an eyebrow.

"I'm absolutely sure," I said, rubbing the side of the horse.

Lupe shook his head, but he saw I was determined. "Okay, then let me help you."

Vicente held the reins while Lupe helped me get on the horse again.

"I'm sorry, *maestra*. I shouldn't have distracted you," Vicente apologized.

"Look, it wasn't your fault either. You were just trying to protect me. I don't want you to feel bad."

"Thank you. I swear I won't distract you anymore."

Lupe interrupted. "Vicente, ride in front of the *maestra*, and I'll go behind."

In a single file, we continued our way through the narrow path in silence, lost in our own thoughts and worries.

At some time, a burning sensation on the palms of my hands forced me to open them. I saw they were scraped, but I didn't know why. The three us continued riding; however, now we were side by side, instead of in a line with me in the middle. When did we change places? I noticed the boys were looking at me in a strange way. I looked down. There was dirt on my pants and my sweater.

What happened? Why are the boys staring at me? Oh, I fell down. But where are we going? Oh, my God, I can't remember! I tried to think. *What's my name? Oh, yes! Socorro Camero. Where do I work? Hmm, I'm a teacher, but where? In Doctor Arroyo, that's it.*

I looked at the boys discreetly, afraid to ask any questions. *What are these boys' names? Vicente and ... and ... Lupe!*

"Listen, guys. Tell me, did I fall?" I finally asked.

"Don't you remember, *maestra*?" Vicente looked at me with a deep frown.

Remember? What? I preferred to change the subject. "Where are we going?"

They looked at each other with an expression of alarm.

The boys seemed worried. I had to remember where it was that we were going. I started to sweat cold, and I tried to remain calm. After a few minutes, I remembered our destination.

"We are going to visit a school." I was happy to be able to answer.

They turned to me, gaping.

"*Maestra*, we were just there. Don't you remember?" Lupe asked.

He affirmed that we had gone to the school and visited a couple of classrooms. Vicente added that I had even talked to a young lady teacher.

I started to remember as if I were in a fog. Nothing was completely clear. Soon we entered Doctor Arroyo again and stopped to return the borrowed horse. Vicente and I waited at some distance. I told the boys I didn't want anybody to see me with dirty clothes.

They asked me if anything hurt. I replied that I was fine, just a little bit tired, and needed to take a nap. I assured them I had a lot of fun, regardless of the accident.

"Send someone to find us if you need anything," Vicente said before they left.

"We'll see you tomorrow, but as Vicente says, call us if you don't feel well." Lupe walked away too, mounting Palomo.

I went into my room, washed up, and changed clothes. Then I went to the dining room and asked for something light. The teachers had already finished. I would retire early to think a little about what had transpired during the day. My momentary loss of memory had been scary.

The next day, Lupe and Vicente came by very early to visit me. They wanted to know if I felt okay. They said they were fearful that something bad had happened to me and had slept outside the hotel's main entrance just in case. I've never forgotten their concern for me.

"You were very lucky, *maestra*. You almost hit your head on the stone," Lupe said.

"Yes, I was very lucky. My guardian angel was very close. Praise God." *And I know my mother always sends prayers my way. Otherwise, how many times would I have been in trouble without them?*

CHAPTER FIFTY-ONE

GOOD START OF A SUMMER

The second fundraising dance had provided us with a respectable amount of cash, and the students had a great graduation celebration.

For that occasion, I taught the students two very different dances. One of them was *"Los Machetes,"* a dance performed by four boys and one girl. Matias Báez kept insisting they should dance with real *machetes*. In it, the dancers cross them several times. Of course, it's exciting to hear the metallic sound every time they hit each other—when performed by professional dancers, but I couldn't take a chance that our amateur dancers would get hurt. Thus, Matias and the rest of the boys had to perform using wooden machetes painted silver. I'm sure the poor girl who danced in the middle was relieved by my decision. At the end, the people rewarded the youngsters' dance with a loud ovation.

The second dance was a big risk for me. I remembered *profesor* Merla warning me the previous year to teach dances to music related to popular taste. However, I dared to put on my own adaptation of a segment of the ballet *Swan Lake*. My girls looked beautiful in their white tulle dresses, the wide skirts below the knee, white ballet shoes, and feather headdresses. I don't remember all the dancers, but I remember clearly that Lupita Torres, Socorrito de la Garza, Minerva, and Irma participated. This was another presentation that was very well received by the audience of Doctor Arroyo, who wished to see dances out of the ordinary. Both the participants and I listened to the ovation of the people with great pride and satisfaction. I sighed in relief.

The rest of the program was a success, too. *Profesor* Merla gave an emotional speech. Some girls shed some tears when he reminded them that they would be leaving their sheltered lives behind to enter the adult world. The recent graduates must have understood at the time that, starting the following day, they wouldn't be part of our school anymore. A new world awaited them; they would have to decide what they wanted to accomplish in it. Several had teary eyes despite smiling.

After the students received their diplomas, we all moved to the large open courtyard next to the theater for the final part of the celebration: the graduates' dance, followed by the popular dance. I felt proud to see my girls who looked like white lilies and the boys so handsome in their dark suits, dancing in the center of the courtyard.

After they performed the graduation waltz that I had taught them, I sat with my friends Nena and the Berrones girls. Just like the previous year, the helpful José had saved several chairs for us, and as usual, he offered to watch our belongings while we danced.

"Congratulations, *maestra*," Nena said, "you did a great job."

"Certainly. An excellent presentation, congratulations," added Eva.

"Thank you; last year's experience helped a lot."

When the end of course celebration was over, I was tired but ready to keep packing. In a few hours I would be back in my own world, with my family and friends.

This was my second year in Doctor Arroyo. Now I would have to wait until August to go to the *Dirección General* to check on the possibility of a teaching position in Monterrey. I had little hope. So far, the teachers of my generation who hadn't accepted jobs outside the city, were still working outside the teaching profession.

"If you could only get a job closer to home," my mother used to say. I didn't want to tell her that if I didn't get something in Monterrey, I would prefer to go back to Doctor Arroyo.

I loved my students and the town with all of its shortcomings, and I was grateful to the people in general for their kind treatment toward me. I had a well-paying job, and even though *profesor* Merla was a strict principal and sometimes moody, his passion for teaching and his high standards had a profound effect on us, the teachers. As I matured, I really appreciated those qualities because they were for the benefit of the students and teachers.

As newly graduated teachers, we were pure wax when we arrived in Doctor Arroyo, ready to be molded. And molding us was exactly what *profesor* Merla had done. He taught us to be fair in grading our students. He showed us, by example, the importance of coming to class with the lessons ready. He never missed work and was super punctual. We learned all of this from him. I don't remember any of us ever missing a single day of work or showing up late.

Profesor Merla also reinforced in us the pleasure of reading good literature. He had an excellent collection of books that he shared with us. I loved to read, but had no time when I was in Monterrey. Since coming to Doctor Arroyo, I had read all the books that he had generously lent me. Often, we discussed them after dinner. That became another way of spending time in a constructive way.

Now, I was back in Monterrey enjoying my summer vacation. Once again, I enrolled in classes I thought would help me in my job. One of them was modern dance and the other arts and crafts.

Cayito was also on vacation at home. We would enjoy him for a short period, and then he would go to Saltillo to spend the rest of his summer vacation.

I was sad when we took him back to the seminary. He would leave the next day with his peers to Saltillo. If he was sad, he didn't show it. He kept joking until the last minute. *I wonder if he is really happy in this new way of life. If he is, I have to get used to the idea of seeing him only from time to time.*

With a broken voice, my mother addressed Cayito. "Write soon, *hijito*, even if it's only a short letter."

"I'll do it at the first opportunity, *mamá*. I promise."

He looked so composed and mature for his age. I tried to hide my grief at seeing him go. *I shouldn't let my mom and the rest of the family know how I feel. I have to be strong for all of them.*

My parents gave Cayito their blessings, and he hugged each one of us. He waved goodbye and entered the building.

We didn't talk much on our way back home. I grabbed Norma's hand and hugged her. I knew it was difficult for her. She wiped her tears and smiled sadly. Cayito was not just her brother but also her playmate. *God, she's so thin! I hope she won't get sick because of Cayito's absence and mine. Unfortunately, there is no way I can take her with me.*

Later on, I asked my mother how she felt about Cayito's decision to study at the seminary.

"As sad as I feel, I wouldn't do or say anything that could deter him from reaching the priesthood, if that's really his vocation," my mother said. "I'll be glad to know he serves God."

"If he changes his mind, he can always serve the Lord wherever he goes," I said.

"Well, there is something else, *hijita*." She stared at me and added, "Now Ernesto is also an acolyte in the Sanctuary."

I was surprised. "What are you saying, *madrecita*? Let's see, tell me about it."

"Last year the Sanctuary was almost without acolytes, because Cayito and five other companions went to the seminary. Father Ochoa, who is the parish priest, summoned the children of the sector to the Masses, and Ernesto decided to register. He is already participating at Masses and baptisms."

"And do you think he might also be interested in the priesthood?"

"Maybe, but what do you think about going to Mass next Sunday where your brother will be helping?"

"I will love seeing Ernesto as an altar boy, and he will be happy to see us there."

As we agreed, I went with my mother and sisters to the Sanctuary for the 12 o'clock Mass. This place, specially dedicated in honor of the Virgin of Guadalupe, *la Morenita*, always gave me a feeling of peace.

The music of the organ signaled the beginning of the religious service, and all the parishioners stood as the parish priest, followed by my brother Ernesto as the only altar boy, processed in. Since we were occupying seats in front, he saw us and smiled slightly.

The Mass began. The priest and Ernesto stood with their backs to the people, as was customary at that time. During the homily, Father Ochoa took the pulpit to address his sermon to us. Ernesto, meanwhile, went to sit on a bench, a few meters to the right of the altar. After a long time, Norma and Julie started whispering to each other and giggling.

My mother called their attention. "Behave, girls; we are in the house of God."

The same thing happened almost immediately, but this time my sisters pointed to Ernesto, who was sitting on the bench—asleep! Now the four of us tried not to laugh.

The priest concluded his homily and came to the altar to continue the Offertory. In this part of the ritual, the acolyte should go to a table and take from there a small towel and also the tray with the cruets containing the consecration wine and water. All this must be received by the officiant, but there on the bench, Ernesto continued to sleep.

After a few seconds of waiting, the priest looked for my brother. When he found him, he began whistling at him, first softly and then openly. The people in the front rows began to laugh quietly, looking at Ernesto fast asleep. Other parishioners began calling him aloud. Abruptly he finally woke up. He turned around, disoriented. When my brother realized that he was the center of attention, he ran toward the table to get what was needed, and the Mass was able to continue.

When we left the Sanctuary, he joined us. Smiling shyly, Ernesto confessed that the sermons bored him, and this time he could not help falling asleep. Then my mother turned to look at me.

"Well, I definitely don't think Ernesto was born to the priesthood. Imagine, sleeping throughout the sermon. Thank goodness he didn't snore." We all, even Ernesto, laughed at her comment.

Around the end of June, Mari Paz came by the house looking for me. We didn't get together as often as before, but whenever we saw each other, we did it with great pleasure. Two years was a long time, and she had made new friends. But I knew I had a special place in her heart and our friendship would be forever. On that occasion, she seemed very eager to ask me something. She almost interrupted what I was telling her. She grabbed my arm and squeezed it like she was asking me to stop.

"Listen, Socorro," she said enthusiastically, showing her perfect teeth. "My sisters and I are going to México City on vacation. We would like you to come with us. What do you say?"

"Well, I don't know." I answered with hesitation, looking at my mother, who accompanied us at that time. "When are you planning to go?"

"We'll be leaving around the middle of July. We will only be gone for a week; you'll have time to come back and spend the rest of the vacation with your family."

"Sorry, Mari Paz, but I don't have money right away for hotel, food, and transportation."

"You just worry about the bus fare. We'll be staying with some relatives."

Her offer sounded tempting, but I felt guilty taking time away from my family.

Squeezing my cheek softly, my mother said, "Go on, *hijita*. It will be good for you. Enjoy your vacation visiting a place other than Monterrey."

"Are you sure, *madrecita*?"

"I'm completely sure." With decision she turned to my friend. "She will go with you, Maripacita. Just let her know the date."

Mari Paz's eyes shone with pleasure. "*Gracias, doña* Petrita. I have to run now because my sisters were getting ready to go to the bus terminal for the tickets. We'll buy yours too, Socorro. You will pay me later."

"They are buying them right now?" I asked, surprised because we still had a few weeks before the middle of July.

"Yes. You know how hard it is to get good seats during summer vacation." She hurried to the door.

I walked with her to the corner of the street to wait for the bus. As she raised her arm to signal one to stop, she said. "I am very happy that you will accompany us. I really wanted you to come. We'll have lots of fun together; just wait!"

"I'm sure of that. I'll start getting ready right away. Thanks for the invitation." I felt in my heart that this was going to be a very special summer.

I didn't have the remotest idea of how special it would be.

CHAPTER FIFTY-TWO

WHAT THE TELEGRAM BROUGHT

Some days before my trip to México City, I was talking to my mother while enjoying a cup of coffee. A knock at the front door and the well-known whistle of a telegram carrier interrupted our conversation. Norma, who was playing with Julie in the living room, ran to open the door.

"Coco, it's a telegram for you!" she said. "Hurry up because you have to sign for it."

As I rushed into the living room, I saw my two sisters by the opened door. Outside, a young man waited with an envelope in his hand.

"A telegram for me? Who could send me a telegram?" I thought out loud. The young messenger shrugged and handed me the envelope. He left as soon as I signed and tipped him.

"It could be your new teaching position," my mother suggested. She had put her coffee mug on the table and was next to me. Telegrams were always received with some degree of anxiety.

Something told me it wasn't about my job. My hands shook slightly when I tore open the envelope. Norma bit her fingernails, Julie jumped up and down, and my mom clasped her hands while her eyes shone with expectation. The three of them waited for me to share the content of the message.

I blinked with incredulity as I read the telegram to myself. For a moment, I was speechless.

"What is it? What does it say?" my mother asked.

"Oh, my God! Listen to this, 'Arriving tomorrow. I'll be waiting for you at 11:00 a.m. at the plaza Zaragoza, across from the Continental Hotel. Love, Martín.'"

We looked at each other. Martín, my long-distance boyfriend, was coming to Monterrey. I wanted to cry, but instead I laughed nervously. My mom and my sisters were happy too.

"Can you believe it, *madrecita*? I wrote him a letter telling him it was now or never. I told him that if he couldn't come to see me this year it would be better if we took different paths. I didn't know what to think, since he hadn't answered me."

"Well, he's showing you that he really loves you and cares about you. Now start getting ready for tomorrow." My mom stroked my head and returned to the kitchen, happily humming a tune.

I opened my wardrobe and pulled out a couple of my newest dresses. "What do you think I should wear, this orange with flowers or the aqua color?" I asked Norma. She was growing up, so I wanted her to know I valued her opinion.

"Wear the aqua color," she answered, as she touched the fabric.

"Good choice. I'll wear that one with my new white shoes."

The following day I got up very early. I'd had a restless night anticipating my reunion with Martín. I bathed and dressed. Then I rushed around looking for a few things while watching the clock on the wall.

"I'm so nervous that I don't know where my head is," I told my mom. "I can't find my new stockings."

"But they are hanging from your shoulder!" Norma laughed at me.

"Relax, *hijita*. Everything is going to be okay," my mother said.

I put on my silk stockings in a hurry, then I looked at my watch. I needed to leave right away because I still needed to go by the beauty academy to have my hair done.

I grabbed my purse and went to my mother. "I'm leaving now, *madrecita*. Please give me your blessing."

With solemnity, she did as I asked her. Afterward she kissed my forehead. *"Ve con Dios, hijita, ¡y buena suerte!".*

"Gracias, madrecita. Say a prayer for me."

My mom, Norma, and Julie followed me to the front door. I kissed them and left.

I rushed across the long bridge that separated my home from the main plaza. Five minutes later, I arrived at the beauty academy, which was only a block and a half from the Continental Hotel.

"Hola, Socorrito. ¿Dónde es la boda?", the lady manager said as soon as I entered the building. I blushed at her question, "Where is the wedding?" It's an expression people commonly use when they see someone all dressed up.

"I'm not attending any wedding. I'm meeting my boyfriend in one hour, and I need someone to fix my hair *pronto, prontito, por favor*".

"That's wonderful," the manager said. "Don't worry. I'll take care of your hair personally."

I told her Martín and I hadn't seen each other in four years so I wanted to give him a good impression.

"Oh, then I'll ask one of the girls to give you a manicure. Who knows? He could give you an engagement ring, and you'll want your hands to look beautiful."

She called one of the girls and continued. "You'll see, you'll look gorgeous when I'm done doing your hair. But are you sure you still remember him after four years? Don't get confused and kiss the hotel doorman." We both laughed.

When she finished I saw myself in the mirror. The hairstyle framed my face very well, and my hands looked attractive with the pink pearl polish on my nails. The manager and the manicurist looked at me, proud of their work—and I was satisfied.

"Thanks for helping me," I told them both. "Now I have to hurry, or I'll be late."

Both wished me good luck and even asked me to stop by later to let them know everything about the romantic encounter.

"Don't forget we want to hear aaaall the details," the manager said. Students and customers laughed at my embarrassment.

I walked the short distance to the Continental Hotel, feeling a surge of elation. A young man coming in my direction gave a whistle as a compliment and mumbled something as he stopped. I looked the other way, and he understood my rejection and continued on his way.

My heart sank when I saw no one outside the building. Maybe Martín was sitting on a bench. I looked both ways. There wasn't anybody. My stomach contracted to a tight ball. *Maybe his plane hasn't arrived yet, and here I am, like a dummy. Should I ask in the Administration?*

Just then, a man came out of the hotel running toward me. *This man certainly doesn't look the way I remember my boyfriend.*

"Are you here to meet Martín?" he asked out of breath.

Oh, my God. Did he contact the hotel to let me know that he will not be able to come? Please, God, I don't want to cry in front of a stranger.

"Yes, I came to meet him. What happened? Did he leave a message for me?" I asked with a cracking voice.

"I'm sorry," the man said. "He asked me to wait for you outside the hotel, but the desk telephone rang, so I had to run inside to answer it. Martín went back to his room to get something, but he'll be back in few minutes. Please wait for him in the lobby."

Aww, thank God! But going into the lobby? Don't even think about it! Can you imagine if somebody sees me going inside the hotel or coming out of there with Martín? What would people think?

"*Siéntese, por favor*". The man pointed to a leather sofa in the cozy lobby.

Without realizing it, I had followed the employee inside the hotel. I was going to sit when Martín appeared at the door. My heart raced and my legs shook a little. He was just as I remembered him, only a little bit taller. Martín looked very handsome in his blue Air Force uniform. He had replaced his curly tuft with a military haircut. He approached me smiling, and I smiled back, feeling very shy. We embraced and shared a light kiss.

"*Hola*. I'm sorry I made you wait. I forgot to bring down your present, so I had to go back to my room. I hope you like it." He handed me a package. "Go ahead; open it."

With my heart beating fast, I looked inside. There was a big white box with Channel No. 5 cologne and a small box of perfume of the same brand. I looked at him, and I'm sure he noticed my happiness because he smiled with satisfaction.

"Thank you so much for the lovely present, but I'm sorry I don't have anything for you. You came completely by surprise," I said, blushing.

"Don't worry. I'm sure you thought I wasn't coming, but you sounded so determined to break up with me that I had to move heaven and earth to come." He pointed a finger at me and shook his head. "You just don't have any idea what I did just to be here."

I felt a bit guilty, but I was happy anyway. Finally, he had come.

"Would you like to eat something?" he proposed. "I'm starving. Do you know a quiet place where we can talk?"

Suddenly I felt hungry. I had been so nervous that morning that I didn't have any breakfast at home. I suggested a restaurant close to the plaza. Martín took me by the elbow, and we walked to the place. The restaurant was small and cozy. There were only two or three tables occupied. We chose to sit in a corner where nobody would disturb us. All of the tables were covered with white tablecloths. On top of each table there was a small crystal lamp and a bowl filled with tiny, perfumed roses. I eyed the menu and ordered something inexpensive, but Martín suggested I order a steak instead. He might have realized I didn't want him to spend too much. Since I didn't drink, I declined the wine and had a Coke with my dinner, while Martín preferred a Mexican beer. The first minutes were a little awkward, but soon the ice broke, and we talked to each other with ease.

Martín told me about his job and his travels, which I found exciting. They were nothing like my life in Doctor Arroyo. I thought he might find my experiences boring. However, he was very entertained when I told him about the students and the town's customs. He loved the story about Dimas García being the region's bad boy and getting

away with it. Martín also wanted to hear about my family.

That afternoon, we went to the movies at Cine Elizondo and had dinner later in a typical restaurant. Finally, our beautiful day together ended.

"How long can you stay?" I had delayed asking the question, afraid to hear that he would leave the following day.

Meeting Martín after four years

"I came for five days," he said. "But before I go, I want to talk to your father. He needs to know my intentions toward you are serious, unless you have changed your mind."

I squeezed his hands, smiling. There was no need to answer what was obvious. "By the way," I said, "I hadn't mentioned to you that I'll go to México City the same day that you are leaving here. I'm going with my friend Mari Paz and her sisters. We'll be there for a week. Since we are traveling by bus, by the time we arrive there you may already be back in the States."

Martín asked me for the address where we would be staying. He would send me a telegram when he reached his destination. I promised to inform him later. We made plans to have lunch and dinner together and go to the movies the following day. Since he wasn't driving and I didn't have a car either, we would only walk through the downtown area.

By then, it was nearly nine o'clock, so I told him I had to go home. We walked slowly across the bridge and stopped at the end of it. I pointed out to him where I lived, and we said goodbye with a soft kiss. Martín stood there watching me until I made it to the front of my house. Then he turned around and went back to his hotel.

I entered my home walking on clouds. My mom was waiting for me, eager to hear how it had been for me to see Martín again. She listened carefully to the details of our encounter and the way we spent the day. She said she had a good feeling about him. I always trusted her maternal instincts and told her I felt the same way. Then I told her about Martín's decision to talk to my dad before he returned to the States.

"It's going to be very hard for your father. I don't know how he will react," my mother said pensively.

I felt a great concern and decided to go to bed before my dad arrived home. Nothing would spoil the happiness I shared with Martín. Once he had left for the States, I would confront any problems with my dad.

Martín and me

CHAPTER FIFTY-THREE

THE GOODBYE AND A PROMISE

The following four days of Martín's stay in Monterrey, I experienced conflicting emotions. I was ecstatic in his company, but I kept counting the hours left for us to be together. How I hated the clock that ticked the hours away toward the end of that wonderful time.

Martín and I shared most of the day. We usually had brunch and dinner in small restaurants where we could talk quietly. We frequently went to downtown Alameda. There we walked under the shadow of the trees or sat on a bench. There were other couples, too. They walked holding hands or kissed, oblivious to anybody else.

Many children came to play on the grass or ride their bicycles. Others fed the noisy pigeons, which flew away every time the kids tried to grab them. The children's laughter mixed with the cooing of the pigeons.

"When we get married, I want us to have lots of children."

"Lots?" Martín asked, placing his arm around my shoulder. "About how many?"

"A dozen," I said without hesitation. As a teacher, I loved being surrounded by children, and we both came from large families.

"A ... a dozen?" Martín asked.

"Yes, maybe six boys and six girls." Martín's reaction amused me.

"Don't you think that's too many? We'll have to provide food, clothes, and education for all of them." He paused. "Besides, we would need a huge house and a bus to transport them!"

"Um, well, you know the Mexican saying, *'Más barato por docena',* 'cheaper by the dozen.' But you are right, a dozen might be too many. What about six?"

We agreed that half a dozen would be a good number. "We might still get a discount for half a dozen," I said.

Martín and I had much in common. We were both born in San Luis Potosí and had been reared with the same kind of moral principles. We shared similar ideals and enjoyed the same things. More importantly, we confirmed that our mutual feelings were real, and that we wanted to share a future together.

"I'm so glad you came," I said. "I wanted to know if, after all these years, the image I had in my mind and in my heart of you was real."

"And what did you find out?" Martín said. He grabbed my two hands and looked deep into my eyes.

"It's like you never left. Even the scent of your cologne and the sound of your voice were always present. What about me? Have I fulfilled your expectations?"

He kept silent for a few seconds, then he tilted his head to one side and said, "So much, that as soon as I save enough money, I'll come back to give you an engagement ring, because I want you to share my life forever."

I was speechless, but surely my smile and the sparkle of my eyes told him the happiness I felt.

"In the meantime, I think the correct thing is to let your family know about my serious intentions toward you," he said.

As on the previous days, he walked me home around nine in the evening. My parents' rule had always been that I had to be home at night before ten o'clock. After we crossed the bridge, he waited until he saw me going into my house, then he went back to his hotel.

In those years, it was not only difficult but also a luxury to own a phone. Of course, we didn't have one; otherwise, Martín and I would probably have talked for hours before going to sleep. I was so happy to be on vacation. In this way, I could dedicate all of my time to him.

The next day, after a light breakfast, I started getting ready. When I finished, I checked my watch and the mirror a dozen times. Finally, it was time to go. As usual, my mom gave me her blessing. Then she and my siblings walked me to the door.

"*¡Te ves muy bonita!*", my mom commented, looking at me approvingly.

"*Gracias, madrecita,* but you see me that way only because I'm your daughter and you love me," I said, giving her a warm embrace.

"Look at yourself. The mirror doesn't lie." Her gaze and voice were full of tenderness.

"It's this pretty dress you made for me." I ran my hand over the French gauze material of my orange, flower-printed dress. It was a two-piece dress on which I had received a lot of compliments. My high-heeled sandals and my jewelry matched my outfit.

I kissed and hugged my mom and my siblings. They stayed by the open door as I walked across the bridge to meet Martín at plaza Zaragoza.

The sound of my heels on the pavement mixed with the beating of my heart. The day was hot, and there wasn't any breeze. I was worried that the walk would make me sweat.

Before crossing the main square, I saw Martín waiting for me in front of the Cathedral. He came to meet me with a big smile. We hugged and shared a short kiss. Then he took a step back to get a better look at me.

"Um, I hope you dress like this only for me."

"Naturally!" I said, grinning.

Cathedral of Monterrey

We sat under the shade of tall trees close to the empty gazebo in the center of the plaza. From our spot, we enjoyed the view of the beautiful mountains south of the city. Dozens of birds flew from tree to tree. Their singing could be heard throughout the area.

The deep sound of the Cathedral bells interrupted our conversation.

"That's a sound of México that I miss so much," Martín said, sighing. We listened with pleasure until the bells stopped giving the hour. Afterward we stood up and walked hand in hand toward the Municipal Palace, across plaza Zaragoza.

Martín seemed grave and abruptly quiet. Suddenly, he told me, "Listen, wait for me here at the Palace. I'll walk to your dad's place of work and ask him to give me some time to talk to him this afternoon."

Palacio Municipal in Monterrey

We were already on the other side of the colonial building, across *placita* Hidalgo. The placita was a small square with a statue in the center, in honor of *don* Miguel Hidalgo, the Mexican hero of the War of Independence. Several benches provided seats to rest, especially for the tourists who abounded in such an area. The square was surrounded by several curio shops, the famous *Hotel Ancira*, a very exclusive restaurant called *Louisiana*, the popular *Café Flores*, and the Municipal Palace. At night, several groups of *trios* walked around playing the strings of their guitars and offering their services.

There were also groups of *mariachis*, waiting to be hired to serenade the locals or the many tourists who visited Monterrey.

From a distance, I saw my father standing by *La Siesta's* front doors. That was the curio shop where I had worked as a secretary while studying to be a teacher. My father was the store manager. That was where I had seen Martín with his family for the first time, but we didn't exchange a word. Not until a few days later were we introduced at a party.

"I'll be back soon," Martín said, adjusting his tie and closing the buttons of his navy-blue blazer. He walked directly toward my father.

This conversation was taking place sooner than I had expected it.

I didn't want my dad to see me. I went inside the courtyard of the Municipal Palace, feeling terribly restless. The brownstone building had two floors surrounding the square courtyard. In the center, there was a small wishing well made of colorful mosaics. I looked inside. Different types of coins in the bottom of the well told of all the wishes made there. *Had any of those wishes become a reality?* I wondered. I opened my small purse and took out a shiny coin. I made a wish and with my back to the well, threw the coin over my shoulder, hoping no one would see me. There were several offices open. People went in and out in a hurry, not paying attention to anything else.

I checked my watch and then the entrance to the courtyard. A few minutes later, Martín came back. I studied his face, trying to guess how my father had reacted to his request. But he was as serious as when he left. Realizing my anxiety, he held my chin and smiled.

"I'll meet with your dad for coffee at the Café Flores at one o'clock."

"Great! I was so fearful that he would refuse."

"Why would he do that?"

"Well ..." I searched for words, but it was difficult to explain that, having been the oldest and also a woman, I had always had a special bond with him since I was little. My family also depended on my financial help to meet part of their needs, and finally, it would be devastating for my father to know that one day soon I would be living away from them. I shrugged and decided to wait for another occasion to share my concerns with him.

A little before one o'clock, Martín took me to a small cafeteria around the corner. I should wait for him there. He put some coins in the jukebox and chose some songs for me.

"Wish me luck," he said. "It won't be long. Your dad said your mom is waiting for him at home." After those words, he disappeared through the front door.

I fidgeted with my straw and my Coke and checked my watch often. I prayed that my father wouldn't be antagonistic toward Martín. After what seemed like an eternity, he finally came back and sat across from me. He asked the waiter for a beer.

"How did it go?" I couldn't hide my anxiety.

"Fine, but I didn't see your father very enthused about our relationship. He wanted to know if we were sure of our feelings. He said I don't know you well. Anyway, it was clear to him that my intentions toward you are serious, and that's fine with him."

I sighed. Wishes do come true. The meeting turned out better than I had expected.

We walked around for a while and then we had dinner in a famous restaurant that specialized in *cabrito al pastor*. The tender meat of young goat is Monterrey's typical dish.

"I had been dreaming of eating *cabrito* again after all these years," Martín said, rubbing his tummy lightly.

Afterward we decided to watch *The Girl on the Red Trapeze* at the Elizondo Theater. The interior of the theater had many Chinese details in its architecture and decorations. It was the most beautiful theater in Monterrey at that time. Unfortunately, it would be demolished twenty years later. This was a controversial decision, but it was necessary to allow the construction of a gorgeous macro plaza, one of the largest in Latin América. The Hotel Continental, where Martín and his family used to stay, would be demolished for the same reason.

The movie ended, and we were sad to have to wrap up another special day. It was getting harder and harder for us to say "good night." Our hours together were running out.

When I arrived home, my mom let me know my dad had told her about the meeting with Martín. I noticed she looked a little worried.

"How is Dad taking it?"

"Well, I told you it wasn't going to be easy for him, but don't worry, *hijita*. He will start getting used to the idea. '*Tu sé feliz con tu muchacho.*'"

It was so sweet of my mother to wish me to be happy with my boyfriend.

"If only Dad could be as understanding as you are, *madrecita*," I said, caressing her hair. "But now let me tell you about my day with Martín."

That night I went to bed early again. I didn't want to face my dad because I knew he wasn't going to be in a good mood.

Martín's last day in Monterrey quickly came. We spent time as on the previous ones, only this time I cried when he walked me home and we said goodbye.

"Don't cry," he said, wiping my tears with the back of his finger. "I promise I'll be back in December."

I felt embarrassed crying in front of him and just nodded my head. Martín hugged me, and I enjoyed the warmth of his chest. After few minutes I pulled apart from his embrace. "I want you to leave first and not to turn around," I asked in a broken voice. "This time it is me who can't walk away from you."

"Okay, if that's what you wish," he said, "but I don't want you to be sad. I'll be back soon. I promise." He gazed into my eyes and gave me a last kiss. Then he turned around and walked away.

I stayed at the edge of the bridge watching him disappear into the distance through my desolate tears. Only then did I go home, with my heart enveloped in a cloud of sadness.

Despite the experience of the previous four years, I knew Martín would be back as he promised. I would only have to wait five more months, but for me, they would be five long, drawn-out months.

CHAPTER FIFTY-FOUR

ECSTASY AND NEW TEARS

After a sleepless night, I prepared to join Mari Paz and her sisters at the bus terminal. I sighed deeply. By that time, Martín would already be flying to México City where he would make a connecting flight to the States.

"Have fun, *hijita*, and take care of yourself," my mom told me as she gave me her blessing. I knew she wanted me to be distracted so I would get over the sadness of Martín's departure.

"I will, *madrecita*, and don't worry. I'll be fine in a couple of days." I gave her a kiss and a smile of reassurance.

Our bus departed early from Monterrey. We were glad to occupy the front seats because the vehicle was completely full. The driver said that it would be a nine-hour trip. Mari Paz's two sisters, Lala and Minga, were traveling behind the driver. Mari Paz and I sat together next to the door. We teased them because both were single, and the man was good-looking. He watched the passengers from time to time through the rearview mirror.

"Hey, girls, don't distract the driver," Mari Paz said to her sisters. "We want to arrive safely."

Minga raised her eyebrows and placed a finger over her lips. Lala, who was quite attractive and always dressed nicely, looked at herself in the driver's mirror, fixed her hair, and smiled when the man noticed her. She winked at us, and we celebrated her mischief.

As soon as the bus was on the highway, Mari Paz said, "I was so glad to hear Martín finally came to see you after four long years. Your mom seems to be ecstatic, too."

"Yes, she is. She told me she has a good feeling about Martín, and I always trust her mother's instinct. She has never been wrong."

"Your mom is an intelligent lady, without doubt, but how does your dad feel about it? It's going to be difficult for him if you get married and leave México."

"Oh, don't get ahead of yourself. Let's wait to see what happens. It won't be easy but at least, my dad appreciated that Martín expressed his good intentions toward me."

"And how do you feel now that you have seen him again?"

"I'm happy he came. The time we spent together helped us to realize that our love is real. I just wish he could have a few more days." I sighed deeply.

"Too bad you didn't introduce Martín to me, but I forgive you." She gave me a playful push and said, "You forgot about the rest of the world these past days. I was afraid you would cancel this trip."

"If Martín had been able to stay longer, I would have canceled for sure, but he had to go back to work. He encouraged me to go ahead with my original plans, so here I am, ready to enjoy the trip in excellent company."

We talked quite a bit the rest of the way, admired the landscape from time to time, and took some short naps before we entered Mexico City. Traffic was intense, going in all directions, and everybody seemed to be in a rush.

On our way to the bus terminal, we admired several towering skyscrapers like Torre Latinoamericana, forty-four floors high, which is an architectural landmark in México City. We saw beautiful buildings like the Palacio de Bellas Artes, whose main façade was constructed with white Italian Carrara marble. We continued along wide avenues where you can admire famous monuments, such as The Angel, a tall column that ends at the top with the sculpture of The Greek Goddess of Victory. We were in awe of México City's beauty.

When we got to the terminal, my friends' cousin was already waiting for us. They introduced us. His name was Magdaleno. He was slightly chunky and of average height. He had a nice personality and laughed easily.

Magdaleno helped us to collect our luggage, then drove us to his home. The house, among others painted in different colors, was in the middle of a lively neighborhood. A group of children played soccer in the middle of the street amidst laughter and screams.

"We'll go out this afternoon, so you better rest for a little bit," Magdaleno said. "My brother will join us and we'll go in two cars." Then he showed us the bedrooms where we would be staying.

We were taking our luggage to the designated rooms when a hard knock at the door startled everybody. Magdaleno rushed to open. Soon he was back with a closed envelope in his hand. "It's a message for you," he said to me.

A message for me? Who can send me a message? Martín must be in the States by now, so it can only be from my mom. God, I hope everything is okay back home.

Magdaleno handed me the envelope. His face was serious. "It's not a telegram. The messenger said he'll wait for an answer."

Everybody's eyes were fixed on me. My heart leapt as I looked at the envelope. *Oh, my God, it's Martín's writing! How can this be?*

"It's from my boyfriend," I told them while I opened the message with shaky hands. I read it. I felt a wave of joy and couldn't hide a smile of happiness. "He says he won't leave until tomorrow so he would like to spend these last hours with me, here in the capital."

"You mean with us," Mari Paz corrected me, joking. "Because I'm not going to let you go by yourself."

"Obviously," I said, blushing with my heart pounding hard. "He wants to know if he can join us, and he sends the name and address of his hotel. I'm supposed to send him an answer." I looked at Magdaleno because after all, we were at his home, and he had already made plans for that afternoon.

"That's fine. Tell him we'll pick him up around five o'clock this afternoon. Just advise him to be ready," Magdaleno said.

I thanked him, and then I wrote a brief note and gave it to the messenger, together with a tip. He thanked me and returned to the taxi that was waiting for him.

Instead of resting, I started getting ready right away. After a while, Magdaleno's brother Emilio arrived. He was good-looking and younger than his brother and he lived in the same house. Soon we were in two vehicles on our way to pick up Martín.

Mari Paz and I rode with Magdaleno, and Lala and Minga with Emilio. My heart jumped with happiness when I saw Martín waiting outside the front door of the hotel. We stepped out of the cars, and he came to meet us right away. We embraced, and he kissed me on the cheek. Then, I introduced him to my friends.

After talking briefly, Martín and I sat in the back of the car, and Mari Paz moved to the front with Magdaleno. Martín placed his arm around my shoulder and held me tightly. I forgot immediately about my previous sadness, enjoying instead the happiness I felt to have him next to me, even if it was for a short time.

"I can't believe you are here with me," I said, squeezing his hand. "I thought you would be back in the States by now."

"My flight was canceled until tomorrow morning. I'm glad I asked you for the address where you were staying," he said.

"Since Martín is coming with us, you better take us to a nice place," Mari Paz suggested to Magdaleno.

"We are going to a nightclub so you can talk and dance. Is that okay with you, Martín?"

"I totally agree, thanks," Martín answered, pulling me closer. I just looked at him and smiled.

I never asked Mari Paz if she had ever been in a nightclub before. Even though I was twenty-two years old, that was my first time, so I felt completely out of place.

The place was semi-dark, and the smell of cigarette smoke filled the saloon. Several couples were dancing in the middle of the room, some with their bodies so close that it looked like they were glued to each other. Not far from us, I saw some couples sitting at their tables and exchanging passionate kisses. I felt my cheeks burning.

Mari Paz, who was sitting next to me, laughed and elbowed me. "Relax and enjoy it," she said.

When the waiter came to our long table and asked me what kind of drink I wanted, I hesitated for a few seconds. I finally asked for a *"Cuba Libre,"* a mix of Coke and rum. This was the only alcoholic beverage I knew, since it was the most popular drink in México. Martín asked for a Mexican beer.

"Next time ask for a *'Piña Colada,'*" Mari Paz suggested.

"Or ask for a *'Vampiro'* or some *'Medias de Seda,'*" somebody else added. The names of the mixed drinks "Vampire" and "Silk Stockings" sounded funny. I wondered if they were just teasing me, but later on, I saw those names on a menu. Anyway, one drink would be enough for me.

"What's the matter?" Martín held one of my hands. "Are you okay?"

"Not really. I've never been in a nightclub before, and it makes me feel uncomfortable, especially with you here."

"I don't like it either," he said. He put an arm around my shoulder to reassure me. The band started playing a popular melody, and many couples immediately went onto the dance floor.

"Go dance," Mari Paz suggested, while she and Emilio also rose from their seats. Lala was already dancing with Magdaleno.

"We prefer to talk," I said.

We moved to a corner and tried to talk over the loud noise of the music and the people. We found it hard, but what was most important was that Martín and I were sharing those last hours together. Even though our relationship had developed mostly through letters, I was surprised to see how quickly we became acquainted with each other's ways.

Finally, it was time to take Martín back to his hotel. I put my head on his shoulder, and we held hands while we made small talk. I tried to sound cheerful. We arrived and he got out of the car. Everybody wished him a good trip. I got out, too, and gave him a last hug and a brief kiss. We felt a little bit self-conscious with so many people around us.

"Have a good trip and write soon." My voice broke, and my eyes clouded with tears.

"Of course! Now go and have a good vacation with your friends. Don't forget that I love you."

"I love you, too," I answered him, wiping an unexpected tear from my cheek.

After a last hug, I got in the car. Martín stood by the hotel door as we departed. I tried to see him through the back window for the last time. He waved goodbye, and I waved back until I couldn't see him anymore. My heart felt sad, and more tears ran down my cheeks.

"Don't worry, Socorro; he'll be back," Mari Paz said. She was now sitting in the back seat of the car with me. "Besides, you still have me." She smiled broadly.

"Oh, be quiet." I smiled back at her and pulled what she called her naturally blonde ponytail.

I sighed and dried my tears. *El tiempo lo dirá, lo que será, será.*

"Time will tell, what will be, will be."

CHAPTER FIFTY-FIVE

DISTURBING NEWS FROM MONTERREY

Martín's departure left a void in my heart. However, after seeing him, I felt more optimistic about our future together.

Martín told me he planned to continue his career in the Air Force. Not only did he love his job, but the government would even pay for his college classes. He described to me in detail the life of the American military families. They had lots of privileges. For example, whenever an active military member flew in a commercial flight, there might not be space on the plane for a civilian, but there would always be room for the people in the armed forces and their dependents. He added that if there wasn't any space, an airline would somehow create it for them.

He also explained to me that military bases were like small cities. They had schools and medical facilities; some had huge hospitals. There were clubs, movie theaters, and stores where people could buy everything from groceries to clothing and furniture at lower prices than outside the base. There were also beauty parlors, restaurants, gas stations, cleaners, libraries, and even a church for all religious denominations. They also had swimming pools, picnic parks, and recreation centers—and many bases even had golf courses.

He described the kind of housing we would have when he reached the rank of staff sergeant if we decided to live on a military base. In general, the houses had a small garden, a fully equipped kitchen, one or two bathrooms, two or three bedrooms, living room, and dining room. He assured me I would love to live there because everything was within reach. At that time, however, Martín was only a sergeant, so we would have to wait for his promotion.

There were thousands of thoughts in my head. I wanted to get married and follow Martín wherever he went. I had always dreamed of traveling and learning about other cultures in exotic and faraway countries. He had been in Korea, and he talked about how much he would like for us to be sent to Japan or Spain, and I delighted in those plans.

However, my heart felt sad whenever I thought about leaving family, friends, my country, and my job as a teacher.

It was better not to think about it and to enjoy the rest of the vacation. Mari Paz's cousins were excellent hosts, and they took us to many interesting places.

"We are expecting beautiful weather tomorrow. We'll have to get up early to go to Xochimilco Lake," Magdaleno said as we were getting ready to go to bed.

We were thrilled. We would visit one of the most popular tourist places in Mexico City.

"I hope we can find a *trajinera* with my name," Mari Paz said.

She was referring to the wooden boats that float through the Xochimilco canals. Each one of them has an arch displaying a woman's name formed with flowers.

"What about looking for one that says Socorro?" I suggested.

"No way, it has to say Mari Paz," my giggling friend said.

"You better go to sleep and stop daydreaming!" Lala laughed.

The following day, just as Magdaleno predicted, was beautiful, sunny, and warm. When we arrived in Xochimilco, we saw lots of people and the canals with dozens of brightly colored and flower-decked *trajineras*. We couldn't find any of them that sported our names, so we settled for the one that looked prettiest instead. After Magdaleno negotiated the price with the friendly boatman, we boarded our attractive *trajinera* and sat on colorful chairs. There was an ambience of festivity all around. Music and the voices of many people speaking different languages created a joyous symphony that delighted our ears.

We slowly traveled on the canal lined with trees. Soon, some canoes came to our side, with sellers offering all kind of merchandise, from embroidered colorful ponchos to attractive jewelry, but more than anything beautiful flowers, since Xochimilco in the Nahuatl language means "flower field place." It was marvelous to fill our lungs with their sweet scent.

"*Señor, señor*! *Flores* for the pretty *señoritas*!" said a woman in a canoe showing several bouquets of mixed colorful flowers. A man expertly maneuvered the canoe, keeping it close to our *trajinera* while the woman offered the merchandise.

"Choose a bouquet, *señoritas*," Magdaleno invited. He opened his wallet and took out some pesos.

We appreciated his chivalry, and we chose the bouquet that we liked the most.

There were several *trajineras* with *mariachis* who offered to sing for a set amount of money. A group of them sang three songs for us while their *trajinera* sailed next to ours. The sound of their voices and instruments mixed with others that could be heard in the distance. The musicians looked very elegant wearing black *charro* suits with golden buttons and their embroidered *sombreros*. As soon as they finished, they rushed to follow another *trajinera* full of American tourists.

The aroma of recently cooked food coming from other *trajineras* awakened our appetite. Each *trajinera* had a specialty, and we couldn't resist trying several. We had some *gorditas*, small thick corn pancakes filled with either pork meat, cheese, *nopales*, *chorizo*, or beans, with cilantro and hot sauce as condiments. They were all delicious.

We finished our *paseo* and returned home with the memory of a beautiful experience that I would have loved to share with Martín. *If we get married and come for our honeymoon to México City, I'll be sure we'll visit Xochimilco.*

A visit to the Basílica de Guadalupe or *La Villa*, as it's commonly called, is an obligatory destination for Mexican Catholics who travel to the capital. The church was built close to the place where—according to tradition—the Virgin appeared to the Indian Juan Diego. I was surprised to see the old colonial building so tilted, half-sunk alarmingly into the ground. This was because México City was built on top of a former lake. Fourteen years after our visit—between 1974 and 1976—a more modern shrine with a capacity of 10,000 people replaced this building. The Basílica houses Juan Diego's miraculous tilma. The image of the Virgin of Guadalupe appeared on this cotton blanket country men wore as a cape, and inexplicably, it has not deteriorated in almost 500 years.

Several millions of devout parishioners and pilgrims visit the Villa de Guadalupe every year, so the shrine is always full. The day of our visit wasn't an exception. Lala had promised she would go on her knees from the entrance of the church to the altar if the Virgin granted her a favor. Since her prayers were answered, Lala was there paying her promise like other faithful. Many of them had come on their knees from a greater distance and had to be assisted by their relatives to fulfill the painful promise. The relatives assisted the faithful by placing blankets on the floor to protect their knees, which sometimes even ended up bleeding.

I wondered what kind of miracles or favors they had received from the miraculous *Morenita*, as people lovingly call the Virgin of Guadalupe.

The sanctuary smelled of candles and flowers. Some pilgrims sang Marian chants, and others prayed the rosary out loud while their companions gave the responses. There were those who only moved their lips in silent prayer. On all of their faces, however, there was an expression of hope and fervor as they came close to the Virgin's image.

Once Lala fulfilled her promise, we sat and prayed for some time. Then we left the shrine with a sense of happiness and inner peace.

Three days before our return to Monterrey, a news report on the radio caught my attention. "This is a flash news bulletin from Monterrey, México," the announcer said. "A severe thunderstorm fell over the hills south of the city, causing a mudslide. Many houses are flooded in the Colonia Independencia." The announcer said at that moment, they didn't know if there were any casualties, but they would try to keep the public informed. My heart started to beat wildly. Our homes were in that sector!

Mari Paz looked at me. Her face was pale, and probably mine was too. "I'm sure our families are okay," she said, fidgeting with her hair. "Otherwise, they would have called us right away, don't you think?"

"Mari Paz, my family doesn't know how to get in contact with me. I hope they're okay," I said in a broken voice. "Remember, my house is on low ground and close to the riverbank."

"How can there be a flood if the riverbed is always empty and it's so wide?"

"I have no idea. Let's ask Magdaleno permission to phone to one of my neighbors in Monterrey. They can check on my family." My concern was growing.

He lent me his phone, and I tried unsuccessfully to call several times. Then Mari Paz placed a call, and luckily the connection went through. She talked to a relative who said they were okay.

"It was a terrible storm," her relative said. "We heard the muddy water washed away several old tool stalls from Querétaro Street and also some cars for several blocks. The debris clogged several sewers. That was why the muddy water didn't drain within the riverbank. Instead, it flooded the nearby houses. Tell Socorro not to worry. We'll go by her house now and check on her family. We'll call you back soon."

I couldn't remain still for the next couple of hours. I kept looking at my watch and wondering what was taking so long since our houses were only ten minutes apart.

"If nobody calls, I want to go back to Monterrey tonight," I told Mari Paz. "Maybe there is something wrong."

"Be patient. I'm sure your family is fine. If not, they would have gone to my house to send a message to you."

I hoped Mari Paz was right, but I kept feeling nervous. Finally, one of her relatives called and informed me my family was okay. My mom told her she wanted me to enjoy the rest of my vacation and not to worry.

This calmed me a bit, but not completely. I counted the hours left before returning home to see with my own eyes that everything was as I had left it.

CHAPTER FIFTY-SIX

DISASTER AND FRUSTRATION

On my return to Monterrey, I found that my concern had been well-founded. My heart filled with anguish when, upon entering my house, I discovered it had suffered extensive flood damage. The living room furniture looked wet, pieces of furniture and books were missing, and there were piles of clothes on the patio.

"What happened here, *madrecita*?" I asked, looking around with bewilderment.

"The day of the storm, it rained suddenly and with great intensity," said my mother with desolation. "Héctor wanted to go check the level of the torrent that was descending our street. He saw that the muddy water was already creeping alarmingly inside, and he opened the door to try to put up a barrier. The level was higher than expected, something that had never been seen. He tried to close the door, but the force of the current prevented him from doing it. Even worse, the door was left hanging because the lower hinge had come off. It was then that the muddy water entered the house."

"But is everyone okay, *madrecita*?" I interrupted her, more concerned about the health of my family.

"Thank God, we are all fine." She sighed and called my siblings. They each gave me a hug, but there was no glee in their attitude. Rather, their smiles were sad.

My mother continued to tell me about that nightmare. She said that as the mud began to enter the house, Héctor yelled for the others to run to the patio in the back. Before leaving, one of them put the basket with the cat and his litter on top of a closet and the dog on the kitchen table. At that moment, the muddy water was rushing inexorably toward the kitchen, so everyone rushed out to the patio. Outside, they stood on some blocks and old furniture, but the flow kept rising.

"Suddenly, the water that was already flooding the back apartments made a hole in our adjoining wall. Cornered and full of dread, we had no choice but to climb the wall that separates our house from Conchita's, and that was another fight for me." When she said the last part, she started to laugh nervously, and my siblings, who had been listening in silence, burst into laughter.

"What's so funny?" I asked.

Héctor said they laughed because even though my siblings were precariously safe, my mom couldn't get up the wall no matter how hard she tried. So, he had to push her up while everyone was yelling for her to hurry up. By that time, the muddy water had already reached them, so as soon as he helped my mom to sit on the wall, he climbed up as fast as possible.

Norma was listening with her eyes wide open, biting her fingernails. My mom later explained to me that my sister had been the most affected by the flooding.

"So, how or when did you all get down from there?" I asked my mom.

"Well, we sat on the wall in the heavy rain. The back door of Conchita's house was closed, so we didn't know if anybody was inside. The mud on our patio started to rise, and we were afraid the wall would collapse."

"We yelled and yelled, but nobody opened the door," Julie said, shaking her head.

My heart felt like it was being squeezed out of my chest just imagining the terror they felt during those minutes.

My mom explained to me that finally, Malena, Conchita's youngest daughter, peeked through the back window and saw them. She called her mom, and they helped the family into Conchita's backyard, which was almost a meter higher than ours, and took them into their house.

"We were completely soaked, so they lent us some towels to keep warm. We waited there until the rain stopped and Dad came looking for us," added Norma with a shaky voice.

Ernesto, who had been silent, said, "I don't want to live in this house anymore. We could get flooded again!"

Seeing my youngest siblings' reactions, I felt concerned about the long-term effect of this event on all of them. I held Norma's hand to comfort her. It felt so thin and cold that I rubbed her two hands between mine. She still looked frightened so I hugged her to comfort her.

"Was Conchita's house flooded too?" I asked.

"No, because hers is on a higher level," my mother said. "In fact, nothing happened to any of the others next to them. It was just our home and the apartments behind our house, because our properties are on lower ground."

Then she told me that when they finally returned home, they saw that most of the furniture was covered with mud. They had to use shovels and hoses to clean what they could. The cat and her litter were safe, but they found our dog full of mud. She had tried to follow the family and ended up swallowing the dirty water. I couldn't imagine at the time that as a consequence of this, my little dog would get sick and die a few days later.

I looked around and noticed a strip of moisture on the inside walls showing how high the water had reached. Suddenly, I remembered something. I ran to look for the box where I had kept Martín's letters. It wasn't there! I felt a pain in my heart. Just then, my mom gave me a different box. As I opened it, I saw Martín's letters, some of them looked slightly wet.

"You should have seen your dad," my mom said with an amused expression. "He grabbed the box where you kept them. It was wet, so he started drying your letters. He saved them and put them in another box, but don't tell him that I told you."

My parents did a good job of cleaning the living room furniture I had recently bought. Mom said they felt terrible because of the money I had spent on it and tried to save it, and they did at the moment, but the humidity finally rotted it.

Even though we suffered a lot of damage, we were thankful everybody was safe. The laundress who came to help my mom had already washed a lot of clothes. Some of them were already folded, and others were still hanging on the clotheslines on the patio of our house. I could still smell the chlorine used to disinfect the walls and to wash the clothes. My parents couldn't afford to throw everything away, but some clothes were completely damaged so they had already been put inside garbage bags.

"*¡Lo siento, hijita!*", my mom said in a broken voice. "We had to throw away a lot of books and clothes, including yours."

"*¡No se preocupe, madrecita!*".

I walked toward my dresser and realized my jewelry box was gone. From the few pieces of jewelry I had, the only ones I cared about were Martín's school ring and a set of gold earrings and pin, a present from my grandmother. They were irreplaceable and they meant so much to me. I turned around, hoping my mom would tell me my jewelry was fine, but all that I saw was sadness in her eyes. I had to hold back my tears.

My father, who arrived at that moment, saw me staring at the emptiness on top of my dresser. He came to me and put his strong arms around my slumped shoulders. "*¡Lo siento, hijita!* We couldn't find your jewelry box. We all tried it together, but it got lost in the mud stream."

That was enough for me to start crying. "There I had kept my grandmother's jewelry. She gave them to me, when she could have given them to one of her daughters. They showed how much she loved me," I said, sobbing. For me they were like a little piece of my grandmother's heart and now they were lost forever. I also cried at the thought of Martín's ring. The irony was that I didn't take it to México City for fear of misplacing it, and now it was really lost.

"Well, at least I still have the *esclava* you gave me on my fifteenth birthday." I wiped my tears and looked at the gold bracelet with my name on it.

"Oh, you still have it!" my dad said smiling. "I thought it was also lost."

"No, I always wear it. It would have been devastating if I had lost this too. I know the sacrifice you made to buy it for me. Thanks, Dad."

"By the way, I had to change some of Martín's letters that belonged to you to another box because the one that you kept them in was completely wet. I rescued them for you," he said with furrowed eyebrows.

I smiled and kissed him on the cheek. "Thank you again, Dad."

"What about your pictures?" I asked my mother, wiping my tears.

"We saved most of them because they were inside a suitcase, but others were completely damaged. Unfortunately, they are unrecoverable. And I also lost my image of the Virgin of Guadalupe," she said in a broken voice. It was an antique wooden Virgin that my mother had had for many years.

"We lost many things, and some we can't replace, but the most important thing is that all of you are okay," I said, trying to smile. "Don't worry. I'll buy you all some new clothes."

I told Mom we had to find another place to live so we wouldn't have to suffer the same bad experience with another unexpected storm. Norma and I spent the rest of my summer vacation looking without success for a house to rent.

The start of the new school year was approaching as we waited every day for the mailman to pass. Finally, my summer vacation was over, and the notification never came. I had to pack my belongings and go back to Doctor Arroyo for the third time, leaving behind a sad and discouraged family.

Andrés and I met in Matehuala. During the four-hour trip to Doctor Arroyo, we talked about our vacation experiences; we also shared our respective disappointment at the null results in the *Dirección General*.

At the bus stop we saw Horacio, José, and some other students, craning their necks trying to find us.

"Welcome back, teachers," they said with a smile. That expression from the students made me feel good. After some hugs, they took our suitcases, and we went home.

Along the way, they told us about some news from the town. Once at the house, they took the suitcases to our rooms and said goodbye.

The reunion with *doña* Susana was completely the opposite of when we met her.

This time, she greeted us with a look of pleasure on her wrinkled face. Claudia came skipping behind her, spinning a hula hoop on her arm.

"You're in your same rooms," she said, "but if you want to move to another, let me know, and I'll tell Teresa to get it ready for you."

"Oh no. I am happy there. Thanks anyway," I said.

Andrés also decided to stay in the same room but said he might change his mind later.

After reiterating that she was glad to see us again, *doña* Susana returned to her work.

Later on, Teresa came to say hello. I was glad to see her again, too. She was a very nice person, always kind and helpful. She asked me about my vacation and my family. I told her about it briefly. Then she informed me that some gypsies had stayed for some days in the hotel, reading the tarot cards or the palms of the hands of their clients.

"Oh, my God! I hope they did not occupy my bedroom. I don't want to find bugs in my bed again!"

"Don't worry," she answered me. "*Doña* Susana learned that lesson, so she respected your rooms. However, since she needed the money, she rented two of the rooms in the back. In fact, the gypsies preferred to stay there because they had more privacy for their businesses."

Teresa said that everybody was happy when the gypsy women left, since there were customers in and out all day. "*Doña* Susana hadn't anticipated this, so she regretted having given them accommodation. She swore never to accept any gypsy again as a guest." When Teresa finished with her stories, she asked me if I needed anything.

"Some warm water for a bath would be really appreciated, Teresa," I answered her.

She said a bucket with warm water was already in the bathroom.

After my bath, I felt refreshed and cheerful. Now I was ready for another year of classes and challenges.

CHAPTER FIFTY-SEVEN

SUPERSTITION, ANGUISH, AND REVENGE

Among all of the new experiences of living in a small town, some of the most shocking were those related to popular superstitions. Two cases in particular stayed in my memory, maybe because they involved two of my students.

The mother of one of these students, who I'll call Benito, was very sick. I don't know if her husband had passed away or if they were separated. The point is that the boy was responsible for the care of the family. He helped his mother as much as he could, in the best way he knew how.

One afternoon, Benito came by my house all disheveled, his flannel shirt wrinkled and half tucked into his pants. He was ashen, and his eyes were red and swollen. I had never seen him looking that bad.

"Benito, what's wrong? Are you okay?" I asked him, feeling tightness in my chest.

He didn't say anything. He stood there looking at me with his lips trembling and his eyes cloudy with tears.

"Sit down," I said, pushing him softly onto a chair. He obeyed without protesting.

I called Claudia, who would surely be listening behind the door. She put her head inside the room, her sparkling eyes wide open, surprised I knew she was there. She came inside walking slowly and eyeing Benito.

"Were you eavesdropping as usual, Claudia?" I asked her, pretending to be offended.

She shook her head, emphatically denying my accusation. Her eyes focused on my distressed student.

"Hmm. Anyway, please go for a glass of water," I said.

Claudia ran and came back right away. I took the glass from her hands and gave it to Benito.

I smiled, thinking that Claudia always took her time doing anything she was asked to do. That time, however, she came right away because she didn't want to miss anything that was said.

She stood next to the rocking chair where I was sitting. Benito stared at the floor silently, the glass of water untouched.

"*¡Claudia, ve a ver si la cochina puso huevos!*", I said, waving my hand toward the door.

Claudia opened her mouth and thought for a little bit about what I asked her to do, to go and see if the pig had laid eggs. Then she understood the double meaning of what I said and left skipping and smiling.

I turned my attention to the boy, who seemed to be in a trance.

"So, what's the matter, Benito? I have never seen you like this."

He drank some water, cleared his throat, and blinked. His voice was shaky. "*Maestra*, you might remember, I told you a few weeks ago that my mom has been ill for a long time."

"Yes, I remember. You explained to me why you couldn't finish some homework."

"Well, lately I noticed she looks a lot weaker. The medicine is not helping her. I felt so desperate that I decided to take advice from some people about asking the *brujo* to see my mother."

"But Benito, I told all of you that there is no such thing as witchcraft and magic potions."

"Wait, *maestra*! That's what I thought, too; but let me finish, and then you can decide."

"Go on. I'm listening."

"I went by myself to talk to the *brujo*," he almost whispered. "As soon as I entered his room, he asked me, 'So, are you coming to ask me about your mother?' This caught me by surprise. How did he know? I hadn't mentioned to anyone the reason for my visit." Benito passed a hand over his forehead. He drank another sip of water before continuing with his story.

"The *brujo* told me he wanted to see my mom. He said he needed to evaluate her condition in person. Since my mom is too weak to leave the house, the *brujo* went to see her that morning."

"What did he say?" I asked Benito, impatient to find out the end of the story.

"He observed her carefully. He frowned and shook his head, which made me feel he had seen something bad. Then he asked me for some fresh eggs, some recently cut roses, a white napkin, and a tray. I ran to get all that he asked me. I found the roses in one of our pots but had to borrow eggs from one of our neighbors." The boy moved nervously on his chair and wriggled his hands.

I sensed that the most important part of the story was coming. Sitting at the edge of my rocking chair and placing my hands on my knees, I asked in a low voice, "So, what else happened?"

"Then, the *brujo* passed the eggs over my mom's entire body. One by one he broke them on the tray, and when he did, the yolk came out, not orange, but black, completely black." His voice sounded altered. "He got rid of the eggs that smelled rotten. He said they showed him my mom had something awful inside her body."

"Next, he washed the small tray and told me to place the fresh roses there, which I did. He covered them with the white napkin and chanted some strange spells that I didn't understand. When he finished, he removed the napkin, and instead of the beautiful roses there were … there were … only ashes, some bones … and many worms." The boy shivered and made the sign of the cross.

"Are you sure, Benito? Did you leave the room at any time? Did *el brujo* put anything else on the tray?" I asked, wondering if the man had played some kind of a trick.

"No, *maestra*. I was right there all the time and saw it with my own eyes," Benito said in an impatient and shaky voice. "I stared incredulously at the tray and even rubbed my eyes to be sure they hadn't deceived me, but the ashes, the bones, and the worms were there. I thought I was going to vomit."

"Drink some water. I don't want you to get sick remembering all that."

The boy drank half of the water in his glass, then he continued. "The *brujo* got rid of the things on the tray, and then he told me, 'I'm sorry, son, but your mom is already dying. She's bewitched, and there is nothing that I can do for her anymore!' I was frozen."

Benito said he thought he had misunderstood and asked the *brujo* to repeat it for him.

"The *hombre* told me the bad news again. He explained to me that somebody had put a hex on my mom and that her time was marked. Unfortunately, it was too late, so she couldn't be rescued."

The boy started crying uncontrollably. I gave him some Kleenex and told him to trust that his mom would recover soon. He had to keep his faith in God and not give up. Benito just shook his head. His ashen face reflected his despair.

"I feel in my guts that the *brujo* is telling me the truth. Some people told me a long time ago to look into this, but I didn't believe it. I'm sure my mom is going to die, and ... and ... I don't know what I'm going to do with my siblings!" Benito finished his story sobbing hysterically.

We talked for some minutes, but I realized he was convinced his mom would die soon. He just didn't know when. Finally he left, with his head down and dragging his feet.

Two months later, Benito and his siblings became orphans.

In the midst of his despair, the boy had said, "If I could only find out who did this to my mom, I could take revenge." I advised him to let God be the judge and not think of revenge. But there was another case in which revenge almost happened. It was a situation very similar to Benito's, and it happened a few months later.

One early afternoon, two of my students came by the house in a hurry. They were agitated, and both were talking at the same time. I asked them to take turns talking because I couldn't understand anything they were saying. One of the boys nodded to the other to tell me what was happening.

"*Maestra*, I don't know if you are aware that this morning, we buried Israel's mother," the one who had the floor began.

"No, I didn't know! He told me his mother was sick, but nobody mentioned she passed away. Otherwise, I would have been there to accompany him. How is Israel?"

"That's the reason we came looking for you," the second boy said. "After the burial, Israel went *loco*. He has a gun, and he said he's going to kill the person who put a hex on his mom."

"What are you talking about? What hex? Where is Israel now?" I stood up from the chair in a hurry, feeling that my heart wanted to leave my chest.

"He was at the cemetery the last time we saw him. He's running around and screaming like he's possessed," explained the same boy.

"Please hurry up, *maestra*. We can't waste time. Israel will listen to you," the other boy urged me, heading to the door.

None of the teachers were in the house at that moment, so I decided to go by myself with the two boys.

"Tell Horacio or any of the teachers to meet me at the cemetery. There is a problem with one of the students," I said to Teresa, who came to the patio, alarmed by the commotion.

I didn't wait for her answer. Right away, I followed the two boys, walking as fast as I could and with my heart beating furiously. I prayed to God to give me the wisdom to find the right words to dissuade Israel from committing a crime.

We arrived at the cemetery. We searched for him for several interminable minutes and finally found him. He was sitting on the ground cross-legged in the lotus position, a pistol propped between his legs. He looked at us with eyes bloodshot from crying.

"Oh, Israel, your friends just told me about your mom. I'm so sorry! Neither the other teachers nor I knew about it. They will also feel very bad when they find out."

As I was talking, I slowly moved toward him. When I finally reached him, he tried to cover the gun with a folded newspaper.

"Why do you have a gun, Israel?"

"*Maestra*, somebody ... somebody put a hex on my mom ... and I think I know who it was. I have to avenge her!" he answered me, with tears streaming down his brown cheeks.

"How do you know she had a spell? Those things are not true; you should know that."

"But they are!" Israel said fiercely, hitting his knees with his fists. "When my mom was in her open casket, I knelt to say some prayers for her soul. Suddenly, a tiny black snake came out from one of her nostrils. I jumped in horror!" He dissolved into tears when he said that. Then he continued.

"They had told me that someone had put a hex on her, but I didn't believe them. I told them my mom didn't have any enemies because she was a nice person. Then I heard my father was seeing another woman, a *querida*, a lover. She must have been who did it. I will look for her to avenge my mother!" Israel turned around with wild look.

I felt chills when I saw his eyes and heard his voice as cold as death. I knew he meant it, so I had to do something to prevent a calamity.

Israel wiped his tears, furious, and stood up with the gun in his hand. That was when I had to try to convince him not to do it.

With a racing heart, I told him, "Before you do anything, think about this! You just buried your mom, and I'm sure her spirit is still around. Do you think her soul will rest after listening to what you want to do? Of course not! Her soul will be grieving, and she will never find peace."

Israel stared at me, as if trying to understand what I was saying. He dropped his arms, the gun pointed at the ground. His breathing was rough. I had to try to make him see reason—and fast!

"Tú siempre has sido un buen muchacho". I reminded him that he had always been a good boy. "Can you imagine how your mom would feel knowing you ended up in jail?"

I continued talking, and he cried a lot. Finally, he handed me the gun, which I placed inside the newspaper where he had hidden it before. I put my hand on his shoulder and told him he did the right thing, and I was very proud of him.

"More important," I said, "your mom must be smiling now, and her soul can rest in peace. Let everything be in God's hands."

After that, the three boys and I walked back to town. I noticed that Israel's friends were relieved that he had not only given me the gun, but also that he had promised me to forget about revenge.

Once again, I had put in this other boy's mind the idea that it was better to let Divine Justice work. I told him that if it had been true that somebody had done such a horrible thing to his mom, the worst punishment for that person would be not to have peace of mind.

Israel walked quietly next to me, while the other boys kicked an empty can in the middle of the silent street.

On the way back, we met Israel's father, who had already learned that his son was carrying a gun. I handed him the gun and commented, "He has suffered a very difficult time losing his mother, but he will be able to recover, as long as you are there for him."

"I'll be there for you, son," assured the man. "Now, let's go home."

"I'll see you there in a few minutes. We'll just walk the *maestra* home," Israel answered.

The father took the gun out of the newspaper and put it under his belt. Then he left, thanking me for helping his son.

Close to the house, I saw Andrés in the middle of the street, rushing to meet us.

"What's going on, Socorrito? Are you okay? I came as soon as I heard there was a problem with one of the students!"

"There isn't a problem anymore," I said, smiling. "Truth, Israel?"

"You have my promise. And thank you, *maestra*. I'll never forget this for the rest of my life."

He put an arm around his friends' shoulders, and the three of them left, chatting in a better mood.

As soon as they were out of sight, a wave of emotional discharge ran through my body and made me shiver. The way I felt then, I wanted to vent by telling the story to the other teachers, not with a coffee, but with a shot of tequila.

The problem is that I didn't drink—and I didn't have tequila either.

Municipal Panteon in Doctor Arroyo

CHAPTER FIFTY-EIGHT

CHALLENGES AT SCHOOL

Life in Doctor Arroyo seemed to pass in slow motion. For this reason, anything outside the usual routine became news, and without my realizing it, I, too, started to enjoy listening to the details about any event.

I wondered how and when the town customs had become part of my behavior. Instead of me changing the environment, the environment was changing me. With time, like everybody in town, I knew who came and who left it and why, mostly by listening to conversations at home or to students' discussions at school.

However, I avoided expressing my opinion. I didn't want someone to say, "*Maestra* Socorro said this or she said that." I remembered my mother and grandmother's saying, *"En boca cerrada, no entra la mosca".* I thought that definitely this was a wise saying: "With closed lips, a fly doesn't enter."

Even the town's sayings became part of my vocabulary. For example, any time somebody said something like, "It hasn't rained," people around would answer in chorus, "And like *don* Teofilito said, 'nor it will rain.'" It sounded prettier in Spanish, *"No ha llovido y como dijo don Teofilito, ¡ni lloverá!".*

Doña Susana had her own saying. Any time someone not involved in a conversation made a comment, *doña* Susana turned around, shook her head in disapproval and said, *"Está como la cochina de tía Cleta:¡comiendo y parando oreja!".* We always laughed because we pictured Aunt Cleta's pig, eating and pricking her ears to hear what was said.

As teachers, we knew that being around students meant our days were always unpredictable. Sometimes, an ingenuous answer from one of them would result in a good laugh or an angry frown.

One Friday, I asked the students to use their plasticine to model a hand during the weekend. Monday morning, I told the students to put their work on top of their desks. I walked around the classroom with my grade book, reviewing the models and giving them a grade. Some hands had plenty of details, like nails and lines; others looked as if they had toes instead of fingers. Some girls even placed a small ring on one of the fingers. Regardless, everyone got credit for their effort.

I noticed that Alfredo, one of the boys sitting at the back of the classroom, bent to whisper something to the girl in front of him. I knew he didn't have his assignment. The girl handed him a box of plasticine. Alfredo got some pieces out of the box and kneaded them under his desk, trying to do it surreptitiously. I walked in his direction and stopped to check the work of the girl in front of him. I watched him from the corner of my eye. Alfredo quickly rolled the plasticine on top of his desk and pressed on one end with the palm of his hand, then stopped because I was almost next to him. He wiggled in his seat and then slid his hands close to the plasticine trying to model it one last time, but it was too late. I walked over to the boy and stared at what he had made. The piece had the shape of a spoon, with a short handle and an almost round flat side. I remained silent for a couple of minutes, tapping my closed lips with a pen. Then I started clicking the pen and looked from the plasticine to his face and back. He rocked back and forth in his chair and started tapping faster on his desk, waiting for me to say something. We played cat and mouse, but I was the cat.

"What's this?" I finally asked, pointing at the piece of plasticine with my pen.

His classmates turned their heads to see what he would answer. Alfredo was one of those wise guys who always had an answer for everything. The girl who had lent him the plasticine sat sideways in her chair to have a better look. She covered her mouth and giggled.

"It's … it's … my assignment," he said.

"I didn't ask you for a spoon. Does this look like a hand, Alfredo? Don't forget that it's for a grade." I continued clicking my pen, waiting for his answer. "Where are the fingers?"

Several students sitting close to Alfredo craned their necks to see his work and giggled, too.

Without blinking, he answered immediately. "It's a soldier's hand, *maestra*. He lost his fingers in the war with a grenade."

Lots of giggles were heard throughout the room. I wanted to do it too, at this unexpected explanation but kept a composed expression. I opened my book and wrote a grade next to his name. Two or three boys craned their necks trying to see what was written. I closed my book and went back to my desk. There was some whispering behind me.

"Did you give Alfredo a grade?" one of the students said in a tone of surprise.

"I certainly did. I have to be fair to everybody. Didn't you hear his explanation?"

I observed different expressions. Some of them raised an eyebrow, others frowned, several smiled, and the rest just waited for the class to continue.

Alfredo looked around, sat straight, and smiled, very proud of his cleverness.

"Yes, but ..." the young man who asked the question began. He shook his head in disapproval.

"Didn't you hear Alfredo's explanation that the soldier had lost his fingers in the war? Well, because of the grenade, Alfredo's possible grade of one hundred has just lost the number one, but I was happy to save the two zeros for him!" I said with a big smile.

This time the class laughed heartily, while Alfredo's face reddened, and he sank in his seat.

I had caught the mouse.

Not all the incidents however were amusing.

I remember, for example, something that happened one afternoon in the schoolyard during recess. The incident involved two students whom I'll call Matías and Eleuterio, two well-behaved boys.

As usual, all of the students had recess at the same time. Here and there, some of them chatted in small groups. *Profesor* Merla and we, the teachers, were outside taking care that they didn't get hurt. Some of them played catch with a baseball. Others kicked a soccer ball. There was shouting and some pushing as the boys kicked the ball from one side of the schoolyard to the other. Some of the girls jumped rope on the sidewalk; others played with hula hoops.

Matías, one of the older students, was talking to several girls. He bent over and distractedly picked up a small stone from the ground. He threw it just as Eleuterio ran to catch the baseball. The stone hit Eleuterio on the back of his head. He touched the back of his neck and looked stunned when he noticed his fingers were tinted red.

Some girls got a little hysterical at the sight of blood and screamed.

The teachers and *profesor* Merla rushed to see what had happened. We couldn't believe something like this could occur right in front of us.

"We must stop the bleeding right away," the *director* said, taking poor Eleuterio aside. "*Profesor* Gerónimo, please get the first aid kit."

Gerónimo ran to the principal's office and came back with the small case.

Matías stood by, shaken and pale. He mumbled a lot of apologies. "It was an accident. I didn't mean to hurt anybody."

"Okay, Matías," Rogelio said. "Go to your classroom. We'll talk to you later."

Matías left with several of the girls consoling him. He was very popular among his classmates and never in conflict. We were sure this had been an accident.

"Who is going to take care of him?" *profesor* Merla asked, looking at us and pointing to Eleuterio's head. Before anybody offered to do it, he handed me the first aid kit and said, "You have this hour free, *profesora* Socorrito, so take care. *Profesor* Andrés will help you if you need it."

I took the case from his hand and nodded, while assessing the situation with Eleuterio.

The *director*, Rogelio, and Gerónimo went into the classrooms to continue with their classes. Two girls stayed with us, after getting permission from *profesor* Merla.

I grabbed a pouch with gauze from the kit and asked one of the girls to get me some scissors. As I applied pressure to stop the bleeding, I saw the girl running back with the scissors in her hand.

"Stop running before you fall and hurt yourself," I advised her. "I can only take care of one wounded at a time."

The girl handed the scissors over to me. "Is Eleuterio okay? He looks very pale," she said, her eyes wide. She looked at him with concern. The boy's shirt was stained with blood.

"Don't you faint on me; it's only a small cut," I told Eleuterio while I squeezed his shoulder. In reality, the wound was larger than I had first thought. When one of the girls held Eleuterio's hand, I said, "See? Today you are going to be a very sought-after *galán*!"

The boy smiled weakly.

"Would you please disinfect the scissors with alcohol and give them to me?" I asked Andrés.

After he did this, I disinfected my hands with alcohol, too. I carefully cut all the hair around the wound; he had so much hair!

Then I cleaned it with a piece of sterile gauze and peroxide. After the wound was disinfected, I put some Merthiolate on the wound and covered it with another clean gauze and a bandage to protect it from infection. I put to good use the experience gained at home with my siblings, especially with Julie and Ernesto, who were very active and frequently got hurt.

One of the students who lived close to school lent Eleuterio a clean shirt. With his patched head, Eleuterio and the girls went back to their classroom. I washed my hands and, after reporting to *profesor* Merla, I went on to teach the next period.

I never considered that I could get some kind of disease by touching somebody's blood. Nobody talked about such things at that time, and we didn't have any disposable gloves at school anyway.

Not even an angry parent came to complain. *Profesor* Merla sent a note with Eleuterio, explaining what had happened. He also let his parents know there would be some consequences for the boy who threw the stone. He would be suspended for two days, even if it had been an accident. All of the students had been warned not to throw stones, and Matías broke that rule. As far as I was concerned, this was one more challenge that I was able to solve successfully.

Today, I get chills wondering if I could have caught an infection from this or other similar circumstances when I acted as a nurse at school, or if I could have been held responsible if the wound had become infected.

I don't doubt God was looking out for me. Surely, He listened to my mother's prayers! And very soon these would be indispensable to help me solve a conflict that is forever etched in my memory.

CHAPTER FIFTY-NINE

TIMELY RESCUE

Our working hours continued to be the same as the previous year. The students attended morning and afternoon classes, with a sufficient interval at noon to eat at home and rest for a while. The big change at our new school had been that boys and girls weren't allowed to walk together, so the girls and I arrived at school ten minutes before the boys, and then we left school ten minutes earlier that they did.

Profesor Merla made this decision to dissipate any concerns parents might have about the relationship between girls and boys outside of school.

"Don't forget the parents entrusted you with the safety of their daughters," the *profesor* reminded me; that had been my commitment when we moved into the new building.

"I haven't forgotten. Besides, all of our girls are good and obedient. I don't have discipline problems with any of them," I said.

One afternoon, the girls waited for me as usual on plaza Juárez. On that occasion we were all present earlier than usual, and we walked back to the school, which was located several blocks from the square. The afternoon classes were waiting for us. The day was sunny and warm, and the only noises on the street came from my girls, talking and giggling.

They walked in small groups in the middle of the street, since there was hardly any traffic on that side of town. They usually walked close to me, but this time, I noticed that two of them, whom I will call Gabriela and Liliana, had gone ahead. They seemed to be carrying on an agitated conversation and, from time to time, they turned discreetly to look at me.

"Stay close," I told them. "Don't go too far from us."

Both waved at me, letting me know they had heard me, but they kept increasing the distance. As they turned the street to go across plaza *5 de Mayo*, they disappeared from my view.

That didn't bother me. They would surely sit on a bench, waiting for the rest of us to catch up with them. As soon as we crossed the corner on the plaza, I saw they were not there. It was unusual for Gabriela not to follow my instructions. She was extremely obedient at school.

Just as I was ready to ask one of the older girls to call them, Liliana reappeared on the opposite side of the plaza. She came running toward us, as if somebody was chasing her. She was crying and waving her arms, almost out of breath. When I saw her by herself, I felt a chill running up my spine and shuddered, sensing something terrible had happened to Gabriela.

"*¡Maestra, maestra! ¡Venga, corra!* Somebody is trying to kidnap Gabriela!" Liliana tugged on my arm urging me to run. She was sobbing hysterically.

"What are you talking about?" My knees went weak, but somehow I reacted quickly, without waiting for her answer.

All of the girls ran with me while repeating, *"Vamos! Vamos!"* "Let's go! Let's go!" A feeling of anguish spread over the entire group.

I still wonder how I moved so fast wearing heeled sandals on a cobblestone street. As we turned onto the street, we didn't see Gabriela. My throat tightened from panic. *How could this have happened to her? She is so quiet, and she has never given us any kind of problems.*

"Maestra, maestra, look! There is one of Gabriela's shoes!" A girl pointed to the solitary shoe that lay on its side in the middle of the street. She ran to pick it up.

Meanwhile, another girl shouted, "Oh, look! There are Gabriela's books, lying on the sidewalk!"

The school was only three blocks away, but there was not a soul in view. We reached an unpaved street. We found Gabriela's other shoe lying on the ground, and her backpack covered in dust. I felt a chill run down my back when I noticed signs of something having been dragged in the loose dirt. Surely this was related to Gabriela.

Then we spotted her. She was standing with her shoeless legs apart, half of her face against the wall, grabbing a door with one hand and resisting being pulled inside a house in the middle of the block. From that distance, I noticed someone's arm.

When she saw me appear with the rest of the girls, Gabriela started screaming in panic. *"¡Maestra, maestra, apúrese, apúrese! ¡Ayúdeme, por favor!".* We ran faster when she said, "Hurry up; hurry up. Help me, please!"

My heart shrank when I looked at her closely. Her blondish hair was disheveled and dirty; her dress and her legs were covered with dirt, too. Tears poured from her terrified eyes; fear was painted all over her beautiful face. *I have to reach Gabriela before the man pulls her inside; otherwise it'll be too late. That would completely ruin her reputation.*

I knew the town's customs. In some cases, girls had lost their honor for less serious reasons than that. The dragging was already bad enough, but if the guy pulled her inside the house, it would be worse. The story would be spread around and the truth distorted.

People would say that she wasn't a decent girl anymore. She could even be forced to marry "to save honor." I couldn't allow that to happen! Gabriela was only sixteen years old. Besides, she was my responsibility.

Almost out of breath, I reached Gabriela and grabbed her hard by her arm. Nobody would take her away from me!

From inside the house a tall, medium-built man looked at me with surprise. He must have been in his early twenties. He wore blue jeans, a long-sleeved shirt, and a cowboy hat. He was still holding Gabriela's hand, which she was pulling back trying to flee.

I glared at him. Then, full of anger, I pushed him as hard as I could while telling him, "*¡Imbécil!* Why did you dare to hurt this girl?"

To my surprise, the guy fell backward and let go of Gabriela's hand. She put her shaken arms around my neck and sobbed louder. Her schoolmates watched, angry, and at the same time heartbroken.

The house was big and old. The entrance was an adobe wall with wide double doors. Only one side was open. The man looked at me in disbelief as he got up off the ground, flushed and blinking nervously. He brushed the dirt off the back of his pants and picked up his hat from the floor.

I pushed the tearful Gabriela gently into the arms of her friends who had formed a semicircle behind me. Two or three of them started to cry, too. Determined not to let the guy run away, I stood in the doorway, with my arms and legs spread to block him.

"I ... I ... didn't mean anything bad," he said. "I was just trying to talk to her."

"Do you think we still live in the Stone Age? How dare you drag her in the dirt, you animal?" I yelled at him. I waved my accusing finger in his face, not caring that he was way taller than me. I had never felt so furious with anybody in all my life. My adrenaline was at its peak.

"I just wanted to talk to Gabriela," he apologized again, turning his hat around and around. His face was ashen.

Minerva, who was never afraid of anything, came closer to me, followed by Josefina, Irma, Matilde, and some of the older girls. I noticed their defiant attitude, and I felt they wanted to give me support.

The house had a large courtyard, and I could see only part of the rooms around it. Surprisingly, nobody in the house had come out to see what was happening. A whinnying and the sound of impatient hooves on the courtyard attracted my attention. I moved to the side and discovered two saddled horses tied to a tree.

"What's the meaning of those two horses there if you only wanted to talk to her?" I pointed to the animals, shaking with anger. I closed my fists, wanting to slap him.

He looked silently at his brown cowboy boots, his hands inside his jeans' pockets.

"*Profesora*, do you want me to run and get *profesor* Merla?" one of the girls offered.

Before I had time to answer, I heard a man's deep voice behind me. "*Qué pasa, profesora*? What's going on, Teacher?"

Oh God! Now comes a friend of this guy to help him. As I turned around, however, I saw a policeman coming down from the jeep he was driving. He approached us with his right hand resting on the gun on his waist and a deep frown on his face.

"Ah, Officer! I'm so glad you are here! Look at what this guy did to one of my students." I pointed to Gabriela who was crying quietly. "He dragged her in the dirt for a block."

"I just wanted to talk to her," the man insisted in a shaky voice. His hands must have been perspiring because he pulled them out of his pockets and rubbed them on the sides of his legs.

"You just wanted to talk to her?" I said to him. "So, why do you have two horses saddled right there?"

The policeman looked inside the courtyard and saw the impatient animals.

"Listen, really ... I don't lie," the man said, switching his weight from one leg to the other. He pulled a red handkerchief from his back pocket to wipe the perspiration from his forehead. "I only wanted to talk to Gabriela."

"You better shut your mouth right now before you make this mess worse!" ordered the policeman.

The man lowered his head and was silent. He looked at Gabriela who was waiting for me with the rest of the girls. "Gabriela, could I at least talk to you?" he insisted.

"Insolent, you have nerve! She's a minor, and you already are in a lot of trouble!" I was infuriated by his insistence. I turned to the policeman, who was talking to someone on a walkie talkie. "Please, take him away, Officer!"

"I have already requested reinforcements, and they are on the way."

"May we leave now?" I asked him.

"Yes. You may, and don't worry, *profesora*, I'll take care of this guy. He's going to have a lot of time in jail to think about what he did to this *señorita*."

"*Gracias, profesora Socorrito*", Gabriela said, putting her shoes on while her friends tried to clean her up a little bit. Afterward we all headed toward the school. All of the girls seemed distraught and talked in whispers.

"We still have to talk," I advised Gabriela, "but I'll wait until later."

As we got closer to school, I saw *profesor* Merla outside the door. His hat was placed sideways on his head, and his arms were crossed.

We all knew what that meant—he was furious! I didn't know how he had found out about the incident. None of the teachers or the boys had passed us. I thought maybe one of the girls had run to inform him what was happening. Or maybe he was going out to meet us, since we hadn't been at the school at the usual time. One thing I knew for sure: I would be blamed and scolded.

Gabriela's fingers tightened on my arm. Sighing deeply, I put an arm around her slumped shoulders. She turned her tear-stained face toward me and smiled slightly.

I had taken care of one problem, but I was sure that it was only the beginning.

The *director's* eyes were narrow with disgust, and the muscles of his face twitched with anger. He straightened his hat, only to put it sideways again. My legs felt weak, and I had a dry mouth. My instinct told me to turn around and hide, but I had to keep moving forward until I stood in front of him.

"Sorry, *profesor.* What happened was—"

"I don't want to hear it!" he yelled. He shook his index finger and said, "You are responsible for all the girls; then you have to explain what happened to her mother!"

He turned around and stormed into his office. The girls and I stood in a state of shock.

As we reacted and started walking toward the entrance door, he reappeared. "Ahh, and I don't want that girl in the classroom!" he said, pointing to Gabriela. "Keep her in the teachers' room!" He again stormed back into the building.

Gabriela started to cry. I told the girls to go to their classrooms, and I took the shaken Gabriela to the office. She was pale, and I must have had an ashen color.

"Gabriela, tell me exactly what happened and, please, tell me the truth. I hope you realize the problem I'm facing now with *profesor* Merla and with the parents of your classmates."

She acknowledged it with a movement of her head. "*Maestra*, Félix (not his real name either) was my boyfriend. My mom found out and forbade me to see him again. Yesterday I told him that we would not see each other anymore, and explained to him why." She stopped to blow her nose. "Félix asked me to return his pictures and his letters today. That was the reason why I started getting ahead. I'm so sorry!"

"Okay, so did you return his pictures?"

"Yes, I did, and I was going to meet the group again, but at that minute, Félix grabbed my arm very hard and said I had to go with him." She paused to wipe her tears.

"What happened next?" I tried to rush her.

"I said, 'No, Félix, no! I don't want to go with you!' But he ignored me and started pulling me. I resisted, but he is stronger than me. That's when I let myself fall to the ground, thinking it would be harder for him to make me move, but he got angrier and dragged me in the dirt." Gabriela stopped when Andrés, Rogelio, and Gerónimo came into the room where we talked.

"*Qué pasa*, Socorrito?", Rogelio asked, frowning at the scene.

Andrés and Gerónimo waited by the door with an expression of curiosity and concern.

"They are going to find out anyway," I said to Gabriela with a sigh. "Let me tell them before they see the *director*."

I told them briefly what had transpired up to that minute and asked them to let me continue talking to Gabriela privately. They nodded and left us alone.

"I don't even remember exactly what happened. I tried to kick him and lost one shoe. I was very scared, fearing that he would force me to go with him, and I thought how much it would hurt my mom!" she said, sobbing inconsolably.

I gave her a glass of water and stroked her hair, waiting for her to regain her composure.

"Listen to me, Gabriela." I held both of her hands in mine. "I want you to answer sincerely because I have to talk to your mother. Do you love Félix?"

"Oh, no, *maestra*! I hate him after what he did to me!" she said, her eyes blazing. "I don't want to see him again, I swear."

"Well, I don't want to stick my neck out just to find out you went back to him."

"I'm telling you the truth, *maestra*. I don't wish to see him or talk to him ever again."

"Okay. That's all I wanted to hear. Never lose your dignity. Somebody who really loves you will never degrade you like that."

Since we didn't have running water, I could only bring Gabriela a small can with water from one of the containers, so she could wash her face and her arms. She cleaned her legs with a wet handkerchief. I gave her my hairbrush to tidy up her matted hair. Then we removed the dust from her dress as best as we could.

When she was more or less presentable, I gave her some work to do and left her with Andrés. I had to teach a class in the next hour and he was free at that time.

The afternoon dragged, even though I taught only a few hours. I kept checking my watch, dreading the moment when I would have to talk to Gabriela's mother. *Profesor* Merla avoided me the entire time.

When it was finally time to go home, he came to the teachers' room and with an icy voice he told me, "Remember that you have to go talk to this girl's mother." He put his hat to the side and left without waiting for an answer. I sighed deeply.

"Wish me luck because I'm definitely going to need it," I told the other teachers.

"Don't worry, Socorrito. It wasn't your fault." Rogelio encouraged me.

"It could have happened to any of us!" Andres added.

"Thanks, your support means a lot to me. You know that I'm a very responsible person and have always taken good care of not only my girls, but also the rest of the students."

"We all know that, and *profesor* Merla knows it, too," Rogelio said. "He's angry now, but you know that tomorrow he will act differently."

The three of them wished me good luck. I walked with all of the girls back to plaza Juárez. They seemed affected by the incident and hardly spoke and when they did it was in whispers. Before I dismissed them, I asked them to gather around.

"Girls, please learn from this lesson. As you all know, Gabriela is a nice girl, and she didn't deserve this humiliation." The young girls listened attentively. "Each woman should demand to be treated with respect. When you are of age to start a relationship, never allow a man to treat you roughly." Some of them approved silently. I also saw two girls biting their fingernails while I talked.

"Remember that from now on, you will be close to me when we go to school and when we return. Once we are in this plaza, we will say goodbye, but I hope that you will go directly home. Now you may go, and please, try not to spread the story."

Afterward, some girls continued the journey with Gabriela and me, and others went their own way. As we went by *doña* Susana's hotel, I dropped off my purse and books. In passing I crossed myself and asked God to enlighten my mind with the correct words to touch a mother's heart.

Then we continued walking to Gabriela's home.

CHAPTER SIXTY

HARASSMENT AND CONSEQUENCES

Just as I had feared, when we walked across the main plaza, I saw four men standing on the corner where the jail was located. They were looking at us. *Oh, no! There is "la comisión." Would they try to talk to Gabriela right now, or are they getting ready to go to her house?*

In Doctor Arroyo, a *comisión* is a group of people, usually relatives or friends chosen by somebody to speak on their behalf, often to ask for a girl's hand in marriage. My heart started beating hard because I knew what this *comisión* wanted—to try to force Gabriela to marry Félix, her now ex-boyfriend.

As soon as they saw us, the four men crossed the street and stood in front of us. Gabriela grabbed my arm, and I felt her trembling. *God help me not to show fear to these men.*

Ignoring my presence, one of them told Gabriela in an imperative tone of voice, "We need to talk to you!"

"I'm sorry, but that's not possible." I got in the way. "She's a minor, and she's with me."

"We need to have a word with her," one of them insisted, placing his thumbs inside his belt. He raised one eyebrow superciliously, trying to intimidate me.

"As I said before, Gabriela is a minor. You cannot talk to her. If you need anything, ask her mother."

When we walked away, the four stubborn guys started following us. Gabriela couldn't stop shuddering. "Just ignore them and don't look at them," I told her. The poor girl was shaking like a leaf. *I wish one of the teachers or Horacio would have accompanied us.*

We arrived at the girl's house. The *comisión* had stopped on a nearby corner. I knew Gabriela's mother was a widow, and as a woman, I hoped she would understand. I prayed for the right words to convince her of what was best for her daughter.

As we went inside, Gabriela called her mother, who I'll refer to as *señora* Méndez. I hoped she hadn't heard anything about the incident.

Señora Méndez came into the living room. She looked surprised at my presence there. I realized she was unaware of the situation. She invited me to sit down and instructed Gabriela to bring me a glass of Coca-Cola.

"I know you are surprised to see me here with your daughter, but something happened today that I need to explain to you in person," I said.

Gabriela came back with the glass of soda and sat next to her mother. She kept wringing her hands and looked very pale.

Her mom looked at her with a frown and asked, "What happened, Gabriela?"

The girl lowered her eyes and blushed. *Señora* Méndez gave me an inquisitive look.

"As you know, Gabriela was in a relationship with a man named Félix," I said. "As she is an obedient girl, she followed your orders and broke off the courtship because she loves you and did not want to cause you anger."

Señora Méndez squirmed in her chair and looked at Gabriela with a worried expression. Then she scrutinized my face waiting for the rest of the explanation.

I explained the serious incident to her, step by step.

Gabriela started to cry. *Señora* Méndez sat silently on the edge of the chair. I told her absolutely everything. She wiped some tears with her apron.

"I know the beliefs of many people in small towns regarding a woman's reputation. Some people might conclude that what happened today means Gabriela is not a decent girl anymore. However, her classmates and I are witnesses and can assure you that nothing of that nature happened. She's a good girl, and she was not at fault. Furthermore, Félix is in jail."

I also told her a *comisión* of four guys had tried to talk to Gabriela on our way home. "I know those people are coming to talk to you. I hope to God you are openminded and won't force your daughter to get married. Otherwise, you'll condemn her for the rest of her life. I want you to realize that if this man is capable of mistreating her now when there is no commitment, once they are married, he will do it even more so, and you will not be able to defend her."

Gabriela started to sob softly, and *señora* Méndez put an arm around her daughter's shoulders. This time the girl put her head on her mother's chest, and her tears poured like water from a broken dam.

"*Señora* Méndez, please, don't worry about "*el qué dirá la gente*". What people will say is not important. Let them say whatever they want. I know we live in a *crystal box*, but don't disgrace Gabriela, *por favor*. Your daughter's happiness is in your hands."

The lady told me not to worry and that she wouldn't even talk to the *comisión*. I left their home after she thanked me profusely for helping her daughter.

"Gracias por todo, maestra". The girl gave me a last hug.

I squeezed her hand and waved goodbye. I left their home still nervous, but feeling better after having *señora* Mendez's promise.

The next day, Friday, we had a normal routine. Somebody brought Gabriela to the plaza where I was waiting for all of the girls. *Profesor* Merla was in a different mood, and I was able to explain everything to him. That afternoon, I walked the girl home. Again, *la comisión* waited at a corner of the plaza. Gabriela's face became a mask of fear when she saw them. I changed places with her and walked on the outside of the sidewalk.

"Excuse us, please," I said firmly and coldly to the men who obstructed the sidewalk.

They stepped aside, letting us go by. One of them cleared his throat, trying to call my pupil's attention. "Psst, psst, Gabriela!" he said.

Gabriela ignored him, but her eyes were full of tears. She told me that they had sent word again about her marrying Félix so he could get out of jail.

"I want them to leave me alone, *maestra*! Why don't they understand?"

"One day this will seem like a bad dream. You'll see." I tried to encourage her.

Gabriela gave a deep sigh and put her hand on my arm. Then she said, "Thank you for everything, *maestra*. I don't know what would have happened if you hadn't been there to help me. Thank you also for talking to my mom. You really made her see what is best for me, regardless of what people want to think."

"I'm glad God put me there to be of some help to you, Gabriela. I hope one day you'll find the happiness you deserve because you are a good girl. Never forget it."

She waved goodbye and closed her front door softly. I returned home, happy to have the weekend for some distraction—going to Mass in the morning and to the movies at night.

Early on Monday, I waited at the usual place to meet all of my girls to walk to school. Gabriela wasn't there. I was very concerned, wondering if *señora* Méndez had changed her mind. Just then, I saw Gabriela's brother approaching us. He was one of our best students, intelligent and dedicated to his studies. My heart pounded hard.

"Good morning, *maestra*." His face was stern. "I just came to let you know that Gabriela isn't coming back to school anymore."

There were several reactions of disbelief. A couple of girls cried silently, especially Liliana, Gabriela's best friend.

He informed me *la comisión* had put much pressure on his sister. She couldn't take it anymore. Their mother, *señora* Méndez, decided to take Gabriela to Monterrey where she would finish her studies. He also said he had already notified *profesor* Merla about it.

I felt a tug at my heart, but I consoled myself, thinking Gabriela would have a bright future ahead of her and hopefully, one day she would find a man who would love her in the way she deserved.

That night, in the solitude of my room, I cried for my sweet Gabriela. I knew I would never forget her.

CHAPTER SIXTY-ONE

MY BEST CHRISTMAS PRESENT

The first dance to raise funds for the next graduation generated a good economic gain. The second dance for the same purpose would take place before Easter vacation. I was sure we would raise enough money to have a better graduation celebration than in the previous years.

For Andrés and me, this would be the third class of students to whom we would bid goodbye. In a way it would be more emotional because we had taught these young people for a longer time. Besides, living in a small town we saw the students not only in school, but also at the movies, church, the plaza, parties, almost everywhere. We practically became each other's family, but we knew we might not see them again. The majority would leave Doctor Arroyo to continue their studies in Monterrey, San Luis Potosí, or some other large city. More than likely, most of them would come back to spend their vacation in town when we would be taking ours in Monterrey.

The town fair at the beginning of December 1960 came and went. Dimas García, the region's bad boy, and his friends were in town during that time. Their arrival, as always, caused a great commotion. People commented on Dimas' habit of entering the *cantina* on his mare and getting drunk. Everybody hoped he wouldn't get in a fight with anybody. Luckily, none of this happened, and we had a great fair.

I tried to avoid any encounter with Dimas. The story about my ride on his wild mare and then jumping off it undoubtedly had reached his ears. I felt ashamed and humiliated to learn that he had found out about my adventure, so I hoped he wouldn't show up to eat at *doña* Susana's. However, he did come in with his friends. Fortunately, we had dinner at different times, and I never saw him during the fair. After Dimas left town, I felt more relaxed. Some time would pass before he showed up again.

The teachers and I finally left Doctor Arroyo to spend Christmas vacation in our homes. As usual, we received many nice presents from the students and their parents. Somehow, they always found ways to demonstrate their gratitude.

December promised to be very special for me, not only because I would be with my family and friends, but also because Martín would be coming to see me. I eagerly awaited his telegram confirming the day of his arrival.

As we pulled into the bus station in Monterrey, it warmed my heart to see my family waiting for me. We kissed and embraced, and it was as if I had never left home. There was lots of laughter and talk as we squeezed inside a taxi to go home. I wanted to prolong every second of that vacation.

I hadn't had time to unpack when a special whistle made me jump up from my chair to greet the telegraph messenger at the door. My hands trembled while I opened the yellow envelope. Martín would arrive the following day! A wave of joy washed over me. Just looking at my face, my mom knew I had received good news.

"What better Christmas present than having Martín with you?" she said with a smile.

"All of you are a gift for me, too, *madrecita*." I kissed her soft cheek. "My happiness wouldn't be complete if I didn't have all of you around."

"How long will he stay?" my mom asked.

"It doesn't say. He only tells me the time we'll meet at plaza Zaragoza. I hope that, at least, he'll spend Christmas with me, but anytime we can share together will be good. I'd better start getting ready for tomorrow. I can't wait to see him again!"

Early the next day, I had my hair styled and my nails manicured. I chose my clothes carefully and paid special attention to my makeup. After checking my watch every ten minutes, I saw that it was finally time to go. I wore a beige cashmere coat with a small fur collar, a brown leather purse, and matching gloves. After getting my mom's blessing, I was on my way.

I had never walked as fast across the long bridge that separated my home from Plaza Zaragoza as I did that day. There was a cold breeze, and some people covered their mouths with their woolen scarves.

As soon as the Continental Hotel was in plain view, I saw Martín at the door. He looked handsome wearing a light grey wool jacket, dark pants, white shirt, and a tie. He met me halfway with a broad smile on his face. That time, our encounter wasn't as awkward as the one on his previous visit. We hugged and shared a quick kiss that filled me with happiness. We had a brief conversation, and then we went to our usual restaurant. Martín and I liked it because it was small and quiet. We sat in a cozy corner where we could have some privacy; we asked the solicitous waiter to leave us the menu and give us a few minutes before placing our order.

"Tell me about your trip. Did you have any problems?" I asked, while removing my gloves.

"None at all. Were you afraid I wouldn't come?" Martín held my hands across the table.

"I didn't doubt your promise to come, but you are a soldier, so I worried you might be sent overseas at any time."

"And if they had sent me, would you have waited for me?" he asked, gazing into my eyes.

"You know I would. I told you before."

He stared quietly at my face without blinking. Then he said, "In that case, I have something for you."

He reached inside his jacket pocket to pull out a small black velvet box. He opened it and took out a ring and slid it on my finger. He did that so fast it took me by surprise. I was trying to understand what was happening when I heard him telling me, "This ring reaffirms our promise. Soon we'll start making plans to get married. Okay?"

I was speechless, looking at the white gold ring with a sparkling diamond that he'd placed on my finger. Feeling a knot in my throat and trying not to cry, I just nodded in agreement. Inside the open velvet box on the table was a second ring. That would be my wedding ring. Martín closed the box and put it inside my purse. Then, in a more solemn tone of voice, he said, "I'll place this other one on your finger the day we marry."

My heart pounded. I was afraid that I was dreaming and that, all of a sudden, I'd wake up. I held my breath and looked at Martín for a few seconds until his voice snapped me back to reality.

"Are you happy?" he asked, holding my hands.

"Of course, I am! It was just ... unexpected." Tears of joy moistened my eyes.

"I wanted to buy you a larger stone, but this is all I can afford at this time."

"I don't need a larger stone. My ring is perfect. I've never had anything as beautiful as this. *¡Gracias!*" I squeezed his hands in reassurance and gave him a kiss. Then I turned my hand one way and the other to admire the sparkle of the stone on my ring.

"I'm glad you like it," he said, smiling broadly. "Now let's order some food. I'm starving."

Well, you can't stay in the clouds all the time, so we called the waiter.

Afterward, we did what had become a routine on his last visit. We left the restaurant, walked around, attended a movie, and sat in the park. The day seemed so short when we had to say goodbye. I looked forward to the following day.

Full of joy, I showed my mom my engagement ring as soon as I stepped inside the house.

"I'm so glad, *hijita*! Congratulations. I'm so happy for you." My mother took my hand and admired the sparkling ring. "That boy sincerely loves you. I know he'll make you happy. You'll see. My heart tells me so."

"Thanks, *madrecita*. I hope so; please pray for us." I kissed her cheek and went to bed, counting the hours left before I would see Martín again.

Martín, my future husband, could stay only five days. That was all the leave he was able to get from the Air Force. Every time I saw a clock, I felt my heart shrink, knowing that the time we had together was ending. I tried not to think about it and to enjoy his company as if he would stay forever.

The moment to part arrived. I went to see him off at the airport, which was on the outskirts of Monterrey. The weather had been very pleasant, so I only wore a sweater over my dress. However, there was a sudden drop of temperature, and I started to shake. Martín took off his gray jacket and put it over my shoulders. I didn't want him to do it, but he insisted I should keep it. He insisted he would be all right.

When his flight was announced, we embraced and had a last tender kiss. I found it very difficult to say goodbye to him. Then he walked away and followed the other passengers. He turned around and waved before disappearing inside the plane. I stood by the large window, watching the plane fly into the sky until I couldn't see it anymore. A feeling of desolation invaded me, and I cried all the way home.

Although I was saddened by Martín's departure, it was enough for me to touch my engagement ring to remember that the separation was only temporary. Soon, he would return to talk to my parents, and we would set a date for our wedding. We wanted to get married in the Cathedral's small chapel. I started making plans in my mind for that special day.

The traditional *Posadas* started on the 16th of December. Every night we got together with family and friends and went through all the rituals of this Mexican celebration.

The culmination was *La Acostada del Niño Dios*, the Laying of the Child God, and the customary Christmas dinner at midnight on the twenty-fourth. As in the previous year, my brother Cayito visited us the following day, Christmas, starting at noon, so he hadn't celebrated this event with us. At seven o'clock he returned to the seminary, where he continued to study the priestly career. We tried to be happy and enjoy until its end the beautiful Christmas season.

I began 1961 with my heart full of joy. I could foresee only happy days ahead.

However, I thought of my grandmother's saying, *"El hombre propone, pero Dios dispone,"* "Man proposes, but God disposes."

May He allow that the dreams that Martín and I set out to make come true.

CHAPTER SIXTY-TWO

GOYITO, THE NAIVE CANDIDATE

Deep in my heart, I had a feeling that 1961 would be a year to remember, hopefully for the right reasons. I was engaged to Martín, and that could be the year I would get a teaching position in Monterrey.

I returned to Doctor Arroyo feeling full of hope and energy, willing to give my best as a teacher, just in case I didn't return the following school term.

Andrés was already at the bus terminal in Matehuala. He met me with a big hug.

As soon as we boarded the bus, Chepa, the driver, informed us we finally had electricity in town. This was big news.

"I would like to listen to a program and go to sleep listening to music," I told Andrés, "but my radio got damaged. If I had known, I would have bought one in Monterrey."

"Let's inquire around who's going to Matehuala who could buy one for us," he suggested, "or we could even go on a weekend."

Horacio, Pedro Castilleja, Catarino Santoy, and several other students were waiting for our arrival. All of them acted as if they hadn't seen us in months, making us feel welcome. They carried our suitcases home.

"*Maestros*, what do you think about not having to use kerosene lamps anymore?" Horacio asked.

"*Profesor* Andrés and I were delighted with the news. Imagine! Now we will be able to read late and listen to music and the news," I said.

"But we don't have a radio. We are making plans to buy one. Do you know anybody going to Matehuala soon?" Andrés asked.

"I'll find you somebody. Don't worry about it. I'll let you know soon." Horacio passed a comb through his kinky hair.

"Great! Now tell us how it was on the first day you had electricity in town," I said.

"Well, I wish you had been here," Pedro Castilleja said while swirling his cap on his right index finger. "The animals were confused by the electric light, so they didn't want to go to sleep. They made all kind of noises and kept everybody awake."

"The roosters were crowing in the middle of the night, believing it was daytime," Catarino Santoy said and giggled.

"Are you serious?" I thought they were exaggerating.

"I swear by this!" said Pedro in the Mexican style, kissing the cross he made with his fingers. "Ask others, and they will tell you the same."

Pedro, better known by his nickname, *Perico*, was Vicente Castilleja's little brother. He was slim, with black hair and dark sparkling eyes. He smiled all the time and had big dimples. The girls liked him a lot, and he was very popular among his classmates. He, furthermore, was a very intelligent student.

Catarino Santoy, Perico's friend, was of medium height and had a quieter personality. He was kind, polite, and a good student, too. Catarino and Perico were together most of the time. Both visited me quite frequently and made me laugh with their stories. After the helpful José graduated and left town to continue his studies in Monterrey, Perico and Catarino kept an eye on my belongings whenever I attended a public dance. The boys were around my brother Cayito's age and reminded me of him.

I didn't have to wait long to enjoy some music. The same week I returned from Monterrey, a person bought me an inexpensive radio in Matehuala. I was ecstatic. How had I survived all that time without music or news? My loneliness and quiet nights were then filled with sounds and human voices.

Even though my mom and I were many miles apart, we had agreed to listen to the same radio stations at a predetermined hour. In this way, we knew we were enjoying the same music and programs. This had a soothing effect on me. I felt in contact with my family and my city.

However, listening to the radio reminded me of everything I wanted to do before coming to work in Doctor Arroyo, mainly continuing my education at the Normal Superior for my master's degree. I felt a little sad whenever my friends in Monterrey told me how much they enjoyed attending classes at that institution.

Another of my dreams had been to learn to swim, the perfect sport for Monterrey's hot weather. However, when I was in Monterrey, between having two jobs and studying to be a teacher, I never had time left to take lessons. The irony was that now I had the time, but not a place to learn.

Learning to drive a vehicle had been another of those unfulfilled dreams. That was something I hoped I could do in Doctor Arroyo.

"I can teach you to drive; all I have to do is borrow one of my father's trucks," Eva said when she found out about my wish.

"You will do it? Really? Thanks, Eva. You don't know what it would mean to me if I could accomplish this."

The trucks, however, seemed to be gone all the time, driving back and forth for merchandise to Matehuala and San Luis Potosí. Eva was able to let me practice two or three times, but that wasn't enough.

One day on the plaza, I bumped into *don* Dustano Muñiz, the *Presidente Municipal*, the mayor.

Removing his hat, he said, "*Maestra*, I heard you want to learn to drive, so you are welcome to use one of our jeeps any time you want!"

I figured he had probably learned this from his children, Alicia and Dustano Jr., who were my students.

"Thank you, *don* Dustano. I'll accept your offer if I find someone to teach me."

"Well, I could tell one of my men."

"Thank you so much, but I don't want to impose on any of your employees. I appreciate the offer, but let me check with one of my friends."

"Very well. You just say when, and as I said before, you are welcome to use one of our vehicles."

Although *don* Dustano wasn't a polished man regarding his education, he had been a great help anytime we needed something related to the school. Personally, he was always pleasant and polite to me.

"My children are very fond of you, *señorita*. They say you are very kind to them," he said.

"I think the other teachers and I are nice to your kids because they are well-behaved and never give us any reason to scold them."

That was true. The fact that *don* Dustano was the *Presidente Municipal* had never gone to his children's heads.

Some weeks after our return from Christmas vacation, we had our second fundraising dance. The students were excited when I told them we had enough money to hire two orchestras for their graduation dance. That had never happened. The great news spread quickly among the population. The kids longed for that day to come. They talked about their graduation all the time, but then something happened that shifted the townspeople's attention in another direction.

With the novelty of electricity, more people went to the main plaza after dark, taking advantage of the pleasant weather. Most everybody strolled around, but some neighbors sat on the benches to chat or to see the people who went by. A small group, however, did it for something unknown to my friends and me.

Several times during our night rounds, we noticed a group of loud, smiling young men surrounding a person. Horacio was part of the group. I was curious about it, so I decided to ask him at the first opportunity what it was about.

That opportunity came the next day when he came by my room to greet me. He knocked softly on my open door.

"*¡Buenos días, maestra! ¿Cómo va todo?*". It was nice of Horacio to ask me how everything was.

"Very good, Horacio, thank you." I noticed that he was taller and leaner. He ran one hand through his curly black hair and placed the thumb of the other inside his belt.

"I won't even ask you if you're having fun this year. I've noticed that you and your friends laugh quite a bit every night. What's this all about?"

"Oh, that!" He smiled mischievously and scratched his head as if he were wondering whether to tell me or not. "Well ... what happens is that, as you know, political elections are just around the corner. We started talking about who would be a good candidate to represent Doctor Arroyo. We listed all people interested in politics, like *don* Peregrino de la Garza and some others. We went through this for several days. Finally, one of the guys said we needed someone new."

"Hmm ... that's very interesting. So, have you decided who will be the candidate?"

"This is the fun part," said Horacio, laughing. "Someone suggested, 'Why not Goyito here? He would be a great candidate!' We all cheered the joke, but Goyito took it seriously."

"Wait, what Goyito are you talking about? Do you mean the one ...?" I identified him by his occupation.

"He is exactly who I'm talking about."

"You're not serious! What does he know about politics?"

Horacio said that they explained to Goyito that to be a candidate he had to know the Mexican Constitution. Goyito had been memorizing it, and every night he recited parts of it to them, and they cheered him with applause.

"My God, Horacio. It's not fair. I can see that Goyito has a good memory, but you must not make him believe that he has a chance of winning."

"It's just for fun, *maestra*. We are not hurting anyone." Horacio shrugged and waved goodbye. He left the house whistling, followed by Duque.

The next time I saw Nena and Eva, I shared my findings with them. They laughed at the occurrence. From that moment on, we knew what the boys' cheering was about.

I was worried about the consequences. Goyito was young, naive, calm, and polite. I wondered when he had started associating with the rest of the boys, and how they had convinced him to be a political candidate.

The joke continued growing when the young people told Goyito about the possibility of taking his candidacy to higher levels. After first telling him that he could be municipal president, they advised him to run for something more important, such as a deputy or senator. The young man had memorized the Constitution following the advice of his friends. They made him get on a bench to deliver his speeches. I don't know if this had any effect on anyone, but the youngsters cheered him anyway.

The group around Goyito began to grow. They made him promise them that he would make certain decisions if he won the election. He, like a true politician, swore that he would do whatever the young people asked of him. Everyone knew it was a joke and laughed every time he delivered his speech and made promises, but not Goyito. He really believed in his future as a public servant.

For my part, convinced of his abilities and his knowledge of the Constitution, I began to think that if someone guided him, perhaps one day he could really occupy an official position, at least in town.

One night, I was walking through the square with Nena, Eva, and her sisters Irma and Licha. We noticed that the boys stopped talking as we approached. They were laughing and pushing each other. We passed near them without problem. However, in our second round we saw that there was a smile on every face as a wave of bodies moved from side to side.

"Hey, let's be careful," Nena warned, raising an eyebrow. "Something is going on. Those guys seem to be waiting for us."

We knew that they would not dare to do anything bad. I was a teacher, and Nena and Eva weren't the type to joke around with young people. Still, we were a bit apprehensive. We walked closer to each other. The youngsters definitely had something in mind. They smiled and whispered as they looked at us. When we crossed in front of the group, they pushed someone toward us. The poor man tried to resist without success. We realized it was Goyito. He had no choice but to come rapidly to our side.

"Excuse me, *señorita* Eva," he said, "could … could I … have some words with you? … alone?" He turned the hat over and over in his hands.

We stopped. Eva looked at us without knowing what to do. The boys continued to laugh, and we did the same. We told her that we would wait a few steps forward. We found it funny to see Goyito's face all red. Eva also blushed.

As soon as we got away a bit, Goyito looked at my friend and then at the ground. He cleared his throat and then blurted out, "*Señorita*, from the first time I saw you, my heart beat for you and ..." The rest of his words were like a rush of water. He told her about his love for her and how he hoped she would reciprocate his feelings. He recited each line so fast that he didn't even pause to breathe. He put his hands to his heart to make his speech more convincing. Eva listened politely, trying not to laugh.

When Goyito finished, he took a deep breath saying, "Think about it. You don't have to answer me right away." He turned around, looking victorious, and went to meet his friends. They cheered and congratulated him by patting him on the back. The poor man took a handkerchief from his pocket to wipe his forehead.

Eva's jaw dropped for a few minutes before joining us. We laughed at what we had witnessed and began to tease her.

"Well, you never told us you had a secret admirer," Irma said.

"Wow, we are jealous." I smiled and shook my head.

"So, what did he say to you? Did he ask you to marry him?" Nena raised an eyebrow and laughed, her tears running, and that made us laugh too.

"Oh, shut up!" Eva then told us about Goyito's declaration of love. "He must have been practicing because the poor man recited it all without even breathing. I wish I could find out who put him up to this," she said, laughing nervously.

"I'll find out soon," I promised her. "Don't worry,"

The following day, I decided to speak with Horacio. He would know for sure.

"Claudia, please tell Horacio to come to my room. I need to talk to him," I told the girl who, like other times, was playing with her hula hoop near my room.

"What do you need him for?" Claudia asked with wide eyes. "Did he do something?"

"Claudia? I told you before that you shouldn't ask questions. Just call Horacio, please."

"Okay, okay, I'm coming." She ran to fulfill my order.

A few minutes later, Horacio appeared, shoving his shirt into his blue jeans and combing his hair. Claudia kept turning her hoop right behind him.

"Claudia, I think *doña* Susana is looking for you. Go see what she wants," I said.

The girl walked slowly toward the kitchen. She turned to see us, showing disappointment because she couldn't figure out why I wanted to talk to the boy.

After the greetings, I asked him whose idea it was for Goyito to declare his love for my friend.

Horacio started to laugh. "Well, you know that Goyito thinks he would be the next candidate for a political position. First, we told him he had to learn the Constitution, and he did. Then, someone explained to him that if he wanted a more important position, he had to be married, as dictated by the Constitution. But he could not marry just anyone, she should be someone special."

"He was intrigued. 'So, who should I marry?' Goyito asked us."

"'Eva Berrones, of course,' we told him. 'She is the daughter of the most important man in Doctor Arroyo. What's more, she is pretty and educated, and her father has money. She would be a really nice First Lady. If she accepts you, you'll have it made!'"

"So, we gave him a page from the book *'Declaraciones de Amor'* to memorize, and he did."

"Horacio, I think this joke is going too far. Now Goyito is waiting for an answer from my friend. How is he going to react when Eva turns him down?"

"Oh, don't worry, *maestra*. We can start thinking about another wife for him. How about my Aunt Nena?" He smirked.

"Horaciooooo. Don't even think about it! You already are in a lot of trouble with her."

Horacio could surely become a great lawyer—for every argument, he always had an answer. I made him promise that they would stop the farce there and that they would leave Goyito and my friends alone.

As the boy whistled away, I was wondering if I had intervened in time.

CHAPTER SIXTY-THREE

AFTER A LAMB, A WOLF

Sometime at the beginning of the new period of classes we learned about something that would create news in our municipality.

Campaigning politicians for the *Partido Revolucionario Institucional*, or PRI, sent word to our authorities announcing their future visit to Doctor Arroyo. *Profesor* Merla received a short letter from the municipal president advising him the date on which the candidate's delegation would arrive. He told us we should stand with our students on the main street to welcome the distinguished visitors.

People from towns close to Doctor Arroyo were invited to come to listen to the speeches. Everybody knew the local authorities wanted to have a large attendance. That would make the town look good. The politicians would leave happy, thinking all of the audience would vote for them. But the rival party's delegation, *Partido de Acción Nacional*, the PAN, would think the same when they came to Doctor Arroyo, since the same audience would be present.

On the appointed day, big trucks carrying visitors from other communities started to arrive in the early morning. They were traveling while standing in the back of the vehicle. Most of them weren't interested in what the delegation had to say. They were there just for the fun of the free ride. People were well acquainted with the politicians' empty promises.

Doña Susana and her maids were awake very early. I could hear the sound of their voices and the clink-clunk of the pots in the busy kitchen. I knew Andrés would be sleeping like a rock despite the rattling. Even Duque got up from his spot and started barking when he heard the trucks going by the house. I smiled, thinking that it would take something louder than that to wake up Andrés. However, once he got up, he got ready very fast.

The delicious aroma of freshly brewed coffee let me know early breakfast was ready. I went to knock on Andrés's door.

"*Profesor* Andrés, we are leaving," I said.

"Oh, okay! *Gracias*, Socorrito. I'll be out in a minute."

His bed squeaked as he got up, and I went into the dining room to have breakfast. *Profesores* Merla, Gerónimo, and Rogelio were already there. We exchanged greetings, and a few minutes later Andrés came in, still tucking his starched shirt inside his pants and his hair slightly wet.

"I hope you were not waiting for me," he said with a shy smile.

"No, we are waiting to be seen," I replied. "It seems that the maids have been delayed a bit."

Teresa came carrying two plates. She placed one in front of *profesor* Merla and the other in front of Rogelio, who had arrived first.

"The others' breakfasts are coming," she said. "I'm sorry we are a little bit behind. *Doña* Susana wanted us to start getting ready for dinner."

"Dinner? Why so early?" Rogelio asked.

"There are many foreign people, so we have to cook extra food," explained *doña* Susana, who had come into the dining room carrying the rest of the plates.

When we finished eating, the *director* went over the plan for the day.

"We'll take the students to the main plaza around midmorning, and somebody there will show us the place where we'll line up. Once the delegation comes, we'll dismiss the students, and we'll go home to rest. After dinner, the five of us will attend the political rally at the theater. Then, we'll go to the courtyard for the dance in their honor."

Andrés and I nodded, but I commented, "I hope the students won't be in the sun too long."

Gerónimo pushed his chair back and raised an eyebrow. "The only good thing about all of this is the dance."

Rogelio kept silent, but his tapping on the table told me he wasn't happy with the plan. He pushed up the tip of his nose and stared at me. I could hear him in my mind saying, "I don't bow to any politicians."

I shrugged. We had to be present because it was expected of us.

"It's time to go," the *director* said, looking at his watch.

We all stood up and left to meet our students. After we gathered them, we took the place assigned to us. The organizers told us the visitors would come around midday. Twelve o'clock came and went. After another hour, the students, in uniform, were already tired, so they sat on the sidewalk.

The caravan finally arrived—three hours late. We were hungry, hot, thirsty, and angry. Several girls were upset because their white skirts got dirty.

"This delay is a lack of respect to all of us," I commented out loud. Rogelio nodded with an angry gesture.

"I wish we didn't have to go to the theater or the dance," he said.

As the cars passed with the delegation, the attendees greeted and applauded. The members of the delegation returned the greeting. We only saw them go by. We, especially Rogelio, were quiet, tired, and upset.

After dismissing the students, we went home for an early dinner. When we finished, we retired to our bedrooms to rest for a little bit.

After a short *siesta*, *profesor* Merla came by our house. We had all changed clothes. The professors were wearing jackets and ties. I wore an orange-flowered silk dress on which I always received many compliments. As we were leaving, Nena arrived. She was late for dinner.

"Have fun at the speeches, *maestra*." Her sarcasm was obvious.

"Ha! Yeah, right. I just hope I won't fall asleep. You said you'll attend the dance; then I'll reserve seats for you and Eva."

"Please do. I might meet somebody interesting from the delegation." She giggled.

I tapped her softly on the arm and hurried to catch up with the rest of the teachers.

When we got to the theater, we saw that it was almost full. Our box was empty, because people understood and respected that was our place. Enthusiastic people held up signs with different sayings. Some displayed the name of the candidate. Others had a petition for their own community. A festive atmosphere prevailed. On the stage there were several long tables covered with white tablecloths. Behind them, several chairs awaited the guests and the authorities. On the right side, there was a podium where the speaker would stand to deliver his speech.

Shortly after, the master of ceremonies announced the names of the people who would occupy those chairs. The spectators kept silent and stared at the stage out of curiosity. One after the other, the guests and authorities made their entrance and took their seats, accompanied by polite applause. Suddenly, a roar from the audience and a great cheer spread through every corner of the theater. The guests looked at each other in confusion; none of them had received such an ovation before.

I looked up at the stage. My eyes flickered in disbelief. Following the guests was Goyito!

At the roar of the people shouting his name, Goyito saluted, raising his arms with a triumphant expression. Then, with great poise, he took the seat reserved for the municipal president, who stood behind him, speechless and with no place to sit. The stunned guests looked at each other in bewilderment, not knowing what to do. Everyone was uncomfortable except Goyito. He seemed to be savoring the moment. People laughed and kept yelling, "Go-yeee-to! Go-yeee-to!"

Someone on the balcony shouted, "Speak, Goyito, speak!"

"Yes, yes, speak!" others chanted. Thunderous applause followed.

There was a gasp as Goyito started to get up from his chair. I felt the blood drain from my face. Was he really going to give a speech? The municipal president's face twisted with rage. He stepped aside and called a nearby policeman. He gave him some instructions. Then the policeman approached Goyito and whispered something to him. He hesitated for a moment, especially when some people started yelling, "Leave him alone!" and "Let him talk!"

Finally, the policeman convinced him to leave the stage in silence.

People kept laughing. It was difficult to silence the audience to start the show. When all was quiet the expert politicians gave passionate speeches, using the expressions on their faces, the movement of their hands, and pounding on the podium to excite the people. The audience cheered and applauded loudly any time the speaker raised his voice. For a moment, people might have believed in their sincerity, but I knew that soon, they would remember about the thousands of promises made to them previously that had never been delivered.

In any case, at the end of the event, everyone agreed—the only interesting thing about the meeting was the unexpected appearance of Goyito. After the parade of speakers was over, the master of ceremonies invited the audience to attend the dance on the neighboring court. Nena and Eva were already waiting for me.

"Hello, girls. Were you inside when Goyito came on stage?" I asked them. They both shook their heads.

"We just arrived a few minutes ago, but what's up with Goyito?" Nena asked.

"Oh, what a show! Let me tell you what you missed."

I told them in detail everything that happened inside the theater. "I think Goyito has a future in politics, maybe you should consider being First Lady," I told Eva.

They both laughed, but Nena did it with such intensity that, as usual, tears ran down her face.

By that time, the music had started. The place was full of people who laughed and talked animatedly. Antonio, the theater owner's eldest son, invited me to dance. He was so tall that I had to look up to talk to him. As we went by the guests, I noticed that one of them said something to the person next to him, while pointing with his head in my direction. Every time we went by, the same man stared at me insistently. I pretended not to notice him while I continued my conversation with Antonio. After the third song, I went back to sit with my friends.

As soon as I did this, the staring man stood in front of me. He extended his hand and asked me to dance with him. Since he was one of the guests, I couldn't refuse. He must have been in his middle thirties. He was medium height, very good-looking, and well-dressed. As soon as we started dancing, he initiated a conversation. He seemed very polite and, other than staring at me, he hadn't done anything else to make me feel unfriendly toward him. I tried to relax. He asked me what all that business was with the guy on stage. I briefly told him the story, and he laughed a lot. The second song started, and he continued to dance and converse with me. He commented that despite the disastrous road, they were all happy to have come because the people of Doctor Arroyo had given them a warm welcome.

"By the way, how is it that such a pretty girl is in this town so far from civilization? I know that you don't belong here."

I felt my face flush. Trying to sound normal, I said, "Thanks for the compliment. I teach in the middle school."

"How long have you been working here?"

"This is my third year."

"Three years buried here? I don't understand. Don't you want to work in the city and be closer to your family?"

I explained to him the circumstances under which I had accepted the position.

The third song had started. I told him my attempts to go back to Monterrey but every year I had been sent back to Doctor Arroyo with the promise they would call me when a position closer to Monterrey became available. "I was supposed to come here only for a year, and this is already my third." I let out a sigh.

"Listen, I know a lot of very important people. I promise you that through my contacts, I'll help you get a job in Monterrey in no time."

"Really? That would be great! I need to be close to my family and also continue my education." *What a wonderful man! We just met, and he's willing to help. Finally, somebody will give me a hand to get what has been denied to me so much.*

The man reached into a pocket inside his jacket and got a business card. "Look, this is my name. The next time you go to Monterrey, send me a letter letting me know you'll be there. We can meet for coffee, and I'll introduce you to some of my contacts. By the way, what's your name?"

I told him as I took the card with a big smile and my heart full of joy. I couldn't believe my luck! *In my next letter I will tell my mom. She'll be thrilled!*

"Well, *mucho gusto*, Socorrito. I just want to ask you something. When you send me your letter, be sure it's addressed correctly to me and write a man's name as a sender. Use something like *'señor* Camero,' and I'll know it's from you."

"A man's name? Why?"

"Well, my wife is a very jealous person."

I heard warning bells in my head. "Why would you hide from your wife the fact that you want to help me?"

"She wouldn't understand that I want to help a pretty lady like you. We have to be discreet. You understand?" He squeezed my hand, as if sending me a secret message.

This time the bells turned into sirens, red flags appeared, and my body stiffened. I felt my face flush with indignation. Trying to suppress my anger, I said, "Here is your card, *señor*! Keep it for somebody more gullible than me! I really thought you were honestly offering to help me, but I just realized I was wrong. Now, I don't want to embarrass you by leaving you standing in the middle of the floor, so take me back to my seat."

I turned around, and he followed me to my chair. He tried to take me by the elbow, but I cringed at his touch and pulled my arm away from him.

"I'm sorry if you got offended, Socorrito. Many other girls would have gladly accepted my help," he said brazenly. He said these words using *tu* instead of the polite form of *usted*, which made his words even more offensive.

I couldn't believe he had the nerve to make such a comment. I stopped and turned around to look at him for a second. "Maybe other girls, *señor*, but not me. I don't have money, but I'm rich in dignity. I would never accept this kind of help. You talked to the wrong girl!"

By that time, we had reached my seat. I didn't even say goodbye. I realized some people were looking at us, but I didn't care. The man went back to his seat, too. My eyes felt heavy with tears. I wasn't sure if it was because I was angry, humiliated, or sad.

"Hey, *maestra*, what's wrong?" Nena asked. "That was a very good-looking man. How come you didn't continue to dance with him?"

"Well, there are wolves in sheep's clothing." I tried to smile when I said that.

"What are you talking about?" Nena asked, regarding me quizzically.

"Looks are deceiving, Nena. I'll tell you later."

"I have to hear that story, too," Eva said. "Now I'm curious."

"Oh, you won't like it, believe me. We better enjoy the rest of the night."

I felt angry with myself. How could I forget he was a politician? He had dazzled me, but I walked away in time. I then thought about another of my *abuelita's* favorite sayings, *"Recuerda, ¡no todo lo que brilla es oro!"*. She was so right, "Not everything that glitters is gold."

What this rascal showed was pure copper.

CHAPTER SIXTY-FOUR

BURYING MY HEART AND MY DREAMS

Some weeks before graduation, I received disturbing news from home. My mom let me know the curio stores where my dad worked were having a hard time. That was hard to understand. I had always heard that "Monterrey had an industry without chimneys," referring to the immense influx of money the city made from tourism. However, it had recently declined drastically. There were rumors that five of the six curio shops that belonged to members of the same family were going to close. My mom told me not to worry, but she wanted me to know; in this way, if my dad were to lose his job, it wouldn't take me by surprise.

I tried not to let the news interfere with my professional performance, and I redoubled my efforts to finish teaching my subjects the last part of the semester. Afterward, we started getting ready for the great day of the graduation.

This event was anticipated with considerable emotion. This group of students had been very cooperative from the beginning. The group always radiated a lot of energy, especially Minerva and her brother Roberto, Irma Berrones, Lilia Nava, Josefina González, Lupita Torres, and several other students. They had been our students for three consecutive years. We, their teachers, saw them grow and change mentally and physically. Now, they were ready to leave the nest and spread their wings in the big city. I would find it difficult to watch them take flight.

María Luisa Berrones, me, and Lupita Torres at graduation. Photo provided by Lupita Torres.

Graduation day was memorable. The students and their sponsors had breakfast after Mass. I did too, because I agreed to be the sponsor of Lupita Torres and María Luisa Berrones. At the end of the afternoon, the young graduates made their grand entrance with the "Triumphal March" of *Aída* in a theater full of family, friends, and curious townspeople.

All the graduates dressed elegantly—the boys in their black suits and the women in their pretty white dresses—for the ceremony.

All was perfectly planned by our principal, *profesor* Merla, who was a master of organization.

Profesor Rogelio was again the master of ceremonies. His deep voice and performance on the microphone created an excellent setting for the event. As expected, I took care of choreographing the dances. *Profesor* Merla gave the farewell speech. Once more, his whole-hearted words and deep thoughts brought tears to the graduates' eyes and prolonged applause from the audience. Andrés and Gerónimo contributed to the program, as well, though I don't remember their activities. We all did something to ensure the event turned out perfectly.

When the graduation ceremony ended, all the people moved to the open courtyard. The graduates lined up by couples inside the theater. Then, with big fanfare, they went out to take their places in the center of the courtyard to dance the graduation waltz we'd rehearsed intensely, *Tales from the Vienna Woods*. In the end, they received a long and enthusiastic applause. They congratulated each other, relieved and proud that their performance was flawless.

Graduation in Doctor Arroyo. Photo provided by Profa. Lilia Nava.

Afterward the dance floor was open to all. New graduates and attendees were delighted that two live orchestras were alternating to play. We received numerous congratulations on the success of the celebration. When the party was over, there were plenty of hugs, laughs, tears, and promises among the students. They vowed to keep in touch and never forget each other.

Minerva and her usual group of friends approached me as I picked up my belongings, safeguarded now by Perico and Catarino. "*Maestra*, we want to thank you for being faithful to your promise of staying with us until we graduated," Minerva said.

"We told you that if you didn't come back, we would go looking for you," Josefina added. She giggled, although there were tears in her eyes.

"I'm delighted I was your teacher during these three years. You know I'm going to miss you."

"You'll always be our teacher and our friend, and we'll never forget you," Lupita Torres said.

My eyes welled with tears at her sincere words. I hugged her in return.

Other students also expressed emotional remarks.

"If you decide not to come back next year, there is no problem," Roberto said. "At least you were with us until the end of our studies. Anyway, we already graduated."

"Roberto! Don't be witty," Minerva said, nudging him so hard that it made us laugh.

I looked at him and smiled, remembering the great surprise he gave us when we returned from our first summer vacation. He had grown suddenly. Now he stood out above the whole class. Even his voice had changed, but inside he was still the same.

"Thank you, Roberto. I'll think about it. Right now, I'll say goodbye because my friends are waiting for me to go home. Without a doubt, you guys must be tired too."

"We'll see you before you leave," Lilia Nava promised.

They all hugged me once more and left.

I thanked Perico and Catarino for taking care of my things and joined my friends. I had been busy all night and hardly had time to talk to them during the party. Besides, anytime I was free, Santiago invited me to dance. I also danced with Pepe Castilleja, the Torres brothers, and others.

"The music was very good. Hopefully, next year you'll have the same orchestras," Eva said. She had danced quite a bit.

"Well, first of all, tell us, will you be back next year?" Nena asked.

"At this time, I'll say that it's more than likely that I'll be back."

We were outside *doña* Susana's house. We said goodnight and promised to get together before my return to Monterrey.

That night, with my mind free from the worries of the end of courses, I had time to think about the problems at home. I hoped the news about the curio stores' possible closing was just a rumor and that everything would be okay by the time I went home.

Two days later, after saying goodbye to half the town, I rode the bus to Monterrey. As soon as I saw *Cerro de la Silla*, Saddle Mountain, I felt at home, knowing that in a few minutes I would meet my family again. My heart jumped with happiness.

When the bus entered the terminal, I saw the eager looks on my family's faces. I opened the window, and they waved their hands when they recognized me. My lonely heart welcomed their hugs and kisses. Even though my parents showed joy, I detected a little shadow in their eyes. Something was amiss. I decided to wait until later to find out about it. I had just arrived and wanted to feel happy a while longer.

I didn't have to ask. My mom gave me the bad news after we arrived home. "*Hijita*, I hate to tell you this, but unfortunately your dad is out of work. The five curio shops closed." She clasped her hands and stared at me, sadness in her eyes.

I kept quiet for a few seconds, trying to digest her words. "When did it happen?" I asked.

"At the beginning of the month. We didn't want to tell you. We hoped your dad would find another job before you came back." My mom's lower lip trembled a little bit.

"And ...?"

"¡Nada! Your dad said that several other curio shops in the tourist area have closed, too. These are bad times." She sighed deeply.

"So, how are you doing with the expenses?" I held her hands and looked into her eyes.

"So far I have been able to pay our debts. ¡Pero qué patrones ingratos! Those ungrateful bosses. Instead of giving your dad severance pay, they decided that they'll pay him a small amount every month, supposedly until they fulfill their obligation."

"No se preocupe, madrecita. ¡Dios proveerá!". Right away after I told my mom not to worry, that God would provide, I went looking for my dad. I found him in the kitchen drinking a cup of black coffee and reading the classified ads in the newspaper. He raised his head when he heard the sound of my heels on the bare floor.

"Daddy, Mom told me about your job. I'm sorry." I put my arms around his neck and kissed him on the cheek. He folded his newspaper and cleared his throat.

"*Si, hijita*. I don't have a job anymore and I'm distressed." He frowned and shook his head. "I've been looking around every day, but I can't find anything. Besides, at age fifty-one I'm considered old. The good jobs are for younger people."

I looked at his handsome face. My father was fifty-one, but he looked much younger. Yet, what he said was true. Sadly, everyone knew it was difficult for a man to get a job if he was forty years or older. For women, it was worse. The newspaper ads most of the time said, "hiring young ladies between eighteen and twenty-five years old." Or "hiring *señoritas* not older than twenty-five."

"Don't worry, Daddy. You'll find something." I tried to sound cheerful. My dad just looked at me with a lost expression in his eyes and went back to searching in the newspaper.

The summer of 1961 was nothing like I had anticipated. Even with Cayito's presence in the house for his vacation, we didn't feel the normal joy. My dad continued his search for a job without success. My mom and I gave him constant words of encouragement, but we could see him become more demoralized day by day. Mom, for her part, immersed in her own musings, had stopped singing, unless we asked her directly.

Arts and crafts classes helped to distract me from worries, and so did the occasional outings with Mari Paz. I wrote long letters to Martín without mentioning my father's unemployment. I was concerned that he might start questioning how this would impact our wedding plans. I hoped my dad would find a job soon so that everything would go back to normal.

By the middle of the summer my dad should have received his third monthly payment, but instead, what they gave him were all kinds of excuses for not paying him. I told my mom not to worry. I would give her my full paycheck, minus what I needed for my rent. My brother Héctor had just started earning some money as a student teacher. He shared his small paycheck with my parents, too.

August came, and my dad still hadn't found a job. Although we had not touched on the subject in our conversations, I knew that my parents' concern was intensified knowing I would be married soon and not able to help them anymore. With a sad heart, I recognized that being the oldest child, I had to make a drastic decision. I couldn't leave my family without my monetary help.

All of my dreams came crashing to an end. There was no hope for me, but I couldn't tell Martín. I was afraid he would think I was asking for his help. I went to the Cathedral's chapel where we had planned to be married and cried. I sat there for a long time, then walked home. I hoped my mom wouldn't notice my red swollen eyes. Luckily, she wasn't there.

That night, I waited until everybody was asleep. Then I got up, and with the greatest pain in my heart, I wrote Martín a letter.

"My sweetheart, I'm so sorry I have to break my promise to marry you. I can't explain my reasons to you, but I'm returning your rings, and I release you from your commitment. Please forgive me and make your life without me."

After finishing the letter, I read it a thousand times with my eyes clouded with tears. For a long time, I struggled with an inner conflict—send the letter or tear it up? Finally, I put it in the envelope and closed it. Then, I let the tears flow freely until sleep overcame me.

Next day, after I sent the letter to Martín, I informed my mom of my decision and we cried together.

A few days later, he wrote me back. He said he wasn't going to pay attention to my words about breaking our engagement. Therefore, he would come to Monterrey in December so that I could explain my reasons to him face to face. I cried reading his letter because it was a proof of his love for me, but I couldn't ask him to wait until my father's situation was resolved. I knew it could take years, and that would be unfair to Martín.

My vacation was almost over. I felt destroyed inside. I had broken my engagement to Martín and doubted I would ever be married since I let go of the man I truly loved. My dad didn't have a job, and only God knew if he would ever find one. The well-being of my family was on my shoulders. From then on, I would be sending most of my salary home, and just when I needed my family's support, I would have to go back to being lonely.

After my suitcases were ready to go, I had another painful task. With my heart broken by sadness, I slowly removed my engagement ring. I held it between my shaking fingers and contemplated it for several seconds. After a last kiss of it, I placed it inside its small black velvet case and closed it. The soft click of the box made me shudder. Like a lid on a casket, I was burying my heart and my dreams of happiness.

Bitter tears ran down my cheeks as I placed the small case in a corner of my empty dresser. I tried to put a smile on my face when my mom entered the room, but she knew me well.

"¡Lo siento, hijita!". She caressed my chin tenderly, looked in my eyes and repeated, "I'm sorry." She ran her free hand over my head and said, "Have faith. If God's plans are that you and Martín get married, eventually it'll happen."

"Well, it better be sooner than later," I said in a cracking voice. "But if it doesn't happen, God knows what's best for me."

My mother looked at me. Her wet eyes and the shadow of a smile invited me to imitate them. *I can't leave her feeling heartbroken for me. She already has enough problems.*

I took a deep breath and tried to smile.

"Don't you worry, *madrecita*. I'll be okay. I promise." I gave her a big hug and kissed her forehead and her cheek. She was my rock.

Then I turned to my dad who was quietly waiting by the door. "I hope you will find another job soon, Dad," I said. "Regardless, don't worry. I'll be here to help all of you."

"Thanks, *hijita*. Pray that we get out of this problem. I can't put all the responsibility on your shoulders." He shook his head and sighed. Then he looked away.

I knew he didn't want me to see the pain in his eyes. He had always worked long hours to support a family of nine. I gave him a hug and put my head on his shoulder like I used to do when I was a little girl.

"The taxi is here," said Ernesto, who was waiting by the open front door.

Javier and Héctor came into the living room and carried my suitcases to the taxi. All of us got into it. There was a long and uncomfortable silence until Julie started chatting. I held one my mom's hands firmly. After all these years, the separation was still painful. I felt sad thinking how much I had missed of my family's lives.

With a heavy heart, I said goodbye to them again. As I kissed my mother's cheek, her tears and mine mixed. We both knew that the rosy picture I had at the beginning of the year was now shrouded in dark clouds.

The day was bright; for me, it was night.

My grandmother was right. "Man proposes and God disposes."

CHAPTER SIXTY-FIVE

FLEXIBILITY AND INJUSTICE

The incident with the visiting politician taught me a lesson: Not all people offer help out of the goodness of their hearts. I thanked God for giving me the wisdom and the common sense to recognize the ulterior motives of that scoundrel. I realized that any effort to change schools would have to come from my mother or me. She was the one who went by the *Dirección General* from time to time to check on possibilities.

We didn't have connections who could pull strings to move me closer to home. My family and I arrived in Monterrey just eight years before, and we had only a few relatives there. The only important people I knew were my bosses from the curio stores where I had worked as a secretary. Those stores, however, had closed, and worse yet, my father was having problems collecting what they owed him.

My father had worked hard for them. He had been a reliable and faithful employee, so I resented the store owners for withholding his severance payment. He couldn't even complain to *Conciliación y Arbitraje* because his name would be put in *la lista negra*, "the black list," that all types of companies or businesses consulted before hiring a person.

However, those same people had been flexible with me. I was the only employee allowed to work half a day so that I could be at my other job as a student teacher. However, I had to make up what they called the borrowed time by working Saturdays from 9 a.m. until 10:00 p.m. and Sundays from 9 a.m. to 4:30 p.m. I had been a reliable and dedicated employee like my father. Whenever something unexpected arose, like the delay or absence of any of the cashiers, my bosses knew I would cover for that person, at least until they could call another employee. Many times, some urgent business letter needed to be written at the last minute, and I did it without complaining. That earned me my bosses' respect.

A year before I graduated as a teacher, my bosses showed me their appreciation for my hard work on one particular occasion. One day, *don* Raúl came to my office. He stopped in front of my desk smiling enigmatically. His expression piqued my curiosity. I stopped working on the ledger to pay attention to him.

After the usual greetings, he told me, "Socorrito, I have some news to share with you. My brothers and I have decided to consolidate all of the stores' offices into one. This will be more beneficial for everyone. Now, we would like you to be our office manager. You would receive extra remuneration, of course."

For a few moments, I was speechless. He sucked his cigar a few times while waiting for my answer.

A little tense, I finally said, "*Don* Raúl, I am infinitely grateful that you have thought of me for this position. Unfortunately, I can't accept this honor. My goal is to become a teacher, as all of you know, so once I graduate, my plan is to stop working as a secretary to focus full time on my career."

Don Raúl said he was sorry to hear that, but he understood my reasons. I suggested another secretary, María Eugenia. She had seniority over me and was a hard worker, too. Besides, she was serious and discreet. She deserved that position. I asked *don* Raúl not to mention that he had offered me the job first. He agreed and the following week announced that María Eugenia would be our new office manager. I felt delighted to see María Eugenia's facial expression go from surprise to beaming with pleasure. My congratulations to her were absolutely sincere.

Some weeks later, after *don* Raúl finished dictating some business letters to me, he stared at me pensively. I waited for more instructions. He put out his expensive cigar on the crystal ashtray and wiped the sides of his mouth. "Socorrito, some weeks back I offered you the management of the offices, but you refused. I accepted your reasons, but now I would like to make you a different proposal."

Don Raúl was a husky man with fair skin and ruddy cheeks. He was clever and had a good sense of humor. He walked around with a cigar between his fingers constantly. I had worked with two of his brothers previously, and the three of them had been good bosses to me. I closed my notebook and paid attention to what he had to say.

He sat behind his large desk, his leather chair pushed back and his hands resting over his stomach. He started to roll his thumbs like he did anytime he waited for an answer. There was a strong tobacco odor in the office, even though he wasn't smoking at the time.

"What kind of proposal, *don* Raúl? As you know well, I want to be a teacher."

"Exactly, and that's where I'm heading. I know you are a very good teacher, even though you haven't graduated yet. My son refused tutoring by three teachers who tried to teach him extracurricular classes, but he loved when you tutored him during the summer. I have to let you know that he has been doing very well in school since then."

I felt pleased with my boss's excellent opinion of me, not only as a secretary, but as a teacher.

"I enjoyed working with your son, *don* Raúl. Once he accepted I was in charge, things went smoothly for both of us. I'm very proud of him." I remember with pleasure the slim, eleven-year-old boy with blue eyes, blond hair, and a handsome freckled face. He had tried to test my patience, but at the end he cooperated with me.

Don Raúl interrupted my memories. "Well, this is my proposition. Why don't we open a private school? You would be in charge, and I would provide the money to finance it. You could hire the rest of the personnel, maybe among your classmates. What do you think? Private schools are a very profitable business. Of course, you can check it out with your father first."

"Thank you once more, *don* Raúl, but I don't need to think about it. I want to work for the State of Nuevo León and so, earn my retirement benefits, but I sincerely appreciate your confidence in me."

Don Raúl re-lit the cigar he had left in the ashtray. I looked at him, expecting some sign of displeasure. Instead he smiled as he sent a cloud of smoke into the air. "That's fine, Socorrito. I understand. But if you ever change your mind, I promise I'll keep my word that you spearhead that project."

"I'll keep it in mind, *don* Raúl. Thanks again. You have to excuse me, but I must finish writing those letters; you told me they are urgent."

"Go ahead and when you finish, bring them to me so I can sign them and send them today."

I walked to my office. On the way, I saw my dad placing a tray full of silver jewelry inside one of the store crystal display cases. I was glad we worked in the same place. This was my first formal job, and it gave me security having my dad around. After all, I was only sixteen when I started working there three years earlier.

"Was *don* Raúl scolding you for some reason?" he asked with a frown.

"It was just the opposite, Dad. He praised my performance. I'll tell you about it later. I have to finish an urgent job for him."

My father smiled. His expression was full of pride.

That had happened only five years before. For sure, I was grateful for the way my bosses had treated me, but now I felt terribly disappointed by the injustice they were doing to my father. Definitely, there was no way to ask my former bosses to intervene on my behalf with the Director General of Education.

CHAPTER SIXTY-SIX

REMEMBERING A BAD TEACHER

My return to Doctor Arroyo was different from previous times. All the way back, I felt a heavy stone on my heart. My mind revolved around the breaking of my engagement and the economic situation back home.

In the solitude of my room, I thought about losing Martín, maybe forever. I remembered my dad's despair looking for a job and my mom's attempts to stretch the money to feed seven mouths. I felt the weight of my loneliness. I had already spent three years of my life in Doctor Arroyo just going to work and back home. Even though I loved my job, my students, and the town in general, I needed to be with my family, now more than ever. I sighed deeply, trying to relieve my sadness.

Coupled with this was the news that *profesor* Rogelio would not return to Doctor Arroyo. In his place was a new teacher, José Guadalupe Gallardo, who Andrés had already introduced to me. *Profesor* Lupito, as everyone was already calling him, was tall, thin, quiet, and shy. He blushed any time I talked to him. I hoped we would get along.

After much thought, I realized that if I continued feeling sorry for myself the months ahead would be miserable, and my students would suffer from my lack of enthusiasm. I came to terms with my reality, and I made it a point to focus on what I loved—teaching.

I had never let myself be defeated before, and I decided right then that this wasn't going to be the first time. I grabbed my books and started writing my lessons for the first week of school. I longed to see my old students again and to meet the new ones.

However, every day I kept waiting to hear from Martín or from my parents, but the mailman never came. I started to feel isolated. I knew that my mom was swamped with work without my help and my dad was looking for a job. I wondered if Martín would ever write me again. After all, I had asked him to forget me.

I tried to distract myself by participating in the *Fiestas Patrias*, México's Independence Day celebration. There was a dance to commemorate the occasion, which I attended with Nena and the Berrones sisters. The teachers and Manuel were there with Santiago. I was glad to see him again. He hadn't been in town since the last school term. I thought that he had decided to stay in Monterrey.

As soon as the music started, Santiago invited me to dance. He told me about his job. Both of us had thought we might not be back in Doctor Arroyo this year, but there we were again.

I observed him and wondered if he had grown more after we graduated. I hadn't remembered him being so tall. Before I had time to ask him about it, he said in a soft voice, "Our Group 'F' was such a neat group, don't you think so, Socorrito?"

"Yes, it was. We had very nice classmates. Eight of us came from Colegio Excélsior, in the second year. Others came from the Normal in Montemorelos. We were like a separate group, the foreigners, and that characteristic caused us to become so close."

"I wish we could be together again." Santiago sighed nostalgically.

Then we laughed, remembering anecdotes of our days as students in the Normal School, the teachers' university.

"Do you remember Professor ...?" Santiago mentioned a name. "The rumor was that instead of grading the tests, he threw them into the air. All those who fell on his bed earned a passing grade, and all those who fell to the floor earned a failing grade. That could explain why so often somebody who never participated in his class earned a grade of 100, while somebody who studied hard failed."

"And how could I forget him? I was even on the point of not graduating because of him." I shuddered at the memory.

"How did that happen?" asked Santiago.

"Do you remember we were gathered in the school gymnasium to let us know who would be graduating? I was not worried because I had good grades in all my classes. Then, imagine my surprise when my name was not called. With a fluttering stomach, I asked the reason for that. They told me that I had not taken the last exam with that teacher, so I did not have a high enough average to pass the subject. I was stunned. I have never missed an exam in all my years as a student."

"So, what happened? What did you do?" Santiago asked.

I told him that fortunately, Ángel Ramiro López, Rasura, and some other classmates were close by. They assured *profesora* Rebequita, our assistant principal, that I had attended the day in question and that I had taken the exam. She instructed me to clarify the situation with the teacher. He, however, was uncompromising and due only to pressure from all my classmates did he allow me to take the test again that day, with only half an hour to prepare.

"I was really upset, especially for his condescending attitude, but I had no choice, so I agreed. Someone ran to get me a book and I read everything I could. Fortunately, I got a good grade on their exam, and my name was added to the graduate list." I sighed and shuddered, thinking of the consequences if I hadn't been able to graduate.

"You should have asked him to look for your test under his bed," Santiago joked.

"Hey, I didn't want to push my luck. I was already scared enough."

He laughed.

Just as this bad teacher affected me, I recently learned that he also affected my friend Mari Paz. She went through a similar situation to mine, but she never protested the unfair final grade he gave her. Because of this, Mari Paz did not graduate with our generation and had to go through school the full year again.

At the end of the melody, I told Santiago, "Listen *amigo*, you better take me back to my seat. We have been dancing for a long time, and I don't want people to start talking."

"Who cares?"

"Oh, I do. I have to live here, and I don't want any *chismes* about me. Gossiping, you know. We live in a *crystal box*."

"Always the famous box," Santiago protested.

"Don't be grouchy. Invite one of my friends or another *señorita* to dance."

"I'll go to get something to drink first. Would you like me to bring you something?"

"No, thanks. I just finished a Coke."

Santiago left me with my friends and went to get his drink. Later on, he invited them to dance. He was a very gentle person, and I knew I could always count on him, too.

Since Santiago was staying at *doña* Susana's, he kept us company during the rest of the week. He had his meals with us, and at nighttime, we played cards and talked in Andrés's room. He finally had to go back to his work in a small village away from Doctor Arroyo.

"I'll be back for the Mexican Revolution Anniversary celebration," he said, mounting his bicycle. "If I can, I'll be back before then."

Santiago rode in a circle a couple of times, then smiled slightly and waved goodbye. We saw him disappear in the distance. He was a lonely rider on a lonely road.

Afterward I focused again on the problems back home. I started thinking that maybe my father could start his own business, even if it were on a small scale. We had owned two successful grocery stores in San Luis Potosí when I was a little girl. My dad had closed them after my younger brother, Betito, passed away. Dad thought that the baby hadn't received enough attention because he and my mom had been too busy with the stores. But my little brother and I were well cared for by a maid named Maria Luisa. She had helped my mom with some chores but mostly took care of Betito and me.

The reality was that there weren't good medications at that time. Anyway, coming back to present time, I realized it would take some time and money to start a new business, but if it worked, I might be able to get married.

Martín had said he would go to Monterrey in December. He wanted an explanation face to face about my decision to break off our engagement. I decided I would let him know exactly what had happened.

I hoped Martín would understand my motives, but I wondered if he loved me enough to understand and wait for me.

My days were still cloudy.

CHAPTER SIXTY-SEVEN

THE PRICE OF DUTY

During the September festivities, many people reminded me that it was another anniversary of my horrendous adventure with Dimas's mare.

"Do you remember two years ago when ...?" they invariably asked me.

Undoubtedly! How could I forget it if they had asked me the same thing during last year' celebration? Despite the time, it still caused me shame and chills.

Three weeks later, a new situation at home would bring me a ray of hope.

At the beginning of October, I received a letter from my mother. The news couldn't have been better. My father had a job! He had come across a friend named Paco Barrón, who he knew from a long time ago. Paco had a curio shop, too. He told my father he had heard about the closing of the rival shops. He, on the other hand, needed someone honest and responsible to take over his well-known establishment. Since he knew my father had those requisites, he offered him a job as a manager. "As you imagine, your dad accepted right away. He'll have a decent salary, plus a commission," my mother said in her long letter. Before finishing it, she added, "Now that your dad has a good job, I hope you and Martín will go back to your original plans."

That was an unexpected outcome. Some tears ran down my cheeks, but that time they were from relief and happiness. *Now it will be easier to explain to Martín, when we meet again, why I broke off our engagement, and how painful it was for me.*

I prayed that he would understand my motives.

Several weeks later, I received some more good news. My family had found a rental house and had already moved to it. My mom had sent me the new address and given me the details of the property. It had a living room-bedroom, two medium-sized bedrooms, a kitchen, one bathroom, and a long patio. The house, located next to a bank, wasn't big, but it was in better condition and in a better neighborhood than the previous one. I wasn't surprised when my mom mentioned that she had already made some friends. Her gift of relating to people was one of her many sterling qualities.

It was going to be a long wait for me to see the new house during my Christmas vacation and meet our new neighbors.

As promised, Santiago came to town for a few days for the Anniversary of the Mexican Revolution on November 20. His company and the patriotic festivities around town changed the routine of the previous weeks.

December arrived, and with it the town's annual fair. There was music throughout the day. Doctor Arroyo came alive with the presence of people who worked in the United States and came to visit their relatives or friends. The generally quiet town now had cars with US license plates driving its cobblestone streets.

We all gravitated toward the main plaza where the town's fair took place. As in previous years, I attended it with Nena, Eva, and her sisters Irma and Licha.

In the lottery, many people simply stopped to observe the excitement of the players. It was fun to see the jubilation of the winner and the frustration of the losers.

The carousel was the children's favorite ride. We adults also enjoyed ourselves, listening to the pleasant music from their speakers and seeing the joy of the little ones, who saluted and smiled proudly at their family members as they went around and around.

The food stands were always full. People found it difficult to resist such enticing aromas. They didn't even mind eating the *taquitos* or *gorditas* standing up when all of the tables were full. Entire families shared these *antojitos*, sitting on the plaza's benches, while the little ones preferred to play on the grass between bites.

However, the main event for the adults was the public dance. The place was always crowded with people who wore their nicest clothes, especially women. There, the most fun was to see who would dance with the foreigners during the long celebration. Everyone wanted to know of any new romances in town.

To top it all, people's morbid curiosity and tension about the presence of Dimas García resurfaced. They never knew what to expect when he was in Doctor Arroyo. Fortunately, Dimas behaved well. Even so, I was careful not to meet him at *doña* Susana's restaurant. After all this time, I still felt embarrassed about the incident with his horse, so I didn't want to see him face to face. I wasn't sure he knew at the time he lent it that I would be the one mounting his horse. However, I was quite sure that he had found out in a matter of minutes. I wondered what his reaction was.

When the town fair ended, my fellow teachers and I welcomed the approaching Christmas holidays. I was eager to join my family in

Monterrey and enjoy the new house. My mind and heart, however, revolved mainly around Martín's coming, as he had promised in his last letter. I would explain the situation to him. I was confident he would understand, and then we could continue with our wedding plans.

My whole being was overflowing with joy. I was impatient for Martín to place my engagement ring back on my finger again. That would be just a formality because in my heart I had never stopped being his fiancée.

Days before I left, one of my students, Herminio García, came to the house. I thought he was there to wish me happy holidays. Instead, after brief conversation, he pulled a white envelope from his shirt pocket. He explained that it was for his sister who lived with some relatives in Monterrey. He asked if I could locate her and deliver that letter to her.

"I know I am inopportune, *maestra*, but it's kind of urgent, and the mail is really slow, especially in December when people send so many Christmas cards," the boy said, looking down as he fidgeted with his cap.

"Don't worry about it. I'll be glad to do it. Just write your sister's address, and I'll look for her and put the letter in her hands."

"The address is already here." He handed me the letter.

I read the envelope, blinked, and read again. Impossible! That was two doors from my house.

Herminio raised an eyebrow observing my reaction. I explained to him about our recent move. His sister and I were neighbors. We laughed at the coincidence.

"I can't believe it; this only happens in novels. I'm very eager to meet your sister. I'll deliver this letter as soon as I arrive," I said, placing the envelope inside my purse.

"As you can see, my sister's name is Rosario, but everyone calls her Chayo," he said, getting up from his chair. "Now I have to go. I promised my dad I would help him in the store. Thanks again, *maestra*. Please say hello to my sister and have a wonderful Christmas."

"You too, Herminio."

The boy waved goodbye and left in a hurry.

On the eve of our departure to Monterrey, our students observed the tradition of coming to say goodbye. They came to wish us a Merry Christmas and to give us all kinds of goodies to take home. I packed all of this in a couple of boxes. Afterward, I carefully placed in my suitcase the dresses that a local dressmaker had made for me. I was very excited that I was going to wear them for Martín.

I said goodbye to all of my friends. Horacio, Perico, and Catarino were the last of my students I saw.

"You'll come back next year, *maestra*, won't you?" Perico asked. He stood by the door, spinning his baseball cap on his index finger.

Catarino looked at me silently and with a big frown. He didn't talk much because Perico talked for the two of them, but Catarino always listened. Horacio tilted his head, crossed his arms, and waited for my answer.

"More than likely I'll be back. Why do you ask such a question?"

Perico shrugged and put on his baseball cap.

"Just curiosity," he said smiling. The boys left after they wished me a good trip and a fast return. I finished putting my belongings together, then went to bed and attempted to sleep. I needed a long time before I succeeded.

The next day, we had an early breakfast. The sun was rising when we were in the bus. Andrés and I sat together and talked about our future plans. I told him that since I would possibly be married soon, I would be happier if he would find a girlfriend and make some plans in the same direction.

"I haven't met the girl of my dreams yet," he said, twisting one side of his moustache.

"Well, you better hurry up. The day I leave, I don't want you to be alone for a long time. Someone has to bang on your door to wake you up!"

"Maybe I'll meet her next year, Socorrito. That will be my Christmas wish."

"Either that, or I'll have to find someone for you myself because she probably won't show up on your shoe."

We both laughed and continued our conversation. Before we knew it, we saw *Cerro de la Silla*, Saddle Mountain. We were in Monterrey. We all hugged and wished each other a Merry Christmas. Then we went on our way to meet our families.

I found the usual reception of kisses, hugs, and exclamations. Cayito wasn't there yet; we would pick him up on Christmas Day. On the way home, my siblings took turns describing the new place to me. My mom seemed content. I was happy to notice the change.

I told my parents about the letter I was supposed to deliver to Chayo and my surprise about the address. My mom said that a clothing and footwear store was located there; it was two houses from ours. As our house was number 1309, theirs should have been 1305, but the owner, *don* Elias Rodríguez, had solicited the number 1313 for good luck. His wife was *doña* Gracia Leija. They lived with their five children as well as *don* Elias' mother, his father in-law, and Chayo. A total of ten people lived there.

"*Madrecita*, I'm sure you've already made friends with them," I said, jokingly.

"Yes, I did. The lady of the house, *doña* Gracia, is quite a lady, very approachable and gentle. All of the neighbors love her. There is a *señorita* close to your age. Her name is Trini, and I know her cousin Chayo, too. She's a sweet girl. I didn't know she was from Doctor Arroyo."

"Well, as I said, imagine my surprise when I found out she was our neighbor. Her brother, Herminio, is my pupil; he is very quiet and respectful. Anyway, I'll meet Chayo sometime after dinner. By the way, you have to see all the goodies my students gave me to share with you. They could last us until summer." Such exaggeration made my mother laugh.

After a long ride, the taxi stopped outside a house with a green façade and Julie jumped out first. "Come on, Coco. Come to see the house," my little sis said, pulling my hand.

For a moment, those pulls reminded me of when she had wanted to go on the bus to travel with me to Doctor Arroyo and I couldn't take her. Julie would never know all the times I had cried in my life remembering that moment. I just hoped she would never feel in her little heart that I had left her out of a lack of love.

I came out of the taxi and looked around. To the left of the house was a bank branch, and next to it a large store, Al Contadito. There were two entrance doors to the store with glass display windows on each side. To the right of our rented house, there was an identical home. Both were painted light green and had a low front wall with an iron fence. For sure they belonged to the same owner. My mom said that the neighbors were a very nice couple, Rosita and *don* Rodolfo Meléndez. They had a daughter younger than Julie. Her name was Rose, like her mom, but everyone called her Chirris.

After placing my luggage in the second room, I immediately went to my dresser. I wanted to be sure that my rings hadn't gotten lost in the move. With a shaky hand for the emotion to see them again, I pulled the drawer open. The blood drained from my face and my heart fluttered. The place where the little box had been was empty. I pulled the drawer toward me, thinking that maybe the box had slid to the other side. There was nothing. Absolutely nothing! I couldn't breathe, and my legs started to shake. Just then, my mom placed her hand on my shoulder.

Of course, she must have put it away when they moved. I turned around to see her. The pain on her face froze the smile that I had begun to outline.

"*Hijita*, I have something to tell you," she said in a strained voice.

"Oh, Mom, please, please, don't tell me my rings got lost during the move here." My hands started shaking. I held them together to stop it.

"No, *hijita*, the truth is ..." Her lips quivered, and her eyes shone with tears.

I stared at her, with my heart full of anguish. I held my breath waiting for her to finish telling me what had happened to the rings.

"Martín's parents came by before we moved here. They were on their way to San Luis Potosi. They said Martín asked them to collect his jacket and the rings, since you had decided to return them to him and break your wedding engagement."

What's she saying? No, not now that a light of hope had appeared! I felt a knot in my throat and tried not to cry, but tears started flowing like a mighty river. I slumped on a nearby chair and covered my face with my hands.

"I'm sorry, *hijita*," my mom said.

I was devastated. Martín didn't want to leave anything that belonged to him behind. He was cutting from the root. I wiped my tears and tried to calm down.

"What else did they say, Mom? Why didn't he come as he said he would?"

"Martín was sent to Morocco. He'll be serving there for a year."

More tears, a sea of tears! *Now he has put an ocean between us. Most likely, I will never have the opportunity to explain my true reasons for breaking our engagement.*

"Well, I guess I've lost Martín forever, *madrecita*. For him to ask for his jacket and his rings back means he is definitely putting me out of his life. Maybe he didn't love me as much as he said." I felt my heart tear apart.

"Oh, no *hijita*. *Eso no.* You know he loves you. I'm sure that love hasn't died. It's just the circumstances. I'm so sorry you didn't have the chance to clarify the situation."

I sighed deeply, trying to get rid of the heaviness in my chest. I wished to run out of the house and cry until I didn't have any more tears, but it was my first day home. I didn't want to cause more worry to my mom who stared at me with her face etched with sorrow.

"It's okay, *madrecita*. It hurts now, but I trust God's plans. He knows what He's doing and what's best for me. Maybe it was not our destiny to be together. Like the song says, *'Qué será, será.'*"

"*Hijita*, I don't know what to say ... Your plans completely broken ... and all because of us." My mom wiped her own tears, wrapped me in the comfort of her loving arms and placed my head on her shoulder.

"No, *madrecita*, don't say such a thing." I wiped my tears, too, and gave her a faint smile. "I'm the oldest, and I did what I was supposed to do. There is no regret. Besides, nothing happens without God's will. I'll be okay. I'll remember that saying: *'Con el tiempo y un tantito'*. 'With time and another little bit,' and who knows? Something good might come from all of this."

At least, I hoped so.

CHAPTER SIXTY-EIGHT

A SPECIAL PRESENT FOR MOM

All of my dreams for a perfect Christmas vacation vanished with the news that Martín not only canceled his visit, but also asked for the return of the engagement ring. Even though he had the right to do so, that devastated me. I decided that somehow, I would hide my pain so as not to cause concern to anyone, least of all my mother. I prayed to God for strength.

Trying to forget the turmoil in my head, that afternoon I went looking for Chayo. She was staying with the Rodríguez family, Al Contadito store owners who were her relatives. They lived on the floor above the business. The long entrance to the house was hidden between the store and the bank next door.

I saw my brother Ernesto playing soccer in the middle of the street with other boys around his same age. They were having a lot of fun.

Julie was on our sidewalk, a few steps in front of the store, jumping rope with another little girl. Their hair and their skirts bounced up and down. Julie and her friend stopped when I approached the front door of the house.

"Hi!" Julie's friend said, looking me over with curiosity. She was a cute little girl with long black hair and bright dark eyes.

"This is my friend Carmelita, and she lives here," my little sister said, pointing to the house where I was about to knock on the door.

"Hi Carmelita! I'm Coco, Julie's sister. I'm looking for Chayo. Is she home?"

"Yes, she's inside. I'll tell her you are asking for her. Do you want to come in?"

"No, thanks. I'll wait here for her." I looked apprehensively at the big Doberman Pinscher coming toward us.

"Don't be afraid of him. He doesn't bite," Carmelita said. She patted the dog's behind as he walked between the two of us. The imposing mascot lay down on the sidewalk looking at the children having fun in the street.

Carmelita ran inside. I heard her yelling for Chayo. A few minutes later, she came back with a friendly-looking young woman behind her. I introduced myself and gave her Herminio's letter. She thanked me and asked about how her brother was doing in school.

"Herminio is a good student, and so far, he has never been in any kind of trouble. All of the teachers, including me, have a good opinion of him. He's a very respectful boy."

Chayo smiled proudly upon hearing my good report on her brother.

As I was talking with her, another young lady came downstairs. She was slim and medium height, with very fair skin. Her face had delicate features. Her golden-brown hair was cut in a modern style. She approached us with a friendly smile.

"Trini, this is Socorrito, *doña* Petrita's daughter. Do you know she's Herminio's teacher in Doctor Arroyo? It's such a coincidence her family moved in the neighboring house. Anyway, he sent me a letter with her."

"Is that so? Nice to meet you. I'm Trini Rodriguez," the newly arrived lady said, extending her hand.

I returned her greeting, and the three of us chatted for a while. Then, Trini apologized and left. I stayed for a few more minutes and returned home after promising Chayo we would get together soon.

I told my mom about meeting our neighbors Trini and Chayo and that I had found them kind and friendly.

"I hope you become good friends," my mom said. "They are excellent girls."

"*Madrecita*, since I work away from Monterrey, it will take some time before that happens, but I'm sure it will. Don't worry."

She looked at me with a downcast expression that saddened my heart. I gave her a hug and a kiss, realizing she tried to make me feel better and was looking for ways to fill the void Martín had left in my life. That would not be an easy task.

Next time I saw Licha and Mari Paz, instead of giving them the good news they were expecting to hear about my future wedding, I informed them that Martín wasn't coming to visit me. It was difficult to tell them in detail all that had transpired when his parents had stopped by my house.

I was emotionally drained, so I didn't mind crying in front of them. After all, we had shared so much through several years of sincere friendship.

My friends tried to comfort me the best they could, giving me words of support.

Mari Paz invited me to a couple of parties, but I only attended one of them, more than anything to show everyone I was functioning normally. I couldn't fool my mom, however. She knew me better than anybody else, and I saw her eyes searching mine for my deepest thoughts.

"I just hope you won't get married to a *ranchero* and decide to stay in Doctor Arroyo," she said one day, pensively. She had mentioned this on a previous occasion, so I knew she meant it, and she was worried for me.

My mother's words made me break into gales of laughter. "You don't have to worry about that, *madrecita*. It will take some time before I date anybody else. The saying, *'Un clavo saca otro clavo'* doesn't apply to me. I don't believe it is always true that 'a nail removes another nail.' It'll take some time because I waited four years for Martín, thinking that eventually we would marry. Now, I have to get used to the idea that this won't be possible."

The reality of my own words made me sigh deeply. I didn't want to worry my mom, and I tried to cover it. "The good thing is that, at least, people didn't see me everywhere with him. It would have been even worse."

My mother seemed satisfied with my comment and informed me of the schedule for the next few days. We were eager for Christmas

Day when Cayito would have permission to spend the afternoon with us.

That night I went over my list of Christmas presents. I usually went to Laredo to buy some clothes for my family and me. That year, however, since there wasn't going to be any wedding, I wanted to use part of my small savings to buy a special present for my mom. My plan was to acquire a washing machine; that way, she would not have to hire anybody to help her with that chore. At the same time, I was concerned that she had so many worries on her mind, so she really needed a distraction. For that reason, at the last minute, I decided to propose two options to her. I knew that any of them would make her happy. I got excited, imagining her reaction.

The following morning, the smell of fresh cinnamon filled the kitchen. My mom had ready my favorite tea, cinnamon, and there was a basket with Mexican sweet bread on the table. As usual, everybody seemed to be in a great mood. We were having breakfast when I said, "*Madrecita*, I want to buy you a special Christmas present, but I want you to choose, so, what would you rather have, a washing machine or a television?"

She turned around with a look of bliss. "Well," she smiled shyly, "the truth?"

Breakfast was interrupted. Héctor stopped joking and Javier closed his book. Norma bit her nails, Ernesto started chewing the top of his t-shirt, and Julie stood up from her chair. All you could hear was the sound of the radio playing in the background. They were all attentive to my mother's lips, and they were hardly breathing. My mom grabbed her hands together and cleared her throat but didn't say a word. She only looked at me the way children look when they know Santa Claus or The Three Wise Men are about to arrive.

The delay in her answer and the expression on her face told me what I wanted to know.

"You want the TV," I said, shaking my index finger at her and laughing. I knew her too well.

There was an explosion of delighted screams from my siblings who applauded, approving my mom's silent choice.

"Look, *madrecita*, the kids agree with you."

"Sure!" Javier intervened. "Why do we want a washing machine?"

"I think Javier is volunteering to do the laundry, *madre*," Héctor joked.

The barrage of jokes that followed showed the atmosphere of good humor that prevailed.

That afternoon we all went to look for that gift. We chose a Zenith TV. We couldn't wait for it to be delivered to us. And of course, we were also looking forward to Cayito's visit, to share the recent acquisition with him.

When the brand-new TV console arrived, it was placed in the living room, as was usual in almost all homes that had this device.

My brother Javier commented, very thoughtfully, "The living room is the best place for the television according to three types of owners: For the generous, because that way the neighbors can watch a program out the window from the street. For the greedy and distrustful, because they charge the neighbors to enter there, without passing through other rooms. And for the vain, because whoever walks down the street will appreciate the status of that family."

His philosophical observation seemed funny to me. "Good analysis, Javier, but we are going to see it here simply because it is the most comfortable place in the house."

In Monterrey at that time, there were three TV channels: one local and two repeaters for each of Mexico City's channels. We had only one television for very varied tastes. How to please everyone?

Ernesto, Julie, and Norma

Julie and Ernesto wanted to see "Bozo el Payaso" or "Teatro Fantástico," as well as cartoons. Norma agreed with them a bit, but she also liked musicals and series with gallants, such as "Doctor Kildare" or "Route 66." Héctor and Javier preferred books and did not care about programming, however, as time went by, they would become fond of some police series, as happened with "The Untouchables," perhaps because of its documentary background. They also enjoyed fiction, as was the case of "The Unknown Dimension." My father would only have Sundays to watch sports and bullfighting. My mother said to conform to whatever it was, but I knew she had her favorite series, one of them being "I Love Lucy."

In the end, I reminded everyone that it was my mother's TV, and that she would decide which shows to watch.

After dinner, we all crowded around the twenty-inch TV screen to watch our favorite shows, obviously in black and white. My youngest siblings, Julie, Ernesto, and Norma, settled on the floor. Julie, as always, couldn't sit still. She crawled on her knees back and forth, while everybody asked her not to move. Ernesto chewed the neck of his tee-shirt, like he did anytime he was nervous, and Norma cracked her knuckles and raised both of her eyebrows from time to time. Javier and Héctor sat on chairs and pushed each other back and forth playfully with their shoulders. I sat next to my mom on the sofa, holding one of her small hands. I loved to caress the softness of her cinnamon skin. It always left me with a sense of internal peace.

Very proud of the honor of inaugurating the set, my father plugged the cord into the wall outlet and pressed the "On" switch. Everybody became quiet. It took forever before something came on the screen, and when it finally did, all that we saw were jumping shadows and broken lines.

"Aww!" was the general expression of disenchantment.

My three siblings sitting on the floor moved closer to the TV screen, trying to see something.

"Move back and let me fix the antenna," my father said. He moved the two metal rods on top of the TV one way and another, until an image appeared, even though it was not completely clear. My father grew impatient.

"I know what it needs," my mother said. She remembered the solution of our previous neighbors. She went to the patio and came back with a small can full of dirt. She cut a piece of wire, placed it around the base of the antenna and put the other end inside the dirt. The picture on the screen became completely clear. Everybody applauded, full of joy, and sat transfixed in front of the TV. We watched something that had nothing to do with any of our favorite programs, yet we all enjoyed it.

"I can't believe we really have a TV," my mother said. She had a radiant face, and her eyes shone with a special light. *"¡Gracias, hijita! ¡Que Dios te lo pague!"*.

For me, my reward was already there, seeing how happy all of them were.

"Madrecita," I said laughing, "since you declined the washing machine, I guess now you will have to spoil the laundress! You need to be sure she won't leave you. Otherwise, you won't have time to watch your TV."

"Don't worry, *hijita*. If she can't come, there is another woman who wants to do it. She has asked me a couple of times. I was thinking of hiring her anyway. She said she really needs the job. Her husband's salary is very modest, and they have small children to feed. From time to time, I share some food with her."

"I hope one day I'll be a little bit like you, *madrecita*," I said, admiring her kindness and generosity.

"You're already a lot like me, *Preciosita*," my mother answered tenderly, softly stroking the top of my head.

That little word of endearment, Little Precious, always left me with a warm feeling. I thought I was so lucky to have family who loved me the same way I loved them. Only Martín had not loved me enough to come to clarify our situation, as he had indicated in his last letter. I shook my head, trying to dismiss his memory.

By the time Cayito came to visit us, we were familiar with the weekly TV programs. He was very excited about the new acquisition. The time he spent with us went by like a sigh. Before we knew it, it was time to take him back. When we arrived at the seminary, there were hugs, kisses, and blessings. I tried not to cry. I found it difficult to accept that Cayito would have a life apart from us. We stood there until he turned once more and waved goodbye. He was already fifteen, but even in his black suit he looked younger. He disappeared from our view at the end of a long, quiet hall, and then we returned home in silence.

I entered the new year of 1962 with a mix of emotions. I felt happy to be with my family but sad about a future without Martín. Soon my vacation was over, and I returned to work.

During the journey to Doctor Arroyo I felt better knowing my family had the TV to distract them. I knew my mom missed Cayito and me a lot. She had lost quite a bit of weight since we left home, and Norma had told me that she had seen her crying. That was very painful for me to hear, but I couldn't leave my job. I needed to continue helping them with the extra money they needed so much. I felt sorry for myself for a while, but once again, I put my faith in God's hands. I knew in my heart that He would show me the way to keep doing, without any regrets, what love and duty demanded me to do.

CHAPTER SIXTY-NINE

A GIRLFRIEND AND A LESSON
FOR ANDRÉS

Upon my return to Doctor Arroyo, several students stopped by the house to pay me a visit. Herminio came, too.

"I gave the letter to your sister," I informed him. "I hope to become better acquainted with her and your cousin Trini on my next vacation during Holy Week."

Herminio told me Chayo planned to come to Doctor Arroyo soon.

One afternoon, as the teachers and I were having dinner, we observed through the restaurant's open doors two girls walking in the direction of the main plaza. The tallest one had dark hair and was of medium build, while the other was medium height and wore a dress with a crinoline. They chatted animatedly.

Andrés and Gerónimo didn't hide their interest.

I identified the girls immediately; they were my neighbors Chayo and Trini. I told my colleagues how I met them. They both showed interest in me introducing them to my friends. I promised to do it at the first opportunity.

In those days, we were busy with a school project. Trini left town before I had the chance to greet her. Later I introduced Chayo to Andrés.

"She is very charming and seems so sweet," Andrés commented after Chayo left.

"If you're interested, you'd better hurry up before someone else gets ahead of you," I advised him.

Andrés narrowed his eyes and smiled silently. Then he twisted the tip of his mustache, as he did every time he was distracted.

I learned on Saturday that Andrés was seeing Chayo when he asked me sheepishly to wake him up early the following day.

"I'm meeting Herminio's sister when she gets out of church," he said.

"Bravo! It didn't take you much time to follow my suggestion about looking for somebody to keep you company. Is she your girlfriend already?"

Andrés crossed his arms, cupped his chin, and smiled coyly. "She will give me an answer tomorrow. That's why I need to see her after Mass."

"Well, I see. In that case, don't worry about it. I'll wake you up in plenty of time, and you will calmly prepare for your romantic encounter."

"I'll get up the first time you call. You'll see!" he said with great certainty.

But promising and doing it were two different things for Andrés. I had to call him several times. Then I warned him Mass was going to end and he wasn't going to be on time to see Chayo. That was the magic formula. He got up in a hurry. Several minutes later, he came out of his room fixing his tie and with his curly black hair still wet. He put on his jacket and as he walked past my room to the front door, he winked at me.

I wished him good luck.

Nena and I attended the twelve o'clock Mass and when it was over, we walked around for a while and then went home. We said goodbye and agreed to go to the movies later.

A few minutes later, Andrés came to see me. I didn't need to ask him about Chayo's response. He had a broad smile, and his eyes shone with enthusiasm.

"She said, 'yes!'" he exclaimed.

"So I anticipated it. I had no doubt. You are a good prize," I joked. "Congratulations!"

"Thanks," he said. "Now, the question is, how we are going to see each other? She doesn't want her dad to find out yet."

The aroma of delicious food coming from the kitchen grabbed Andrés's attention.

"Hey, I left in such a hurry that I didn't eat anything, and I'm really hungry. Do you want to have an early dinner with me?"

"Let's see if *doña* Susana has already prepared something. Otherwise, you will have to wait with a cup of coffee."

Since it was Sunday, there were many people from other small towns who had come to attend Mass or the movies, so dinner was ready earlier than usual. We sat at our regular table. We greeted the other diners, as is traditional in small Mexican towns, as a sign of courtesy.

Teresa and another maid came and started to attend the customers or clean the tables.

Lupito and Gerónimo came from the street and joined us.

Andrés gave me a discreet signal to not say anything in respect to Chayo. I nodded slightly. A few minutes later, *doña* Susana came to our table.

"Congratulations, *profesor* Andrés, I heard the good news!" she said loudly and with a big grin.

Andrés pushed his chair back and shook his head in disbelief. He pulled down the knot of his tie and started tapping on the edge of the table looking sideways at *doña* Susana. She crossed her arms waiting for a response from Andrés. When she didn't get one, she went back into the kitchen.

"Would you believe it?" he asked me.

"I do. Have you forgotten after all these years that we live in a *crystal box*?"

"What are you two talking about, and why did *doña* Susana congratulate you?" Gerónimo asked.

"I'll tell you in a little bit," answered Andrés, glaring at the customers who were watching us carefully.

"I certainly don't live in any *crystal box*," Gerónimo said, arising an eyebrow and looking around him.

Andrés and I looked at each other and burst out laughing.

"We live in it, Gerónimo. Everybody can see what we do, and don't forget it," I said.

"I couldn't care less," he said shrugging. "I have nothing to hide."

His cockiness made me smile. I remembered the day the *director* scolded him in front of the group. In a few hours, many people found out. I wondered if he would ever learn the meaning of this expression "living in a *crystal box*."

From then on, every Sunday it became routine for me to wake Andrés up just before I left for church with Nena. He was a heavy sleeper, and he struggled to get up.

"Don't wake him up, *señorita*. I think he needs to be taught a lesson," *profesor* Merla advised me on several occasions. There was a mischievous expression on his face every time he said that.

"I don't mind calling him, really. He needs to get up to meet his girlfriend when she gets out of church."

Invariably, the *director* would raise an eyebrow and shake his head in disapproval.

One Sunday, he arrived just as I was calling Andrés for the third time. *Profesor* Merla was late for breakfast, so he went straight into the dining room. I heard him talking to *doña* Susana and Teresa.

"I'm leaving for church, Andrés! Get up! Don't be late!" I knocked loudly on his bedroom door.

"Don't worry, Socorrito. I'll get up in a moment."

Satisfied with his answer, I went to chat with the *director* for a few minutes.

"Did you call *profesor* Andrés?" he asked.

"Yes, I called him three times. He said he's getting up now. I hope so because Nena is already here, and we are leaving. Could I ask you for a favor? Could you please knock on his door if he doesn't come out soon?"

"Don't worry about it, *señorita*, I'll take care of that."

"Thank you so much. *Profesor* Andrés will appreciate that."

"I'm sure that he will. Now run or you'll be late for your Mass."

My goodness, it surprises me how much the director's attitude has changed. I never thought one day he'd rush me to go to church.

"Okay, then. I'll see you this afternoon for dinner. Enjoy your breakfast!"

Profesor Merla raised his hand in response while taking a sip of his coffee.

I joined Nena who was waiting for me outside the house.

When Mass was over and we left the church, I didn't see Andrés or Chayo around the plaza as usual. I thought maybe they went for a walk, but the only place they could have gone was to the *aljibes*, where the water for the town was collected. However, walking alone that far was exposing oneself to gossip, and I was sure Andrés would avoid that at any cost.

Nena, who by this time was already aware of the courtship, also noticed their absence.

"I don't see *profesor* Andrés nor Chayo around. Didn't you say they were meeting after Mass?"

"Certainly, that's why he asked me to wake him up. This is weird. I don't think they went anywhere where *don* Panfilito could see them."

"Maybe Chayo didn't come to church today, and she let *profesor* Andrés know at the last minute."

"Maybe. I'll find out soon if Andrés is home, but in the meantime, let's go for some ice cream."

We walked to the ice cream parlor and chose a table where we sat for half an hour chatting and watching people stroll around the main square.

As soon as I came back home, Andrés came by my room with a deep frown and clenched jaw. Seldom had I seen him angry, and that was one of those exceptions.

"Hey, Andrés. Are you okay? I didn't see you in the plaza."

"Someone put a lock on my door!" He gestured furiously without answering my question. "I know it wasn't you, but do you have any idea who would do that?"

"Wait, calm down and give me the entire story." I sat with my hands on my lap, ready to listen.

"Someone locked my bedroom door from the outside with a padlock, and when I tried to get out, I couldn't do it," he said in a hoarse voice. "I had to hit the door hard for a long time because nobody came to see what was happening."

"So, who opened the padlock?" I asked, trying not to laugh. I didn't want to make the situation worse. He was really upset.

"*Doña* Susana did, but it wasn't right away. She had to try several keys until she found one that adjusted the padlock."

"Well, I'm glad you were able to get out."

"The thing is, I was really late, and by the time I went to the plaza, Chayo had already left. I'm going to find out who played this prank on me. *Doña* Susana swears she doesn't know, but I'll try to get the truth from Claudia. I saw her giggling, so she must be aware. Believe me; it wasn't funny." By that time, he was squinting, which, in his case, meant he was really angry.

"Well, you can be sure it wasn't me, Andrés. You know I always worry about waking you up in time. In fact, before I left, I asked—Uh-oh!" I covered my mouth with my hand.

"What?" He stared at me suspiciously.

"Well, I asked *profesor* Merla if he could call you."

Suddenly, I realized who put the lock on the door. It was certainly the *director*. I remembered how he smiled when he said he would take care of waking Andrés up. I also thought of his repeated advice that he needed a lesson and how he rushed me to church. I didn't doubt that he instructed *doña* Susana to delay opening the door. My laugh came out spontaneously.

I told Andrés about my suspicions and reminded him how *profesor* Merla enjoyed playing pranks. He listened to me in silence and then left without saying a word.

That afternoon, Andrés was very serious when he saw *profesor* Merla. He, on the other hand, smiled mischievously.

"Okay. I know you figured out who locked you in your room, but please don't be mad at me, *profesor*." The *director* put an arm around Andrés's shoulders.

"You made me late for an important meeting," he grumbled, frowning and crossing his arms.

"Hmm, but you know what?"

"What?" Andrés asked.

"I'm sure next Sunday you'll be up and ready even before I come to breakfast, with a padlock in hand." *Profesor* Merla gave him a friendly pat on the shoulder.

Andrés did not know what to answer and had no choice but to laugh, and we did too.

CHAPTER SEVENTY

INNOCENT PRANKS

Doctor Arroyo had changed drastically in the four years I had been there. Now we had electricity, and the town was alive. Our radios brought music to our routine and kept us informed of the latest news. Some people even had television, so their small world had expanded to include remote places where they learned about other cultures and new ideas. Doctor Arroyo was becoming modern.

In my immediate world, life was different, too. A feeling of loneliness started closing in on me, especially with my dreams of marriage cut short.

The teachers and I no longer got together to play cards. Andrés's new romantic interest kept him away quite often. Lupito stayed by himself most of the time, and Gerónimo had his own agenda. From time to time they went some place together. I read a lot and wrote letters I never sent. I didn't want to sound sad to my mother. Hopefully, there would be better times ahead for me.

Many of my former students who used to visit me frequently were now studying far away. However, the visits of other faithful students: Perico Castilleja, Catarino Santoy, Socorrito de la Garza with her sisters Cuquita and Malena, and some others alleviated my loneliness a bit. Their companionship distracted me until the time that Nena closed her store and came by the house. Then, the two of us went for a walk around the plaza. Now that we had streetlights, more people were encouraged to go out at night. Of course, we would never have another opportunity to play a joke like the one we played on Andrés and Manuel, some time ago, taking advantage of the dense darkness of the plaza.

That reminded me of another prank the students played in similar circumstances.

One day, all of us teachers, as usual, watched over the students during recess time. We noticed they had placed two chairs—one beside the other—outside the classroom. Two kids sat on them while others stood around them. The two who were sitting started a very personal conversation while the rest laughed aloud. They were acting. All of a sudden, we saw Gerónimo's face redden, and he stormed inside the building mumbling something. We looked at each other, puzzled by his reaction.

Profesor Merla went to talk to the students and came back laughing. The actors confessed to him that the previous night, some older friends convinced them to hide behind the bench where Gerónimo was sitting with his girlfriend. These two youngsters were so short and the plaza so dark that the couple never realized there were spies listening.

"So, what they were doing was repeating the romantic talk of Gerónimo and his girlfriend. Of course, he recognized the conversation, and that was the reason for his anger."

We couldn't help laughing in private, but we scolded the kids for doing something so inappropriate. Geronimo would now have to admit it: he too lived in a *crystal box*.

I remembered another prank played with the complicity of the night and of *profesor* Merla.

One afternoon, I was reading my notes in the teachers' room when the *director* came in. Lupito, Gerónimo, and Andrés were teaching at that moment.

"*Señorita* Socorrito, has *profesor* Andrés complained to you about the students?" he asked.

"No, *profesor.* Is he having some discipline problems?"

"Well, in a way." He had an amused expression on his face.

"What do you mean 'in a way'?"

"Well, do you know that *profesor* Andrés and his girlfriend Chayo talk outside of her house every night after *don* Panfilito goes to bed?"

"No, I didn't know. No wonder I never see them in the plaza."

I knew Andrés went to see Chayo every night. I suspected they talked outside her house, but he had never said anything to me. Andrés was very discreet, and I respected his privacy.

"I'm glad they chose to meet like this instead of going to other places," I said, "but, what does that have to do with the students?"

Profesor Merla settled in a chair. He placed his hands on his legs and bent forward. He lowered his voice. "I heard they have been playing a prank on *profesor* Andrés."

"A prank? What kind of prank?" I was alarmed it could be something that could damage his relationship with Chayo.

"The kids form small groups, and then they parade in front of *don* Panfilito's house at the time *profesor* Andrés and his girlfriend talk outside the front door. I was told that from the opposite side of the street, they yell in chorus, 'Good night, *profesor* Andrés!' You can imagine how the poor man feels. He doesn't want *don* Panfilito to wake up and find that he's outside talking to his daughter."

By that time *profesor* Merla slapped one of his legs and burst out laughing.

"*Profesor* Merla! Do you have anything to do with this joke?"

"*Señoriiita*, please, how could you think I would do such a thing?" He pretended to be offended, yet he couldn't stop laughing.

"Because I know you, *profesor*. You are terrible. I'm sure your hand is behind this." I was laughing, too. I could imagine Andrés not answering the boys, his arms crossed in front of him and his eyes squinting. "You have to tell the boys to stop doing this. I'm sure Horacio is one of them, so I'll talk to him, too."

We heard the sound of the students' desks and some voices coming from the nearest classroom. *Profesor* Merla stood up.

"We better stop laughing now. The teachers are coming, and it's time for you and me to go to work," he said. We both took our books and went to our classrooms.

That afternoon, Andrés told me what had happened. He said he didn't want to make the situation worse and asked me to talk to the students that he identified by their names. Horacio was one of them as I had thought. I told Andrés not to worry and that I would take care of the problem.

"Horacio, I need to talk to you before you go." He had just dropped his books in his bedroom and was ready to go. I stopped him outside my bedroom door.

"Sure, *maestra*. What can I do for you?" He showed his most gracious smile while combing his kinky hair.

"I found out that you and your friends have been playing a joke on *profesor* Andrés."

"Meeee?" He asked, in a malicious tone. He stopped combing his hair. Then he shifted the weight of his body from one leg to the other.

"Yes, you! Don't bother denying it because I have all the details directly from the *director* and *profesor* Andrés."

"Hmm, we just wanted to make *profesor* Andrés sweat a little. We had no bad intention, I swear. You know we all like him."

"That's not a way to show it to him, so I'm going to ask all of you to stop those jokes immediately."

"Okay, *maestra*. We won't do it again. I promise."

"Thank you. I trust your word. Now you can go, and please don't forget to talk to your friends as soon as possible."

Horacio waved and walked away whistling. I went to knock on Andrés's bedroom door.

"I talked to Horacio, and he said they 'just wanted to make you sweat a little bit but there wasn't any bad intention in them.' Anyway, he promised that it would not be repeated."

"Thanks, Socorrito. I really appreciate it."

"You are welcome. Let me know if it happens again."

I never told him than probably it had been *profesor* Merla's idea to play this prank. We all needed to have fun from time to time, but Andrés was definitely not laughing on this occasion.

CHAPTER SEVENTY-ONE

TREASURING NEW FRIENDS

The season of Lent seemed to drag. I went back to Monterrey for my two-week Holy Week vacation before the end of the 1961–1962 school term.

The company of my family had a soothing effect on me. Hearing my mother's voice lifted my spirits and warmed my lonely heart. She didn't even have to be in the room for her presence to caress me. I felt her love from every corner of our small home. I was not surprised to learn that she had already made many friends in the new neighborhood. With her kindness and friendliness, she always earned the affection of everyone around her.

The second day, I went by Mari Paz's home to say hello. The mutual appreciation was still intact, but during my long absence she had made new friendships, and I understood that. On this occasion, she was about to go out with some friends. She asked me to accompany them, but I felt out of place. I declined the last-minute invitation. Afterward, the only times I went out with her were when it was just the two of us.

My other close friend, Licha, not only lived farther away, but she also didn't go out much. Her father was very strict, and he didn't allow her go anyplace unless her aunt Isabel accompanied her. My old acquaintances now had their own agendas, new friends, and different interests from mine. I felt isolated and sad.

"How come you came back so soon, *Preciosita*?" my mother asked when I entered the kitchen. "Weren't you going to have lunch with Mari Paz?"

"She had a previous engagement with some other friends. She didn't know I was coming. There was no way to let her know, since neither of us has a phone." I forced a smile, but my mother looked at me with concern. "Mari Paz did invite me to join them, but I didn't want to be an imposition. Anyway, I would rather spend the day with you." I hugged my mother and kissed her on her soft cheek.

"I'm glad you are with me, but you need to go out and have fun with girls your age."

That afternoon, Julie's friend Carmelita brought me a short message from her sister Trini.

She asked if I would like to get together with her after they closed their store that night. Of course, I accepted. That invitation couldn't have come at a better time. I started to sing with my mother while she was getting dinner ready. At dinner time, the food tasted better than ever.

That was the first of many nights on which Trini and I would talk for hours outside her house. Often, we sat there, eating delicious, steamed tacos from a small restaurant across the street.

Trini and I enjoyed watching the activity on our street. My brother Ernesto and Trini's two younger brothers—Pancho and Elías—played soccer with other boys in the middle of the street. Julie, Carmelita, Chirris, and other neighboring girls jumped rope on the sidewalk and sang a children's song.

My sister Norma, already an adolescent, talked with Rosa, another of Trini's sisters. Whatever they talked about made them elbow each other frequently and giggle. Everybody in my family seemed to have a Rodríguez friend of similar age, and even though I was six years older than Trini, we got along very well.

On Holy Thursday, Trini and I visited the seven churches, as tradition dictated. As in previous Holy Weeks, I met many people whom I had not seen in a long time. This celebration would become routine among us in future years.

Trini told me she was dating one of Minerva's oldest brothers, Antonio. Theirs was a long-distance relationship too. Toño, as he was called, was one of the nicest single guys in Doctor Arroyo. Everyone knew the dedication with which he helped his grandmother Lupita in her clothing store. Toño and Trini were involved in their respective family's businesses. They were perfect for each other. I hoped one day they would get married.

I confided to Trini about my broken engagement to Martín. She told me not to worry and that maybe it would all work out in time.

I preferred not to talk about it anymore. I just wanted to enjoy her company.

A few days later, my mother and I were sitting in the kitchen talking when she commented, "I'm so glad you and Trini have become such good friends, *hijita*. I'm sure she is just like her mom *doña* Gracia, one of the nicest people I know."

My mom told me about this remarkable lady.

"*Doña* Gracia takes care of Paulita, an old woman who lives by herself across the street. The *viejita* has ulcers on her legs, so *doña* Gracia goes by her house every day to wash them and apply medicine and bandages on the poor woman's legs. Can you imagine? Not everybody would be willing to do such a task with someone who is not even related to her."

"You are right, *madrecita*. Trini also has a kind heart like her mother. I have noticed it through our conversations."

I felt very lucky to have her as a friend. And my fortune increased.

It was at this time that Trini introduced me to two friends of hers from childhood—the sisters Santa and Guille Mendoza, with whom I would later develop a great friendship, not only with them, but also with the rest of their family. Both were very polite and pretty. Santa was a girl with delicate features and a sweet character. Her sister Guille stood out for her big green eyes and strong personality. As I was already at the end of my vacation, we only saw each other on this one occasion.

In the blink of an eye, it was time to return to Doctor Arroyo. The last night in Monterrey, I went by Trini's house to say goodbye.

"I'm going to miss you, Coco. I wish you didn't have to go," she said.

"I wish I could stay, Trini, and I'm going to miss you, too. This vacation has been special. You don't have any idea how much your friendship means to me. I'll be back soon, and we'll have a great summer!"

My visit was brief since I had to pack my bags and go to bed early.

As I traveled back to Doctor Arroyo, my mood was different from the last trip because I had a new friend waiting for me back home. The thought of how much we had shared and learned about each other in such short time made me happy. I would eagerly await the time to return and continue those pleasant moments with her.

The next weeks were busy with the end-of-the-year exams. Then came the rehearsals for the graduation's artistic program and waltz.

On the day of the great celebration, everything went perfectly. In reality, it was much better than predicted. The students had a special Mass followed by a reception. The graduation ceremony was in the early afternoon, with the theater packed from side to side. People came from small towns around Doctor Arroyo and even from Matehuala. I'm sure many of them didn't know any of the graduates, but they came to attend the ceremony and, more than anything, to enjoy the free dance with two great orchestras.

When the ceremony ended, the graduation dance followed. For this occasion, we arduously prepared the Mexican waltz *"Sobre las Olas."* As I proudly watched the twists and turns of the graduates, my eyes filled with tears. *What if this is my last graduation at Doctor Arroyo?*

Afterward, the two bands played the rest of the night. Everyone was cheerful and talkative.

When the dance ended and people started to leave, my girls came to hug me once more, and many of them cried. The boys also came up to me to say goodnight. Several of them said they would visit me the next day to say goodbye.

I didn't talk much as I walked home with Nena and the Berrones girls. I promised to see them before I left. It saddened me to part with them, who had supported me with their friendship throughout this time, making my loneliness more bearable. On the other hand, I was excited about the idea of meeting again with Mari Paz, Licha, and my new friends in Monterrey.

The next day, I packed my belongings. There were not many, so it didn't take me too long. As I had promised, I got together with my friends and finally had to say goodbye.

Everyone asked the same question, "Will you come back for the next course?"

"I don't have any idea. I should wait and see what happens." I could not answer them otherwise.

Many of the recent graduates, as well as other students from different grades, came throughout the day. Several of them would go to the university in San Luis Potosí. Others, like Perico Castilleja, would continue their studies in Monterrey.

"I'll visit you at your home to let you know my progress, *maestra*," he said with his characteristic big smile.

"I'm sure you'll be somebody important one day, Perico. I have faith in you. Just study hard and choose your friends carefully. 'You show me who your friends are, and I'll show you who you are.' Remember the saying."

Perico nodded. "I'll do that, *maestra*, I promise. You'll be proud of me. You'll see."

Soon, all the students had left. *Doña* Susana said she would have breakfast ready for us. We had to be at the bus by five o'clock in the morning, and we were happy to know that we would get something to eat before leaving.

Next day, as soon as we finished breakfast, it was time to say our last goodbyes. I thanked Teresa and the other maids for all that they had done for me. Then I went and gave a big hug to *doña* Susana, who waited on the side.

"*¡Gracias por todo, Abue!* I hope to see you in August."

"*¡Vaya con Dios, Niña!* I hope you'll be back soon." Her usually dry eyes looked sad and moist as she said goodbye to me.

Horacio, Perico, Catarino, and some other students showed up to help carry our belongings to the bus. I couldn't believe all the presents there were in the luggage. I didn't worry because I would have many hands to help me once I was in Monterrey.

When the old bus took to the dusty road, I waved a last goodbye to my students. Every year I felt the same sadness, knowing that some of them would no longer live in town because they would continue their higher studies in another city. I was happy to think that I had contributed to their desire to reach for something better. I felt comfort remembering that some other students would be waiting for my return to Doctor Arroyo.

A few hours later, as always, the majestic *Cerro de la Silla* was the first to welcome us from afar. I was home. I didn't know for how long, but I would try to enjoy my summer vacation. My family and my friends from Monterrey were waiting for me, and I would make every minute count.

CHAPTER SEVENTY-TWO

SPECIAL SUMMER: BULLS AND RETURN

I had left Doctor Arroyo anticipating the time I would share with my friend Trini. However, a few days after my arrival, she left on vacation to Doctor Arroyo. Now she had two reasons to go there—her boyfriend, Toño Rodríguez, and her cousin Chayo.

Once more, I enrolled in summer classes knowing they would be useful to me, especially if I were to go back to Doctor Arroyo. For the previous four years, I had taken special courses to compensate—in part—for not being able to attend formal graduate courses.

Mari Paz came by the house in the second week of my vacation. As always, I was delighted to see her. Her bubbly personality always made me feel good. Despite the time and distance between us and her new friends, our warm friendship always remained.

After a brief greeting, she raised an eyebrow and said, "I can't believe you are back in Monterrey and you haven't been to see me."

"But I just returned a few days ago." I pulled playfully on her ponytail. "Besides, you work during the week, and now that you have a boyfriend, I feel like I have to make an appointment to see you."

Mari Paz smiled, showing her perfect teeth. Then she told me about her job and her relationship with her boyfriend, Juan Antonio. Both of them worked at a well-known radio station in Monterrey.

She was one of the teachers who hadn't found a teaching position. My mother knew about this situation. Always empathetic, one day, reading the newspaper, she found out that there was a vacancy at a certain radio station. Wasting no time, she commissioned my brother Javier to go to Mari Paz's house to give her the newspaper clipping with the data. My friend went, applied, and was hired right away. She worked in the control room, and Juan Antonio was an announcer. He always joked that he should be introduced as "The most beautiful voice on the radio." In fact, he sported a pleasant and deep vocal timbre.

Juan Antonio had a second job. On Sundays, he was a bullfight chronicler, then he published his bullfighting column in a major local newspaper. He knew a lot about this art because he had been a *torero* when he was younger. After Mari Paz started dating him, she became a regular at the *"Fiesta Brava."* That summer she formally introduced me to the *Mundo Taurino*, the bullfighting world.

Previously, I had attended a *corrida* twice. On those occasions, when the moment came for the *matador* to kill the bull, I had always thought, *"¿Qué hago aqui?"* "What am I doing here? I'll never come back." Now, however, I was listening to Mari Paz talking excitedly about how her nephew Roberto was being groomed to become a *torero*.

"My God, Mari Paz, Roberto is just a little boy. What does your sister Carmela say about it?"

"Well, this is something he wants to do. Of course, Carmela doesn't like that, but he's passionate about it. He's training hard, and Juan Antonio says he's sure Roberto will go far. He's already in the *cuadrilla de niños*, the group of little boys learning the *torero* skills."

"Well, it doesn't sound bad—Roberto Martínez, *matador*." I traced the name in the air, on an imaginary poster.

"There is a boy who is already getting famous; his name is Eloy Cavazos. Roberto and Eloy are training together. Hopefully one day they will be *novilleros* and after that *matadores*." She let out a long sigh.

"I hope so. I'm sorry for your sister Carmela. She must be very uneasy."

"Forget about it. Come tomorrow around three o'clock, so you can join us." She stood up with her purse, ready to go.

"Wait! I don't know if I have something to do tomorrow," I said, trying to remember a valid excuse not to go. I squeezed her arm softly.

"Don't be silly. I don't want to hear about it. I'll expect you at that time, and don't be late. Juan Antonio must be at the plaza on time." She laughed and waved goodbye.

So, that Sunday and on the following ones, I was there, on time. I remember listening to a famous announcer saying, "A bullfight is a ritual between life and death."

And I attended such a ritual for five Sundays of my summer vacation.

Cayito came home for a few days before leaving for Saltillo with his seminary classmates. There they would continue their vacations in a huge, old property. He enjoyed watching his favorite programs on our new TV and playing soccer with Trini's brothers Pancho and Elias, our brother Ernesto, and other neighborhood boys. Cayito seemed to adjust perfectly well to the old family routine. Time passed quickly, and after he left, the family felt incomplete again. We missed him and eagerly awaited news from him.

A few weeks later, my mother received a letter from Cayito. With a beaming expression, she opened it.

"I bet you he's letting us know the date he'll be back in Monterrey. He must be eager to see us." As soon as she started reading it, her smile disappeared.

"What's wrong, *madrecita*?"

"It would be better if you see it yourself and tell me your opinion." My mom sat with a pensive expression. She squeezed her hands and waited silently while I read the letter.

In it, Cayito said he had concluded that he didn't have the calling to become a priest. He said he had struggled with this fact for a long time but had found it difficult to let us know about it. He was worried that we would think he had failed us.

I finished reading the letter, closed it, and gave it back to my mother.

"What do you think, *hijita*?" she asked in a shaky voice.

"*Madrecita*, if Cayito doesn't have the vocation for the priesthood, it will be better if one day he becomes a good parent and not a bad priest. Don't you agree?"

She was silent for few minutes, turning the letter over a couple of times. Then she said, "You are right, *hijita*. We can't force him to become something that he no longer wants to be."

"I'll answer him right away." Full of joy, I must confess, I wrote him a long letter urging him to follow his heart and assuring him we were happy with his decision.

Cayito came back from Saltillo a few days later. My father had double joy that night; Sultans of Monterrey, the city's professional baseball team, were crowned league champions, and minutes later Cayito arrived by taxi. The family was complete again, at least until the end of my vacation.

Trini returned from Doctor Arroyo a month before my vacation ended. We visited every single day after dark. Guille and Santa came to meet with us several times, and we really hit it off. We would get together to have a snack or just to talk. A bond of close friendship was formed that has lasted for decades.

I enjoyed a good summer, but it distressed me to think of my mother's sadness if I would have to leave one more time. Every day she was very attentive to the time the mailman went by our house. I had two reasons to wait for him, too—a new job notification and some news from Martín—but the mailman, like in recent vacations, never came.

I tried to lift my spirit thinking about how much my students needed me in Doctor Arroyo. For some of them, attending school represented a challenge. I had to be there to give them the tools to graduate. That made me think of a particular case.

At the beginning of the previous school year, I had noticed that two students were constantly late for the first class of the day. One of them was named Tiburcio and the other Agustin, who was Francisco Molina's half-brother, one of our most distinguished students and of whom I have very fond memories. I was surprised *profesor* Merla hadn't said anything about it, since he was always very punctual.

One afternoon, before leaving for the day, we gathered in the *director's* office to review some school projects. I thought it was a good time to ask about the boys, since we were all present.

"Excuse me, *profesor*," I said. "A couple of students have been arriving late every day. They not only interrupt the class, but they are also missing half of it. Should we talk to them?"

"No, *señorita*. I'm aware of their delay, and the reason why we won't say anything is because these two boys make the effort to come to school from a small town outside of Doctor Arroyo."

"Oh, I had no knowledge of that. I just thought they might be getting up late."

"When their parents came to register them, they advised me that the boys would possibly be late often because they have to walk several kilometers."

"You are right, *profesor*. I just found out that they leave home very early in the morning," Lupito said. "I almost scolded them, but one their classmates told me about it."

"It was my mistake; I forgot to inform you of that." The *director* closed his notebook. "As you realize, it's harder for them than for the rest of the students to attend class. Somehow we'll work with these boys to help them with the part of the instruction that they are missing."

From that day on, I really appreciated those students' presence in class. I was particularly impressed by Agustín. I wondered how it felt to be a foreigner and the oldest student in the entire school, at nineteen. It made me sad to think that maybe middle school would be the limit of studies for him. More than likely, he would have to stay at home to help support his family.

At the same time, we were able to recognize the humanity and concern of *profesor* Merla to bring culture to all those thirsty for learning and progress. He was an exemplary teacher.

I waited until the last minute to pack my belongings. No notification arrived from the *Dirección General*, and I would have to go back to work in Doctor Arroyo for another year. At least I had a job, even if that meant leaving my family, friends, and home, and putting my dreams on hold. Before leaving, I asked my mother not to be sad. She tried to smile as she gave me her blessing.

"*Hijita*, please promise me that you will not marry a *ranchero* and stay there," she insisted.

Her comment was funny. "*Madrecita*, you asked me the same thing before. What worries you the most, that I would marry a *ranchero* or that I would stay in Doctor Arroyo?"

She looked at me shyly without answering. We all laughed at her reaction. That was a very opportune time to say goodbye with smiling faces, although inwardly our hearts cried once more.

CHAPTER SEVENTY-THREE

UNEXPECTED MIRACLE

The ten-hour trip back to Doctor Arroyo gave me plenty of time to think about all that had happened during the summer of 1962. More than ever, I realized what I was missing: my family's warmth, my friends, the proper diversions for girls my age, and the continuation of my education.

Even though the *Director General* had promised to bring me back to Monterrey as soon as there was an opening, that hadn't materialized.

I learned that several teachers assigned outside Monterrey at the same time as I had—or worse, later—were now working there. Others had jobs in towns close to the city, so they went back and forth to work every day, or they came home on weekends. Why this injustice?

After a long and boring trip, I finally arrived in town. Lupito, Gerónimo, and Andrés were back, too. *Profesor* Merla welcomed us, and we went through the usual procedures of preparing for the beginning of classes.

My friends Nena and Eva were still on vacation. I enjoyed seeing my old students again and meeting new ones. I accepted that I would be there for at least another year and devoted my attention to the subjects I would teach.

One afternoon, around the second week of September, I had just sat down to eat when a municipal office employee stopped his jeep in front of the restaurant. *Doña* Susana, the diners, and I looked at him with curiosity as the doors swayed behind him. I thought he was coming for dinner. To our surprise, he took big strides toward me.

"I'm glad to see you, *maestra*," he said, without preamble. "I was just going to inquire for you. You need to come with me to the *Presidencia* to receive a radio message."

My heartbeat quickened. "Did they say who is calling me?" I asked as I stood up in a rush.

"I don't know. I'm sorry. Someone else received the message. They just told me to fetch you and to hurry up."

Doña Susana and the maids paid a lot of attention as did a couple of diners.

"I'll be back, *Abue*," I said, as I followed the man outside. I got into the jeep, and in two minutes we were in front of the municipal building. The driver politely helped me out of the vehicle.

I rushed inside. I was afraid, not knowing who would be contacting me with such urgency. *I hope everyone at home is alright.*

There were three or four employees in the office. They stared at me, and I greeted them. One of them was sitting in front of the radio console.

"The *maestra* is here," the employee announced to somebody on the radio. He handed me the microphone.

My heart pounded and my hands shook while I held the small apparatus. After I said hello, an unknown feminine voice informed me that she was calling from the *Dirección General*—yes, the *Dirección General*!

"*Profesora* Camero, there is a position for you here in Monterrey as a middle school teacher in *Secundaria 8*," she said. "If you accept it, you should report immediately."

I wondered if I was dreaming.

The woman's voice continued. "So, you have to decide right now if you will accept this job or not. We have a long list of people behind you waiting for the position."

I brought the microphone close to my lips, wanting to be sure she heard me. "Of course, I accept! But, what about my principal here? Are you calling him now to let him know?"

"No, we will call him as soon as we select the person to replace you. Here in Monterrey, the principal of Secondary 8 will be notified of your assignment immediately, and he'll be waiting for you. Good luck, *maestra* Camero!"

Overwhelmed with a mix of emotions, all I could say was, "Thank you so much!" Those words came sincerely. The call marked the before and after.

I returned the microphone to the employee and thanked the people in the municipal office. I knew they had overheard the conversation, and soon everybody in town would find out that I was leaving Doctor Arroyo. I hurried home, afraid to wake up from my dream. A miracle had happened! I would finally return to my family.

Happiness invaded my being, but soon, a chill ran down my spine, thinking about *profesor* Merla's reaction when I informed him about my new assignment. I was sure he would not share my happiness.

I walked into the dining room where Gerónimo, Lupito, and Andrés were waiting. Everyone was watching me in silence. I understood that *doña* Susana had already informed them of my hasty departure to respond to the radio. I tried not to let my face show any emotion as I sat at the table, ready to eat with them. Gerónimo started tapping the table, and Andrés cupped his chin with one hand, waiting for me to say something.

Doña Susana and the maids peeked inside the dining room as soon as they heard my voice. Everyone observed me in silence.

Finally, I couldn't hold back anymore. Smiling broadly, I told them, "I have been offered a position in a middle school in Monterrey—and I accepted it!"

The teachers looked at me, trying to discern if I was serious or playing a prank.

"You are joking. Truth?" Lupito asked.

Looking at me sideways, Andrés said, "Don't say that, Socorrito. Seriously, who called you?"

"I'm telling you the truth. They called me from the *Dirección General* in Monterrey to ask me to report immediately to my new school."

The maids started to whisper among themselves, and *doña* Susana sent them inside the kitchen. She stayed close, pretending to clean the table next to ours. Little Claudia came back with a rag and started wiping another table.

The teachers were silent for few minutes. Then, realizing I was telling them the truth, they said they would miss me, but they felt happy for me.

"I would not like to be in your place when you inform *profesor* Merla that you will be leaving, Socorrito," Andrés commented thoughtfully.

"Well, he'll have to accept it," Lupito said. "It was bound to happen eventually. Don't you worry, *maestra*."

"Hmm. I bet you the *director* is not going to be happy, *señorita*." *Doña* Susana shook her head as she carried some empty plates into the kitchen.

Claudia, walking behind her, looked at the restaurant door with a worrisome expression. *Has she spotted professor Merla?*

"Please, don't make me more nervous." I wrung my hands.

My legs felt weak when the *director* came into the dining room. He greeted us cheerfully. Then, I dropped the bomb, and my worry became reality.

He reacted worse that I had anticipated. As soon as I told him, his facial expression changed, and he looked at me with withering eyes.

"I knew it!" he said with trembling lips, hitting the table hard with his fist. "They always do that. They don't care if I don't have any teachers after classes have already started."

"They'll be sending somebody to replace me soon, *profesor*."

"You go ahead with your plans and leave. I don't care." He pushed his chair back and stood up. After putting on his hat sideways he stormed out of the house without eating.

We all stared, dumbfounded, at the dining room's swinging doors. After an uncomfortable silence, I said in a broken voice, "I'm sorry he's taking it so hard, but it has been a long assignment, and it's time for me to go back home."

"Don't worry," Andrés said. "You know him. Soon he will reconsider, and everything will be fine."

I knew he was right. Fortunately, *profesor* Merla never stayed angry for very long. After the first explosion, he always acted as if nothing had happened.

Doña Susana and Teresa were sad to hear I was leaving.

Within two hours it was common knowledge that I was being transferred to another school. I went to the telegraph office to send a telegram to my parents. I was eager to share the great news with them. Along the way, several people stopped me to let me know that they already knew about my change.

"We are sorry to hear that you are leaving us."

"We are going to miss you. After all, you were here several years."

Many of them wanted to know how *profesor* Merla was taking it.

"He's upset at the minute, but soon it will pass," I told them.

"Do you know who's going to replace you? Will it be a man or a woman?"

I assured them I didn't have any idea, but the *director* would be notified soon.

My father sent me a telegram back. He informed me that at home they were happy with the news. He would come in two days to thank *profesor* Merla and the rest of the people for taking care of me during those four years.

I started gathering my belongings and saying goodbye to the closest persons. Unfortunately, Nena was not back in town yet. *Profesor* Merla came by the house in a better mood and apologized for becoming angry. He said he was sad I had to go, but he understood I wanted to be with my family. What infuriated him was the fact that the *Dirección General* decided to make the change when the classes had already started. He didn't know how long it would still take for them to send a new teacher. Meanwhile, all of them would have to work more hours to teach the subjects that had been assigned to me.

I told him I understood his reasons for being angry and that he had nothing to apologize for. Also, that I was very grateful for all I had learned from him. I added that after four years of working together, I understood it would be hard for him to start anew with somebody else.

My students were shocked to hear the news. Some of them told me they thought I would never leave Doctor Arroyo. Others wanted to know the reason I had to go back to Monterrey. Saying goodbye was very painful. Several girls hugged me and cried, and some boys didn't even hide their teary eyes.

"It has nothing to do with you, with my coworkers, or the townspeople," I said, holding back my tears. "I love all of you. The teachers are great, and everybody in town has always been kind to me. But I have my family that misses me and awaits me in Monterrey. Besides, I want to go back to school to continue my studies. I'll never forget you; I promise. Come to see me in Monterrey or write. I'll leave you my address."

I had a difficult time teaching that afternoon because the students were so upset that they couldn't pay attention or participate in class. However, there was nothing they or I could do about it. I would be leaving forever.

My father arrived two days later, covered with dust like the rest of the bus passengers but smiling with happiness. I saw Toño Rodríguez, Trini's boyfriend, coming down from the bus, too. He said hello, and my father commented later that they had been traveling companions.

I was elated to see my dad. I ran to hug him and kiss him on the cheek.

"It was a long and hard trip, *hijita*. Now I know what you had to go through every time you took the bus."

"You get used to it, Dad. The only thing I never got used to was arriving dusty."

As promised, my father thanked people for their kindness to me, especially *profesor* Merla, *doña* Susana, and the rest of the teachers. I had reserved a room for my dad at the hotel, and since I had everything packed, all that we had to do was to get up very early the next morning to go back to Monterrey.

That night, I said goodbye to Lupito and Gerónimo. Andrés would walk us to the bus. Claudia came and hugged me, crying. I told her one day I might be back and I would bring her my red shoes. In reality, if my economic situation had been better, I would have left them for her.

The next day, my father and I awoke around four o'clock. The morning was pleasantly cool. The aroma of fresh coffee reached us from the kitchen, and *doña* Susana announced that breakfast was ready. My father and I sat down to eat with hearty appetites. *Profesor* Merla and Andrés showed up in the dining room a few minutes later and had some coffee and *pan dulce*. I looked at my watch. It was time to leave. I went to my room to collect my belongings. Everybody waited by the front door.

At the moment of saying goodbye, *doña* Susana began to cry. "*Por favor*, take care of my girl," she asked my father.

That touched me deeply because I had never seen *doña* Susana cry. I hugged her and gave her a kiss on her wrinkled cheek. She wiped her eyes with the end of her *delantal*, her old apron. I tried not to cry, but my tears didn't obey.

"One day, I'll come back to visit, Granny. *¡Gracias por todo!*".

Teresa cried, too. I hugged her, and then everybody else. Afterward, I left with my father and *profesores* Andrés and Merla, who walked us toward the bus.

It was almost five o' clock, and the sun was just beginning to rise. We walked down the middle of the street followed by Duque. I patted his head. "Thanks for taking care of me, Duque!" was my farewell.

Horacio and some students were already waiting for me. There were lots of hugs and some tears. The final sad moment was saying goodbye to Andrés, as well as *profesor* Merla, who wiped a tear away with the back of his hand.

"Thank you again, *profesor* Merla, and don't hate me for leaving." I tried to lighten the moment. "You are a great teacher and an excellent human being. I'll never forget you or my dear Doctor Arroyo!"

"Good luck, *señorita* Socorrito." He gave me a big hug and tried to smile.

"*Profesor* Andrés, thank you for your friendship and support. Take care of yourself."

I knew my departure would be harder for him. We had always been close since we arrived in Doctor Arroyo together four years before.

"Take care, Socorrito, and good luck! I'm going to miss you." Andrés smiled sadly.

I also tried to smile. "I'll miss you, too, but I know you are well cared for with Chayo. You were born for each other and will end up being married."

Andrés just smiled and gave me a hug. I felt a knot in my throat remembering how gentle and protective he had always been with me.

My father and I boarded the bus and sat in the front seat behind Chepa. As the old bus started its way toward the road to Matehuala,

I waved to everyone for the last time. I looked at the plaza with its gazebo in the middle, the white church with its steeple, and the cobblestone streets. I tried to fix these images in my memory as they grew smaller until they ended up fading into the horizon.

As we left the town that I had learned to love, the sun shone brightly with the promise of a great day. On that trip, I didn't mind the swaying and jumping of the old bus or the alarmed cackling of the caged chickens on top of it. Nothing bothered me anymore. My heart was singing, "I'm going home. I'm going home!"

Tears rolled down my cheeks, but I knew that I would never forget the small and great experiences lived in the beloved *crystal box.*

CHAPTER SEVENTY-FOUR

REVELATIONS

As Doctor Arroyo disappeared in the distance, I reflected on my past and contemplated my future. With a sigh, I put my head on my father's shoulder.

"Can you believe it, Dad? I'm finally going home. After all these years the *Director General* at last made good his promise to bring me back to Monterrey."

For a few moments, my father gave me an enigmatic look. Then he looked straight ahead. "Well, you could have stayed there for God knows how long if it hadn't been for your mom."

"I owe this to Mom?" I picked up my head and turned slightly toward him to look at his face. "What do you mean?"

With a smile, Dad began his story. "After you left, your mom started trying to get an appointment to see the *Director General*, but he was always busy. After much insistence, she was finally able to speak to him. After letting him know that she was your mom, she reminded him of the promise he made to you to bring you back to Monterrey in a year or as soon as possible. Then your mom told him, 'We can understand that in one year there are no places open, at most in two, but it is already four years!'"

"And what did he answer?" I asked.

"He remembered it. He said that it was indeed the case, but there was a particular reason in your case why he had left you there."

"One reason?" Now I was really intrigued. "I do not understand."

Dad looked at me with an expression between amused and proud. "You won't believe it, *hijita*, but the *director* told your mom that every summer they received a letter with a long list of signatures. It was from the students' parents requesting that they not move you from Doctor Arroyo. They said they didn't want another teacher because 'they were so happy with *profesora* Camero'!"

I was speechless trying to digest that revelation from my father. I blinked several times.

"Your mom told me that she was, like you, completely surprised." Dad paused again. "The *director* told your mom he was amazed that you didn't know all that. Then, he added, 'Ma'am, you must be happy that people love your daughter that way. Most of the requests that come to my desk are to remove a teacher from his or her position.'"

"Poor Mom! She must have thought they were going to keep sending me to Doctor Arroyo indefinitely."

My father turned to look at me for a few moments and then continued his narration. "Your mother assured the *director* that, naturally, the detail he had shared with her made her feel very proud of you. But with more reason it showed that you had already made enough merits in time and quality to be assigned to a closer place. She explained to him your desire to continue your studies at the Superior Normal and appealed to his condition as a father. In short, she used all the resources mothers have to move hearts."

My father's voice cracked slightly. He took out his handkerchief to wipe his eyes. "The *Director General* told your mom that he would try to find something for you. We had almost given up hope until we received your unexpected telegram with the good news." He finished with a happy smile.

I heard all of this in surprise. Shaking my head, I said, "I can't believe the parents sent those requests and I didn't even know it. Now I see why dear *profesor* Merla hinted every year that I would come back; after all, having a woman on the school staff is very important. On the other hand, I suppose that from the first year he liked my work. He also knew that I supported him unconditionally."

Then I talked to my father about everything the principal had to go through, from working a year without salary in order to be authorized to found the school to getting the funds for the construction of our own building. Dad listened in silence, shaking his head from time to time.

"I hope that one day all those who were his students will recognize his efforts and name the school after him. Nobody deserves it more than him," I said.

"Hopefully, *hijita*. Unfortunately, humans sometimes easily forget."

"No, Dad. The people of Doctor Arroyo are always very grateful. I am sure that the alumni will never forget that, had it not been for the creation of this school, many of them would not have studied beyond primary school."

"I hope you are right, *hijita*. The praiseworthy work of *profesor* Merla must have a just reward. It would be a disgrace and an injustice if it were not like that."

After a short silence, I added, "Well, I have to thank Mom for her intervention."

"By the way, *hijita*. In your telegram you only let us know that you had been moved, but you did not tell us where."

"I'll tell you, Dad; only let me be the one to inform Mom and my siblings."

"Of course, *hijita*. It's your right."

When I told him, his face showed me the happiness my news had provided him.

This time, Mom and my siblings waited for us at home. My mom came to the door with open arms, and even when her eyes shone with tears, her beaming face reflected her feelings at that moment. As I hugged her, I whispered in her ear, "*¡Gracias, madrecita!* Dad told me all you did to bring me back."

"Of course, *Preciosita*, how would I not do it? I'm your mother." She gave me a kiss on the cheek, while my dad and my siblings happily watched us. "But tell me, you have us on edge. Where did they assign you?"

With the most serious face that I could show, I asked, "How far is Villa de Juárez?"

"Villa de Juárez?" My sister Norma clapped. "That municipality is close!"

"It takes a little less than two hours by bus," Héctor reported.

"How nice, *hijita*. You can come and go every day," my mom said, clasping her hands.

At the back of the room, Dad was trying to hide a smile. I decided it was enough.

"Well, that's good, because I won't have to go there. My change is here, in Monterrey. In the Secondary 8 of the Buenos Aires subdivision!"

The hubbub was general. My mom hugged me, tears rolling down her cheeks. She crossed herself and muttered something, probably a short prayer.

My eyes also clouded with tears. "And everything, thanks to you, *madrecita*."

"No, thank God," she replied.

And she was right. Thank God! Finally, the miracle had taken place and our family was complete again.

CHAPTER SEVENTY-FIVE

WEDDING BELLS

When I left Doctor Arroyo forever, all my problems and those of my family, which arose in the course of those four years, had practically been solved. All but one, and that corresponded to my romantic relationship. In that regard, what happened after the *crystal box*?

Two years after my return to Monterrey, sometime during the summer, Martín's mother, *doña* Margarita, her daughter Azucena, and a young woman surprisingly came to my home. I didn't know what to say or how to react to their visit. Azucena was Martín's older sister, and I knew from her that *doña* Margarita had been upset with me for breaking up with him.

However, they were very cordial. They explained to us that they had come to México to help the young woman who accompanied them. She was their relative immigrating to the USA. They had to arrange for her visa and passport in Monterrey. That required waiting for an appointment at the American Consulate. *Doña* Margarita said they were staying at the Hotel Continental. She asked my parents if they would let me stay with them at the hotel during the weekend and keep them company since they didn't know the city well.

I thought my father would be reluctant for me to spend time away from home, but to my surprise, he answered, *"¡Con mucho gusto!"*

The three of them seemed to be very pleased. That night I could hardly sleep, thinking about what they would have to say about Martín. My heart felt heavy, worried with the possible news that he was happily married.

The next day I stayed with them. We talked but didn't mention Martín. Later, Azucena asked me about my work and whether I was dating anybody. I told her I wasn't, but I didn't dare ask her the reason for her question.

I got along really well with the three of them.

A few days later, *doña* Margarita said, "Okay, Coco. I want to know the real reason why you broke off your engagement with Martín."

My face reddened and my heart started to race when I told her the facts starting from my father's job loss.

"As you can understand, *doña* Margarita, my dad couldn't find a job, and there seemed to be no hope. Then, being the oldest, I had to support my family. I became their only source of income overnight." I tried to hold back, but rebellious tears gave away my grief.

Doña Margarita hugged me and scolded me for not telling Martín what had happened. Her show of affection calmed my spirit, but even more so what followed.

"Look, we have something to confess, too. We came looking for you because Martín asked us to do so. He wanted to know if you were still single. We realized he is still in love with you, so we decided to do whatever was necessary to bring the two of you together. However, before saying anything, we wanted to be sure you are free and that you still love him."

"I'm free and never stopped loving him," I confessed. "I guess deep in my heart I always hoped that one day he would look for me again."

A few days later, a letter arrived from Martín, who was now in the Philippines. He said he had received information through the mail from his dad and also from Azucena telling him about me, and he wanted to thank me for helping his family. I told him we were having a great time going to the bullfights on Sundays and listening to the mariachis every night.

During the month or so that *doña* Margarita and her family spent in Monterrey, Martín and I exchanged several letters. Finally, he said if I were still willing, we would get married after he returned to the United States. Full of joy, I read the letter to *doña* Margarita and the girls.

Doña Margarita smiled and said, "This time you'd better get married. Oh, and don't worry; I promise you I'll be the best mother-in-law in the world."

"Thanks, *doña* Margarita, and I'll be the best daughter-in-law to you, too." I smiled and gave her a kiss on her cheek.

Martín and I had made plans to get married during the summer of 1966. To my dismay, in mid-September 1965, he asked me to advance our wedding plans to December, as he had orders to go to Vietnam early the next year. This would be the second time he would go there.

This change of plans created chaos in my life for the next three months. The Cathedral's chapel was only available on December 28 at 6 a.m. This was a ridiculous hour for a wedding. I had no choice but to make the necessary arrangements to get married in the church that belonged to my sector.

I had to travel to San Luis Potosí to get a copy of Martín's baptismal certificate. His mother told me that he had been baptized in the church of San Sebastián, which was the one where his other siblings had received this sacrament. As there was no record of him in that place, I inquired at the *Iglesia de la Compañía*, a centralized parish where I had been baptized. To my surprise, Martín was registered there. So, we were not only born in the same city, but were baptized in the same church, in the same christening font, and, most extraordinary, by the same priest.

I had no doubt that our destiny must have been written in the stars.

Outside of my closest friends and family, I didn't tell anyone that I was getting married. I needed to be sure that Martín would come to Monterrey.

I was afraid that he might be sent abroad ahead of schedule. Since it was December, I had a thousand difficulties getting everything I needed: the church, reception room, music, and invitations. In addition, I had to get the permission of Foreign Relations, since, although Martín had been born in México, he was considered a foreign citizen. The permit barely arrived in time.

This, along with the semester exams of my students, and mine, as a student of the Normal Superior, added to the tremendous stress of the wedding preparations. There was a time when I was afraid I was on the verge of a nervous breakdown.

During this exhausting period, my friend and colleague from work and studies, Ernestina Treviño, supported me unconditionally, accompanying me wherever necessary. She and I had met as high school students and again as teachers in *Secundaria # 8*. We also attended the Normal Superior together in the specialty of *Idiomas* (Languages). I don't know what I would have done without her valuable support. Thank God, by the time Martín arrived, everything was settled, and I was feeling relatively calmer.

Our first encounter was very sweet. As on previous occasions, he was already waiting for me outside the hotel. We hadn't seen each other in four years, except through pictures. There wasn't any doubt in my mind, however, that we would pick up where we had left off the last time we had been together.

Martín strode to meet me before I'd crossed the plaza. He was as I remembered, only a little darker and more serious looking. After a hug and a gentle kiss, I put my head on his chest and released a few tears of relief. Everything about our breakup had already been explained. I was so full of happiness to see him there. I took him home to introduce to my mom and siblings. After all that time, he finally met my family and vice versa. My mom, who had been eager to meet him, told him she grew fond of him even before she met him in person.

Almost ten years after we met, Martín and I finally married. Right after the wedding ceremony, the priest baptized Carina, the baby of our neighbors and friends *don* Rodolfo and Rosita Meléndez. Martín and I were her christening godparents. According to local beliefs, the baptism of a baby for whom the couple are godparents right after the couple is married attracts more blessings to the marriage. That morning, it rained during our ceremony, which is considered a good omen. The rain stopped, and for the rest of the day we enjoyed a pleasant temperature.

Norma, Petrita (my mother), Martín, me, Arcadio (my father), and Julie

My sister Norma and my dear friends Trini, Licha, and Santa and Guille Mendoza, kindly offered to be maids of honor. My brother Héctor and my friend Ernestina were our *lazo padrinos*, and my little sister Julie was our flower girl. Mari Paz and Juan Antonio acted as sponsors of the civil ceremony. In México, the civil and religious ceremonies occur separately. The civil ceremony takes place before the church. It can be the same day, or several days before the religious. Martín and I were married in a civil ceremony at nine in the morning, in my home, with only my immediate family, our sponsors, and closest relatives present.

Our maids of honor Licha, Norma, Trini and Santa.

After the religious ceremony, we moved to a reception hall. The waltz that Martín and I danced to the chords of a marimba orchestra said what my heart felt at that moment—"Fascination."

Among my special guests were *profesora* Lupita Martínez and her husband. She was the principal of the elementary school who had to leave Doctor Arroyo due to a nervous breakdown. We met at the Normal Superior and established a beautiful friendship. She corroborated the stories of harassment that I had heard four years earlier in Doctor Arroyo and that at that time I found incredible.

"I was too young and inexperienced," Lupita told me. "Today I have acquired maturity and experience. If I would go back now, things would be very different."

*Juan Antonio R. Córdova and Mari Paz Rodríguez,
our civil ceremony sponsors.*

Martín and I had an almost two-week honeymoon in México City and Guadalajara. During that period, some days I felt ecstatic, and on others, I felt deeply depressed, knowing Martín would leave for the war.

On those occasions he would say, "Listen, don't worry; there is still no bullet that ends the life of one of the Martínezes!" referring to himself and his older brothers Fabio and Fred, who were also fighting in the war of Vietnam. I was sure that their wives Betty and Liz felt the same as me, but it must have been worse for their parents, *don* Martín and *doña* Margarita, because they had three children in the combat zones.

For a long time, I cried without knowing if Martín would return. Would our marriage be shorter than our courtship? Would he be injured? And even more, would he survive the war?

I put everything in God's hands.

EPILOGUE

Thank God, Martín returned from Vietnam. In October 1966, I left family, friends, my job, and my country to move to the United States, where I would start a new chapter of my life with my husband.

We have been blessed with three wonderful, loving children who are our pride—Patricia, Juan Carlos, and Omar. Our life has never been dull. Martín and I have had the adventurous experience of traveling the world, exploring the exotic places I always dreamed about, and meeting amazing people who have expanded our list of friends. I have never regretted my decision to wait for Martín. In 2015, we celebrated our Golden Wedding Anniversary in Monterrey by renewing our marriage vows in the Cathedral's chapel, a dream fulfilled half a century later!

Profesor Merla continued to teach. He passed away at age eighty-five after educating many generations of students. He has been honored with having a night school named after him. A street in the town of Doctor Arroyo bears his name: Fancisco Merla Moreno. He is survived by the daughters who were his pride and adoration, Lydia, a teacher, and Delia, a nurse.

As a new teacher, I learned his work ethic and his love of education. Throughout my entire teaching career, I followed his golden rule, "When one rates his students, he is rating oneself." For us teachers who worked under his direction, *profesor* Merla was, in a way, a father figure because he protected us and cared for each one of us. In my case, he made me stronger as a teacher, and I'll always be grateful for his guidance and support.

Andrés found the woman of his dreams in Rosario "Chayo" García. After a short courtship, they married in Doctor Arroyo. They have three children, one girl and two boys. He became a school principal and served in four schools. Then he retired to a tranquil place in the country, not too far from Monterrey, where he grows fruit trees as a hobby.

Lauro and Esperanza Martínez made their dream of love come true and got married in Monterrey. They had six children, three boys and three girls. They shared forty-two years of happy marriage until the passing of Esperanza. Lauro is retired and lives quietly in Monterrey with one of his children.

After returning to Monterrey, José Luis taught in several schools. Later, he held the position of Director of the Normal Schools of the State of Nuevo León. He married and had three children: two girls and one boy. After retiring, he ran a small sporting goods business. He died in Guadalajara and one of his last wishes was that his great friend Lauro be notified. Friends until the end.

Mari Paz and Juan Antonio R. Córdova married, too. They have four girls. With time, she was able to find a job as a teacher and practiced her profession until she retired. Juan Antonio retired from the radio, journalism, and bullfighting worlds. His bullfighting friends, as well as his fellow journalists, continue to visit him.

Trini and Antonio "Toño" Rodríguez married and established their home in Monterrey. They have three girls and have been very successful in business. Now they live peacefully and happily on a beautiful *finca* outside the city. They are the godparents of our youngest son. We became like family.

Licha married a federal schools inspector, *profesor* Armando Villarreal, who was also from Villaldama, as Lauro and José Luis. They had two girls and a boy. She retired from the private school system. Unfortunately, Armando passed away, and Licha continues to miss the serenades he used to give her with his guitar.

Ernestina continued to teach English as a second language. She married a wonderful man, Olaff Quesnel, with whom she had five children. He passed away very young, so Ernestina became both mother and father to their children. She retired as a teacher after twenty-six years of service.

My friendship with all of them has continued through all of these long years.

After Martín and I married and left for the United States, my brother Héctor, who was a teacher then, took my place in helping my father financially to support the family. During this time, he entered school to study medicine. When the rest of my siblings were already grown up, the last of my brothers, Paquito, came into our family, filling our lives with joy.

Thanks to my parents who sacrificed for our education, all of my siblings and I became professionals. All of us married and have happy families. We continue being a close-knit family honoring a family motto, *La Unión Hace la Fuerza*, Unity is Strength.

Today, many of the people who were once part of my life aren't here anymore to read my story. Gone are my parents and my sister Norma. Gone are my in-laws, *don* Martín and *doña* Margarita, and my sister in-law Azucena. Gone are *profesores* José Luis Pérez, Rogelio de León, Gerónimo Llanes, Santiago Cantú, and, of course, the mentor and guide of all of us, the unforgettable *profesor* Francisco Merla

Moreno, our *director*. Gone also are *doña* Susana and recently her daughter Nena, my friend and companion in adventures of that time. Gone are some of my most faithful students: Ernesto Rodríguez, Pepe Rodríguez, Jorge Martínez, Irma Berrones, María Luisa Berrones, Sergio Sánchez, Alicia Muñiz, Matías Báez, Pedro Castilleja, Lupita Torres.

I honor the memory of all of them by bringing them back to life through the pages of my memories. They will always live in my heart.

Even now, in this year of 2021, I still keep in touch with several of the students I met in Doctor Arroyo between 1958 and 1962. I also communicate with several other students from *Secundaria # 8* in Monterrey, whom I have known since 1962.

My greatest reward as a teacher is knowing that they have never forgotten me and that I inspired many of them to pursue the most beautiful career in the world: teaching. Several other students have expressed how much my words influenced them to stay on the right track to achieve their dreams.

In this regard, knowing how many of them are now successful professionals and prosperous people, I feel that I reached my own expectations, and this knowledge fills my heart with happiness and satisfaction.

I retired from the Texas school system in the United States in 2004. Even though the schools where I worked were modern, well-equipped, and comfortable, I have always remembered with fondness and nostalgia the modest middle school in Doctor Arroyo, Nuevo León, my students, and the kind people with whom I shared my life ... *Living in a Crystal Box.*

Camero Haro Family: Ernesto, Cayito, Coco, Héctor, Norma, Javier, Julie, and parents Petrita y Arcadio

Silver anniversary, with our children Omar, Carlos, and Patty

50th wedding anniversary, some of the attendees

ABOUT THE AUTHOR

María Socorro "Coco" Martínez, maiden name María del Socorro Camero Haro, is a freelance writer and author of a memoir.

Coco was born in San Luis Potosí, in the state of San Luis Potosí, México, but grew up in Monterrey, Nuevo León, México. She worked as a teacher of grades seven through nine, as well as an Assistant Principal for a year, in a middle school in Doctor Arroyo, Nuevo León, México, from 1958 to 1962. She later taught in middle schools in Monterrey, Nuevo León, México, from 1962 to 1966.

She then married Martín H. Martínez, a US Air Force member, and moved to the United States. She was a stay-at-home mom to her three children until she returned to work as a bilingual assistant at elementary schools in North East ISD in San Antonio, Texas, from 1985 to 2004.

Co-founder of the Spanish for Children program, National Autonomous University of México (Universidad Nacional Autónoma de México, UNAM), San Antonio, Texas, she led double summer sessions from 1988 to 1995.

Since 2002, she has worked part time for Tri-Lin Integrated Services in San Antonio, Texas, as a Spanish consultant and freelance writer of standardized test passages in Spanish for elementary students.

Living in a Crystal Box is her memoir describing her experiences as a young city girl facing the hardships and taboos of working as a teacher in Doctor Arroyo, a rural Mexican town, in the 1950s.

A NOTE FROM THE AUTHOR

If you enjoyed my memoir, would you recommend it to other readers? I would greatly appreciate it if you would tell your relatives and friends and write a brief review online. Just a few words saying what you liked about the book would be very helpful. Reviews on Amazon.com and Goodreads help others find books they like.

I'd love to stay in touch with you. You can reach me on my Facebook page, Socorro "Coco" Martínez, (*https://www.facebook.com/ socorromartinezwriter*) or by email at *msm.pub2021@gmail.com.*

DISCUSSION QUESTIONS

1. Was the author able to get your attention in the first chapter? Why or why not?

2. What is your opinion about the educational authorities sending women to dangerous communities in the 1950s?

3. Should Socorro have turned down the job offer and sought a position at a private school so as not to cause pain to her family?

4. Do you think that the presence of another female teacher would have been preferable to having Andrés as a coworker?

5. Should Socorro have dismissed the advice of José Luis and *doña* Susana and continued the friendship with the divorced woman?

6. Was Socorro wrong when confronting *Professor* Merla about her Christian beliefs? If so, how should she have handled the situation?

7. Is the general behavior of the inhabitants of Doctor Arroyo different from that of other small towns? If so, how?

8. Why were the people from Doctor Arroyo who lived in the United States so attached to a small town with so many deprivations?

9. Do you think that at some point *profesora* Socorro could foresee that some of the girls in the school could be in a dangerous situation? Why?

10. Do you think *profesora* Socorro should have waited for another teacher or Horacio to accompany her in the cemetery incident?

11. Do you consider that the moment when *profesora* Camero fell from Palomo was something serious?

12. Should *profesora* Camero have agreed to have a gun in her room? Why?

13. What was the intention of the two teachers' questions to Socorro in the tertulia?

14. Do you think the rancher and the lieutenant recognized the horse that *profesora* Socorro was riding?

15. Did she do the right thing by jumping off Dimas's horse? What would you have done instead?

16. Why do you think the priest and the lieutenant showed up at the airfield together?

17. Was *doña* Susana right to be so angry with *profesora* Socorro after the accident? Why?

18. Do you think that Judicita was aware of how dangerous Dimas's mare was?

19. What is your opinion of Socorro's decision to break her promise to marry Martín? Should she have confessed the fact that her father was out of work?

20. In the incident with Gabriela, did Socorro have the right attitude towards all the people involved?

21. Should she just have rescued Gabriela and let the guy go? Should she have allowed the commission to speak to the girl?

22. Should Gabriela have stayed until the end of the school year? Why?

23. Do you think this incident positively affected other girls?

24. What do you consider was Socorro's greatest challenge at Doctor Arroyo?

25. In your opinion, what was the most difficult situation that Socorro faced in this story?

26. Which chapter in this book caught your interest the most?

27. For you, what secondary character stands out in this story and why?

28. Do you think Socorro ultimately achieved her goal of earning the affection and respect of Doctor Arroyo's people?

If you liked this book, would you recommend it to your friends and family? If so, kindly leave a review on *Goodreads* or *Amazon.com* or a comment on my Facebook page (*https://www.facebook.com/socorromartinezwriter*).

Thank you!
Yours sincerely, the author,
María Socorro "Coco" Martínez
msm.pub2021@gmail.com

Made in the USA
Coppell, TX
05 March 2023

13775777R00365